4

Douglas Slick
322 Shawnee Hall

Patterns in the Sand
an exploration in mathematics

Maurice Bosstick
Assistant Professor of Mathematics
Miami-Dade Junior College

John L. Cable
Assistant Professor of Mathematics
Miami-Dade Junior College

GLENCOE PRESS
A Division of The Macmillan Company
Beverly Hills, California
Collier-Macmillan Ltd., London

GLENCOE PRESS
A Division of The Macmillan Company
8701 Wilshire Boulevard
Beverly Hills, California 90211
Collier-Macmillan Canada, Ltd., Toronto, Canada

Library of Congress Catalog
Card Number: 77-127943

First printing, 1971
Second printing, 1971

To OUR PARENTS, without whose concern, past and present, this book would never have been written.

contents

preface

The mathematical road for the individual who has not chosen to major in mathematics is not always as smooth and straight as he would like. For this person we hope to whet the appetite enough to make mathematics more alluring and recreative.

Our endeavor is not necessarily geared to the "appreciation" of mathematics, but rather to an understanding of the language and ideas important in making decisions. The language of mathematics—simple shorthand terminology—is a specter that frightens many away from the subject. An aftermath of the modern revolution in mathematics is a tendency to make mathematics appear less possible, less relevant, and more unseemly. To help the student overcome this difficulty, we have included enough—but not too much—language in an informal conversational style to enable him to solve the problems and make mathematics a useful tool. The asides and attempts at humor need not be taken seriously. They are there to tempt the appetite and ease the reader's way.

Properties and operations of numbers in many cases can be more easily understood if they are presented through a pattern approach. We have resorted to this technique hoping the student may make some discoveries about these properties on his own, much as Archimedes may have done with his patterns in the sand.

The pre-requisites are at a minimum: a working knowledge of arithmetic computation, a speaking acquaintance with algebra, an open mind, and enough physical strength to express oneself either by writing or by talking. With this frame of mind and these tools at hand, the apprentice can grasp an understanding of the approach to many types of problems that face research work in our complex society.

Due to curriculum changes that have taken place in the past decade, we feel that the bulk of individuals who read this book will have already played hopscotch with Venn diagrams, sets, and subsets. Consequently, we have presented no formal chapter on sets, but have integrated these ideas within the material, especially in Chapter I, Logic, which deals with the translation of English into the language of mathematics. Chapter I also includes a short history of computers, which have become a way of life.

Chapters on numbers and algebra are presented for a better understanding of the modern approach to mathematics, but are approached without losing sight of the primary goal—problem solving.

The chapter on probability is a building block for statistical concepts. The use of games of chance is not intended to create speculators, but to give color to the presentation and supply a tangible means of expression. We have tried to provide enough statistics for the liberal arts student so that he will have an understanding of formulas and terms needed for his research papers. Statistics can also be important in evaluating an individual's progress or achievement, preparing plans, predicting weather, space probes, family budgets, and credit cards.

Although we have emphasized the practical side of mathematics, Chapter 6 provides an opportunity to explore the structure—the finite detail, the orderliness, and the precision—of mathematics.

Chapter 7 contains supplementary material which is an extension of the basic ideas developed in the text to more advanced mathematical problems. It is hoped that the more advanced reader will find these topics interesting and challenging.

We have hinted at many things, any one of which could produce a lifetime of enjoyment or concern. Our intention is to provide the material for a terminal one-semester course which will give the student a glimpse of the variety of uses for modern mathematics.

We are sincerely grateful to Patricia Bosstick for her cheerful responses and suggestions as she typed the manuscript. We also wish to extend our gratitude to our associates who gave us helpful suggestions and unpremeditated reassurance, and to all our unnamed students on whom we practiced what we preached.

January, 1971   Maurice Bosstick
                                                 John L. Cable

Chapter 1
LOGIC

> *Logic was, formerly, the art of drawing inferences; it has now become the art of abstaining from inferences, since it has appeared that the inferences we naturally feel inclined to make are hardly ever valid. I conclude, therefore, that logic ought to be taught in schools with a view to teaching people not to reason. For, if they reason, they will almost certainly reason wrongly.*
>
> Bertrand Russell

1.1. Statements: English and Mathematical

"Everybody doesn't like something, but nobody doesn't like Sarah L.," claims a television commercial. "In a certain small town in France, everyone is shaved by the barber who doesn't shave himself. Then, who shaves the barber?" asks Bertrand Russell. "It sounds like something written by a Philadelphia lawyer," asserts John Q. Public.

In 1735 Carl von Linné, a Swede, first classified life forms and placed man in the genus *Homo*, species *sapiens*, aside from other orders of primates of the class Mammalia, because, he reasoned, we have a more developed brain, giving us the ability to think and reason. We are "wise men." But even with this great gift, we, as often as not, fail to communicate effectually due to our lack of basic procedures in logically reasoning through complicated dissertations.

Logic may be thought of as a reasoning process, sometimes consisting of awkward trial-and-error procedures, by which we reach conclusions that follow from given statements. We agree beforehand to use these specific given statements, *hypotheses,* as foundations on which to build. That is, when two statements are related in such a manner that the second must be true if the first is true, we say that the second is a *logical conclusion* of the first, or that the argument is *valid*. The first statement is the hypothesis and the second the conclusion.

By far the most popular approach to a conclusion in mathematics is *deductive reasoning*. We draw our conclusion only by proposing some general statements in advance, then arbitrarily agreeing to use them as the basis for our argument.

For example, we may on occasion be fortunate enough to find ourselves in the following predicament. We are given the conditions — hypotheses — that we have an 8-gallon keg of Tennessee's finest mountain dew, an empty 5-gallon keg, and an empty 3-gallon keg. The conclusion is a method of equally dividing the booty with another reveler. We find three obvious avenues of reasoning. There is the entertaining solution of sitting down and disposing of the contents; then the problem is solved on the spot. Surely there would be few to argue whether or not the division was equal. Second, if we were to reserve the liquid for further use and had plenty of time, patience, and luck, we might succeed in a direct experimental method by pouring from one container to another until the required division was accomplished. The third approach — reserved for those addicted to reasoning deductively — does most of the pouring mentally. We reason that if we fill the 5-gallon jug, 3 gallons will remain in the original container. Making a mental note of this fact, we proceed in this manner with less labor and greater speed than the actual experimenter. If we fill the 3-gallon jug from the 5 gallons, empty that back into the original 8-gallon jug, and continue the pouring, then we can see from figure 1.1 the number of gallons left in each jug after drop-by-drop calibrations.

The final result and the steps leading to it suggest that reasoning in the human logic machine is made possible by the reasoner's previous knowledge, his experience, and his ability to store the chain of mental experiments without losing track and arriving at an erroneous conclusion.

Often it seems impossible to find the necessary statements on which to base an argument, or if we find such statements they suggest no obvious step-by-step approach to a valid conclusion. In such cases we resort to itemizing many particular instances similar to our argument, and then come to a probable conclusion without further proof. This is an important process in scientific experimentation and everyday life called inductive reasoning. A budding four-year-old scientist, for example, may release his grip on his jelly sandwich (to his mother's dismay) and discover that it falls stickily to the floor. So do his ice cream, toys, paper, and even he himself, when he loses his balance. Young Newton's conclusion is, then, that anything not supported will fall to the floor. But, even though this is a highly probable conclusion, it is premature, for when he lets go of his gas-filled balloon, he finds that it falls to the sky.

4

8 GALLON
JUG

5 GALLON
JUG

3 GALLON
JUG

8 gal.

3 gal.

3 gal.

6 gal.

6 gal.

1 gal.

1 gal.

4 gal.

5 gal.

2 gal.

2 gal.

empty

5 gal.

4 gal.

4 gal.

3 gal.

empty

2 gal.

2 gal.

3 gal.

empty

Figure 1.1

There are pitfalls for the logician at every step. He may fail to take into consideration all the variables that enter into the picture, or he may encounter bad reasoning dressed up to sound good. There are those, such as debaters and orators, who practice this type of *seductive logic.* Their intention is to pursuade rather than to seek the truth. We shall hope to recognize and unmask this deceptive reasoning. A Herculean fellow with more muscles on his back than in his head dug a hole in the ground. When he attempted to fill it up again he was more than dismayed to find that the hole would not hold all the dirt that he took out of it. Scratching his head, he decided, "I just didn't dig the hole deep enough."

Our aim here, then, is to try to make reasonably good sense from statements by reducing them to simple patterns of letters and symbols. This does not mean that we need never think or reason; we are only attempting to clarify patterns of thought and to avoid errors whenever possible. That is, we shall let our mechanical characteristics take over whenever convenient and become thinking machines — walking computers!

As computers then, we need a component labeled "input," for we can get no more out of a brain, mechanical or otherwise, than we put into it. We must have a "control" component to tell us what to do; a "logic" unit, the nuts and bolts to do arithmetic and manipulate decisions; a "memory" unit, our warehouse of facts, numbers, symbols, and strings around fingers; and an "output" component to display the results.

In the beginning, we shall feed into the memory unit only simple propositions, some letters of the alphabet to represent these propositions, and some conjunctions, or *connectors,* to put these propositions together.

Let us look at some simple expressions, English and mathematical.

1. Uranium is used to make atomic energy.

2. $5 - 3 = 2$.

3. Three astronauts landed on the moon in July, 1969.

4. $2 + 7 = 5$.

5. Miami is the largest city in Florida.

6. 2 is larger than 7.

7. His name is Frank.

8. $x < 7$. (Read, "x is less than 7.")

9. If I were a millionaire

10. Indianapolis is

Referring to our English courses, we know that simple sentences are complete, have a subject and a predicate, and convey a single idea. Simple sentences that can be determined to be either true or false are called *statements*. We can generally decide whether a sentence is true or false by reading it. Expressions 1 and 2, then, are statements since they are both true. Similarly, since 3 and 4 contradict indisputable facts (only two astronauts actually landed on the moon on the first try, while the third piloted the command module) we claim that they are false statements. Sentences 5 and 6 present some controversy. When we say that Miami is the largest, are we comparing cities by population or area? Likewise, in number 6, do we mean value or physical size of 2 and 7? Since ambiguity exists, we shall not classify them as statements until more information is given.

We cannot make a logical determination of the truth or falsity of example 7 until we know to whom "his" refers. Therefore we cannot classify it as a statement. Example 8 is of the same type, since it cannot be classified as true or false until a substitution is made for the mathematical pronoun x. Examples 7 and 8 are called *open sentences*. Open sentences are sentences that contain pronouns. We cannot determine whether an open sentence is true or false until a replacement is made for the pronoun. The *set* of all elements, or nouns, of the replacement set that causes the statement to be true is called the *truth set* or the *solution set*. An open sentence, then, sorts the *replacement set* into two *subsets*, one containing those replacements for which the sentence is true and the other containing those for which the sentence is false.

The thoughts in examples 9 and 10 are not complete and do not convey any meaning at all. They are neither statements nor open sentences.

PROBLEM SET 1.1

1. Which of the following are statements?

   (a) Close the door!

   (b) Where is the book?

   (c) If you drink, don't drive.

   (d) New York City is the capital of New York State.

   (e) Make love, not war.

   (f) Wednesday follows Friday.

   (g) On Sunday John usually

   (h) That dog is a poodle.

   (i) This sentence is not a statement.

   (j) This statement is not an even numbered statement.

   (k) $9 - 3 = 7$.

   (l) A man jumped off the roof of the Empire State Building and wasn't injured.

   (m) It is an orange.

   (n) $x + 2 = 7$.

   (o) $x < 4$.

   (p) He is president of the Student Senate.

   (q) _____ is a month that begins with the letter p.

   (r) Put the homework on the blackboard.

2. Of the sentences in Problem 1, which are classified as open sentences? For each, give a replacement set which will make the statement true.

   REMARK: Most of the following situations can be solved logically and may not need to be computed mathematically. They may prove to be entertaining and somewhat frustrating.

3. Nine points are arranged as in the figure below.

With a pencil, start on any one of the points and draw exactly four straight line segments which will include all nine points. This must be done without lifting the pencil point from the paper.

4. A two-volume set of books is arranged in proper order on a shelf. The total pages in Volume I measure 2 inches in thickness and those in Volume II, 1½ inches. The thickness of each book cover is ¼ inch. A bookworm is on the first page of Volume I. He plans to eat straight through to the last page of Volume II. How far must he travel?

5. You are given eight identical-appearing coins and a balance scale. Seven of the coins weigh exactly the same, but the eighth is lighter. As many of the coins as necessary are to be placed in each pan and balanced against each other. You may use the balance scale only three times in determining which coin is the lightest. Can you do it?

6. Duplicate the following equations using matchsticks. By moving only one stick in each equation you should be able to make a true statement.

> (a)   I − I I I = I I   (b)   I I + O = I
>
> (c)   X − I = I   (d)   V I = I I

7. If 78 players enter an elimination tennis tournament for a singles championship, how many matches have to be played to determine the winner? (Each person must play at least one match, with the winner advancing to the next round. Finally, two players meet in the last round.)

8. (a) Six coins of the same denomination (e.g., six pennies) are placed in a triangle as shown. Move the coins, one at a time, so that as each coin is moved it comes to rest tangent to *two* other coins. The last move should result in the coins forming a hexagon.

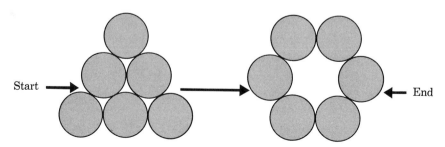

(b) After mastering this problem, return the coins to their original position. Move any two coins so that the point of the triangle is pointing in the opposite direction.

9. A man buys a shirt and a tie for $9.50. The shirt costs $5.50 more than the tie. What does each cost?

10. Write a numeral for 100, using only four 9's and any of the arithmetic operations (addition, subtraction, multiplication, and division).

11. Grandfather winds his clock on Monday morning at 10:30 a.m. The clock will run for exactly $8\frac{1}{4}$ days before it is completely run down. If it takes the pendulum 2 seconds to make a period (over and back), how many periods will it make before the pendulum stops?

12. What is the smallest number of coins needed to make change for all amounts less than one dollar (i.e., 99¢, 98¢, etc.)?

13. Two guards lead a prisoner into a room containing two doors. The prisoner must select one of the doors. One leads to freedom and the other leads to certain death. He is allowed to ask one of the guards one question. One guard is a habitual liar and the other always tells the truth. What question should he ask to guarantee his freedom?

14. A ship is moored in a harbor. At 11:00 a.m. its bow is 20 feet above the surface of the water. If the tide is going out at the rate of one foot per hour, how far above the water level is the bow at 3:00 p.m.?

15. It takes precisely five seconds for a clock to strike 6 o'clock beginning at 6:00. If the strikings are uniformly spaced, how many seconds does it take to strike 12 o'clock?

16. Farmer John, who has been in the not-raising-chickens business, plans to switch into the fowl business. He plans to spend $100 for a total of 100 roosters, hens, and baby chicks. How many of each kind can he purchase for his $100, if roosters cost five dollars each, hens a dollar each, and baby chicks five cents each?

1.2. The Connector "AND"

Frequently it is much more convenient to use a letter to represent a simple statement than to write out the whole sentence. Once we know what the statement says and agree upon a suitable letter to represent the idea involved, we can store this information in our memory bank, and whenever we are to use this information we need only recall the letter for manipulation purposes. For example, we can let the letters p and q represent the following statements:

p: This person likes pie.

q: That person likes cake.

Now, since each of these statements has a pronoun for a subject, we must define a replacement set for each. Let us define the replacement set for the statements p and q as being the set of all people who live in the Midwest. A graphic device for showing our replacement set is the interior of a simple closed figure (circle, square, etc.), generally referred to as a Venn diagram in honor of John Venn (1834-1923) — although Léonard Euler (1707-1783), the most prolific mathematician in history, and many others have also used them. We could draw, if we were endowed with artistic ability, a map of the Midwest, as in figure 1.2, to represent our replacement set; however, the interior of a simple rectangle, as shown in figure 1.3, will do just as well.

Midwest U.S.A.

Replacement Set
for a simple sentence

Figure 1.2   Figure 1.3

The people who satisfy the statement p and live in the Midwest, then, belong to the truth set, or solution set, of p. Let us call this set P. Then everyone in the Midwest who doesn't like pie does not belong to set P. They are in the remaining portion of the replacement set, which we call the *complement* of P, or P_c.

In addition, we can assume that Q is the truth set of all alternatives that can be used for the pronouns in statement q that will make it true, and Q_c, the complement of Q, are those replacements that make q false. Then,

p: This person likes pie.

P: The set of Midwesterners who like pie.

P_c: The set of Midwesterners who don't like pie.

q: This person likes cake.

Q: The set of Midwesterners who like cake.

Q_c: The set of Midwesterners who don't like cake.

For statement p we have:

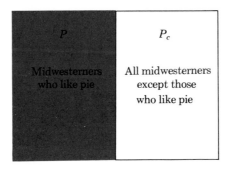

Figure 1.4 Replacement set for *p*

and for statement q, we have:

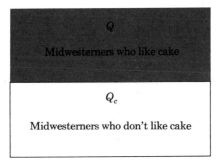

Figure 1.5 Replacement set for *q*

We should not be misled by Venn diagrams into believing that there are always elements in both P and P_c. There may be instances in which one or the other has no members at all. If, for example, it could be shown that everyone in the Midwest liked cake, then Q_c would be empty. On the other hand, if it could be shown that no one in the Midwest liked cake, then Q would be empty. Whenever there are no members in a set, it is called the *empty set* or *null set*. The symbol ϕ represents the empty set. In any event, our Venn diagram as shown in figures 1.4 and 1.5 can still be used.

Since there are no strict rules for size and shape of our diagrams, we may construct them arbitrarily to present a solution.

In figure 1.4 a vertical line divides P and P_c into their respective subsets, and in figure 1.5 a horizontal line divides Q and Q_c into their respective subsets.

It is necessary to let our replacement set contain *all* of those elements which, when substituted into our sentence, make it either true or false. Thus the replacement set can also be called the *universal* set, and we denote it by the italic capital U. Since P and P_c contain only those elements that are also in U, we say that P and P_c are subsets of U, and write symbolically

$$P \subseteq U$$
$$P_c \subseteq U$$

and also

$$Q \subseteq U$$
$$Q_c \subseteq U$$

On occasion, a statement is given in a negative sense. Such a statement may also meet all of the earlier criteria in logic — completeness of sentence, subject, predicate, single idea, and trueness or falseness. For example, "Uranium is not used to make atomic energy" is a false statement and, "It is not true that three astronauts landed on the moon in July, 1969" is a true statement. In our sentence structure with symbols, then, if we let $\sim$ stand for "not," then its use will reverse the truth or falsity of the sentence with which it is used. If p represents, "It is raining," then $\sim p$ states, "It is not raining," and $\sim (\sim p)$ is another reversal which would mean "It is not true that it is not raining," or simply our original statement, "It is raining."

This notion is consistent with our idea of sets and Venn diagrams. If we are given statement p, then the members of the replacement that make p true form the truth set P. Members of the replacement set that make p false are all those members that are not in truth set P. They are in the complement of P, or P_c, and we can picture the replacement sets for statements p and q as shown in figure 1.6. It will prove to be convenient if we agree to shade that area of our rectangles that includes the truth portion.

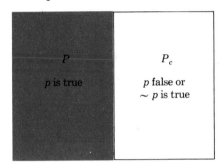 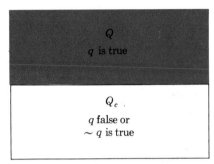

Figure 1.6

Let's consider two sentences that have the same replacement set and superimpose the Venn diagram of one on the Venn diagram of the other to form the rectangle shown in figures 1.8 and 1.9. We are given that the replacement set is the days of the week — that is, our *universal set* is

$$U = \{\text{Mon., Tues., Wed., Thurs., Fri., Sat., Sun.}\}$$

or

Monday
Tuesday
Wednesday
Thursday
Friday
Saturday
Sunday

Figure 1.7 Replacement set for p and q

Then, for the two statements

p: Niki goes to her mathematics class today.

q: Niki goes to her English class today.

we define the following truth sets for the statements:

$P = \{$Monday, Tuesday, Thursday, Friday$\}$

$Q = \{$Tuesday, Wednesday, Thursday, Friday$\}$

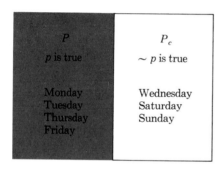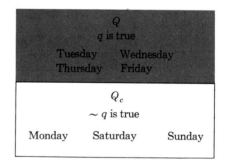

Figure 1.8

Finally, by transposing one replacement set on the other,

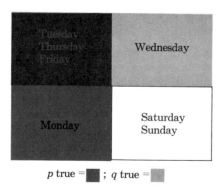

Figure 1.9 Combined replacement set for _p_ and _q_

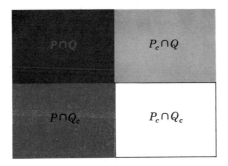

Figure 1.10 Shaded areas where *p* ▮, and *q* ▮ are true and *p* ∩ *q* ▮ is true

We should be able to generalize from our diagrams and form some conclusions concerning the given statements *p* and *q*. For the replacements of Tuesday, Thursday, and Friday, statement *p* is true and so is statement *q*; thus, *p and q* is true. For "and" we use the mathematical symbol ∩ (sometimes called "cap") as a connector combining simple parts; we write $p \cap q$ (read "*p* and *q*"). A sentence constructed from two or more simple parts (clauses) joined by a connective is called a *compound* sentence or statement. Compound sentences using the connector "and" are referred to as *conjunctive* sentences.

We wish to investigate the truth of the compound sentence, "Niki goes to her mathematics class today *and* Niki goes to her English class today." Since both sentences have the same subject, we write it in a more compact and pleasing form, and state, "Niki goes to her mathematics *and* her English classes today." From our Venn diagram of truth sets, we see that it is necessary for both simple statements to be true for our compound "and" statement to be true.

If we did not wish to write the conclusion in English, but simply to indicate the solution set for the compound statement $p \cap q$, we would have

$$P \cap Q = \{\text{Tuesday, Thursday, Friday}\}$$

and we say the *intersection* of *p* and *q* is the days of the week that must satisfy statement *p* and also statement *q*.

We should also notice that the area of the Venn diagram that represents the truth set for the statement $p \cap q$ is the doubly shared portion. A more simple version of our diagram may be as in the shaded portion of figure 1.11, where U is the replacement set for both statements p and q; P is the truth set for statement p; Q is the truth set for statement q; and $P \cap Q$ (the shaded area) is the truth set for the statement $p \cap q$.

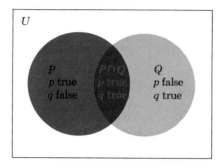

Figure 1.11   P ∩ Q

Let us look at another area of our congruent rectangles, the area P_c and Q, where p is false and q is true for the truth set {Wednesday}. In English we would say, "Niki does not go to her mathematics class today and she does go to her English class today." It would also be correct to use the conjunction "but" here to enhance the sentence. "Today Niki goes to her English class, but not to her mathematics class." Both of these compound sentences have the same logical meaning. In symbolic logic we can write this compound sentence $\sim p \cap q$ (not p and q).

Or, using set symbols, we have $P_c \cap Q$ (intersection of Q with the complement of P). Using our simplified version of the Venn diagram, our solution is figure 1.12.

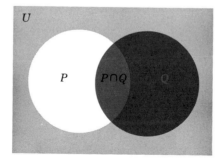

Figure 1.12   P$_c$ ∩ Q

At times, we may wish to find the intersection of three sets. Suppose *P* represents the set of people with blue eyes, *Q* represents the set of people with brown hair, and *R* represents the set of people under 6 feet tall. If we use *U* as the set of all people in the United States, then we can represent the above situation with the following Venn diagram, where the shaded area represents $P \cap Q \cap R$, or all people in the United States who have blue eyes, brown hair, and are under 6 feet tall.

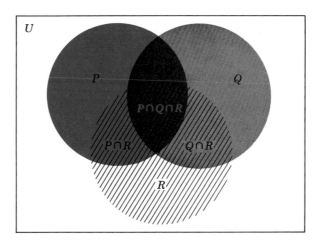

Figure 1.13 $P \cap Q \cap R$

PROBLEM SET 1.2

1. Write the following sentences in symbolic form where:

   p: It is Monday.

   q: It is raining.

   (a) It is not Monday.

   (b) It is Monday and it is raining.

    (c) It is not raining and it is Monday.

    (d) It is Monday, but it is raining.

    (e) It is raining, but it is not Monday.

    (f) It is a rainy Monday.

2. Write English sentences for each of the following symbolic forms where:

$$p: \text{She is wealthy.}$$

$$q: \text{She is happy.}$$

    (a) $\sim q$ (b) $q \cap p$

    (c) $\sim p \cap (\sim q)$ (d) $\sim (\sim p)$

    (e) $\sim p \cap q$ (f) $\sim (p \cap q)$

3. Using Venn diagrams, shade the appropriate area where P and Q are intersecting sets.

    (a) P_c (b) $P \cap Q$

    (c) $P \cap Q_c$ (d) $(P \cap Q)_c$

    (e) $P_c \cap Q_c$

4. If P, Q, and R represent three intersecting sets, shade the areas represented by:

    (a) $(P \cap Q \cap R)_c$ (b) $(P_c \cap Q) \cap R$

    (c) $P \cap (Q_c \cap R_c)$ (d) $P \cap (Q \cap R)_c$

5. Given the replacement set $\{1,3,5,7,9\}$, find the truth set for:

    (a) $3a = 15$.

    (b) $n + n = 2n$.

    (c) $5a = 3$.

6. Which of the following are compound statements?

    (a) $3 + 2 = 5$ and $2 + 5 = 7$.

    (b) $3 + 2 = 9$ and $2 + 5 = 7$.

    (c) $3 + 2 = 5$ and $2 + 5 = 9$.

    (d) $2 = 7 - 5$.

    (e) $x + 2 = 5$.

(f) $x + 2 = 5$ and $2(3 + 4) = 6 + 8.$

(g) Saturday and Sunday are the first two days of the week.

7. For each of the compound statements above, list the simple parts.

8. Write English sentences that are the negation of the following.

(a) All men are good drivers.

(b) All women are good drivers.

(c) No men are good drivers.

(d) At least one man is a bad driver.

1.3. The Connector "OR"

In our previous example, the statement "Niki has mathematics today" is false when we choose Wednesday from the replacement set, while the statement "Niki has English today" is true. It should be apparent, now, that we cannot combine these two simple statements into a single true compound sentence using the connector "and" (*conjunction*). We can, however, use another connector, "or" (*disjunction*), and have a true compound statement. Our mathematical symbol for the connector "or" is $\cup$ (sometimes called "cup"). Using our new symbol, we can now write $p \cup q$, which represents, in a modified interpretation, "Niki has mathematics *or* English today." In relation to sets we write $P \cup Q$ (read "*P cup Q*" and referred to as the *union* of P and Q), which is the set containing the members of the truth set for statement p and also those members of the truth set for statement q. The union of sets is something like addition, but we cannot necessarily add all the members in one set to the members of another set, for we must be careful not to count any element more than once. However, our definition of "or" is such that it also includes those members of $P \cap Q$. Thus $p \cup q$ has the meaning of "*p and/or q*." The truth set for the area of $P \cup Q$ in figure 1.10 is the entire shaded portion, making up three-fourths of the total area of the replacement set. An easier diagram to construct for the compound statement $P \cup Q$, using a Venn diagram and the connector "or," with P the truth set for statement p and Q the truth set for statement q, both chosen from the replacement set U, is:

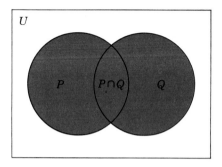

Figure 1.14   P U Q

A specific example of the usage of "or" is given by the statement $3 \leqslant 7$ (read, "3 is less than 7 or 3 is equal to 7"). We know that 3 is not equal to 7, but since 3 is less than 7 the statement $3 \leqslant 7$ is true since *one* of the conditions is true.

Here is another example: "In 6 years Kelly will be more than 22 years old. Five years ago, he was 13 or less than 13 years old. How old can he be now?" First we should analyze each statement to see if it can be condensed into a more simple form. If Kelly is to be more than 22 in 6 years, then he should be more than 16 now and we write:

> *p:*   Kelly is more than 16 years old.

as an equivalent expression to the first statement in the problem. We may also write $k > 16$ (read "K is greater than 16"), where K represents Kelly's age. Next, by the same logic, if he was 13 or less 5 years ago, then he is 18 or less now; thus,

> *q:*   Kelly is 18 years old or less than 18 years old.

In mathematical symbols we can state $K \leqslant 18$ (read "K is less than or equal to 18"). The statement "Kelly is more than 16 and less than *or* equal to 18" now seems trivially true if we construct our diagram. We see that Kelly is either 17 or 18 years old. (Obviously he can't be both ages at the same time.)

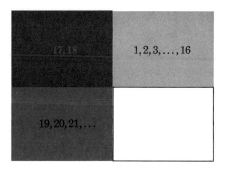

Figure 1.15 $K > 16$ true ■ ; $K \leq 18$ true ■ ;

$K > 16 \cap K \leq 18$ ■

PROBLEM SET 1.3

1. Write the following sentences in symbolic form where:

p: Roses are red.

q: Violets are blue.

(a) Roses are red or violets are blue.

(b) Roses are not red or violets are blue.

(c) Roses are not red or violets are not blue.

(d) It is not true that roses are red or violets are blue.

(e) It is not true that roses are not red or violets are not blue.

(f) Roses are red or violets are blue, and violets are not blue.

2. Write English sentences for each of the following symbolic forms, where:

p: He lost his job.

q: He did not go to work today.

(a) $q \cup p$ (b) $\sim (p \cup q)$

(c) $\sim p \cup (\sim q)$ (d) $\sim [p \cup (\sim q)]$

(e) $\sim p \cup q$ (f) $(p \cup q) \cap (\sim p)$

3. Using Venn diagrams, shade the appropriate area:

   (a) $P_c \cup Q$ (b) $(P \cup Q)_c$

   (c) $P_c \cap Q_c$ (d) $P_c \cup Q_c$

   (e) $(P \cap Q)_c$ (f) $(P \cap Q)_c \cup R$

   (g) $(P \cap Q) \cup R$ (h) $P \cap (Q \cup R)$

   (i) $(P \cap Q) \cup (P \cap R)$ (j) $(P \cup Q) \cap (P \cup R)$

4. The replacement set for n is $\{1,2,3,4,5,6,7\}$. Give the truth set for each of the following:

   (a) $n < 6$ (b) $n > 4$

   (c) $n < 1$ (d) $n \leqslant 1$

   (e) $n \geqslant 1$ (f) $2n \leqslant 6$

   (g) $2n < 4$ (h) $(n < 3) \cup (n < 6)$

   (i) $(n < 3) \cap (n < 6)$ (j) $(n < 6) \cap (n > 4)$

   (k) $(n \leqslant 5) \cap (n > 3)$ (l) $(n > 4) \cap (n < 4)$

5. In seven years Tracy will be less than 24 years old. Six years ago he was at least 9 years old. What is his possible present age?

1.4. Conditional Statements

Penelope Pitfall was always wishing and daydreaming: "If I were a millionaire I would pave the streets with gold." But, as a matter of fact, she couldn't even spread a little cement on her own sidewalk. "If my Prince Charming comes along, I'll marry him." Yet Penelope lived the life of a lonely bachelor girl. "I'm going on a diet, but only if my doctor advises it." But Penelope was climbing up to a trim 250 pounds — give or take a few (and she took at every opportunity) — and is still climbing. Penelope was always vowing, "If this . . . ," "If that . . . ," but we claim that she harmed no one with her idle promises. Most of her statements depended upon some condition to be fulfilled before she could be accused of untruths. Most of us are guilty of using this type of invention, called a *conditional statement*. Such statements are most commonly in the form, "If . . . , then . . . ." Many times the "then" seems superfluous in a sentence and it is left out, as in:

1. If I can get away from the job soon enough, I am going fishing.

2. If your wife wants you to start a garden, the first thing to dig up is an excuse.

There is a confusing variety of ways to state the "If . . . , then . . . " form, which sometimes seems to veil the true meaning of a compound statement. Those who practice misrepresentation or falsification have become artists in using this in their roguery.

Before investigating more forms of "If . . . , then . . . " we should, to satisfy those ordainers of symbols, find a way to shorten the writing by some mathematical or logical device. If we agree to use an arrow as the connector, we can save much time and effort, as in the following example: "If you attend class regularly, you get an A for the course." (Note: you must consult your respective professors for the actual truth of this statement.) First, as with the other connectors, let us examine the following:

p: You attend class regularly.

q: You get an A for the course.

Then using our new connector we have $p \rightarrow q$ (read "If p, then q").

This does not have the same meaning as $q \rightarrow p$ ("If q, then p"). We shall discuss this later, but for now we must be able to point out the conditions that must be met before the conclusion is required to take place. In this instance, our condition is that you attend class regularly.

When will our compound statement $p \rightarrow q$ be true, and when will it be false? If such a statement were made to you and, at the end of the semester, you discovered that you did *not* get the grade that was promised, having fulfilled the given condition p, you would probably question the integrity of the professor. Obviously the compound statement was a falsehood. On the other hand, if p is true, you did attend every class, and if q is true, you did get the A, everything is on the level — a truth has been told. What if you didn't attend every class, but did receive an A? That is, p is false ($\sim p$ is true) and q is true. Does this mean that the

professor told a falsehood when he said, "If p, then q"? No. The condition was not met, so the original statement was not binding on any action
that followed. Then, with p false and q true, the conditional statement
is still true.

The same argument holds if both p and q are false, for, since the
condition p is not satisfied, the consequences are not restricted by that
condition.

Using this information, constructing a Venn diagram, and shading
that portion where $p \rightarrow q$ is a true conditional statement, we have
figure 1.16.

	P	P_c	
	p true q true	p false q true	Q
	p true q false	p false q false	Q_c

Figure 1.16 $p \longrightarrow q$

Our simplified version for the Venn diagram is the same as that
for the compound statement $\sim p \cup q$ (see exercise 3a, problem set 1.3),
as shown in figure 1.17.

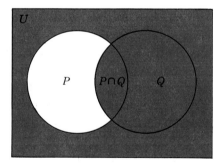

Figure 1.17 $p \longrightarrow q$

From figures 1.16 and 1.17, we can conclude that any member
of the set P that is in the true set of $p \rightarrow q$ is also in the set Q. That is,
the truth set of P is a *subset* of the truth set of Q and we write $P \subseteq Q$
for the compound statement $p \rightarrow q$. We now have three ways of investigating the truth or falsity of compound statements: symbolic, Venn
diagram, and set notation. Let us take another example.

p: It is a Buick.

q: It is a car.

We are not advertising any particular brand of automobile, but "Buick"
is a short name, and easy to spell. It should not be too difficult for us
to accept the premise that all "Buicks" are automobiles. Then the conditional logic statement $p \rightarrow q$ is, "If it is a Buick, then it is a car." We
can also write in set symbols $P \subseteq Q$. We have only to make a picture
diagram as shown in figure 1.18, and our work is nearly complete.

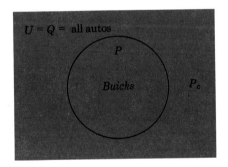

Figure 1.18 $P \subseteq Q$

Since our replacement set and the universal set are the same, the
set of all automobiles, $U = Q$, and again $P \subseteq Q$. We conclude that
$P \subseteq Q$ and $p \rightarrow q$ are statements having equivalent interpretations. One
uses set theory, the other employs mathematical logic.

Suppose our statement was, "It is a Buick only if it is a car." Does
this have a different meaning from our original statement, "If it is a
Buick, then it is a car"? Possibly we can best answer by investigating
$p \rightarrow q$ and figure 1.18 together. A friend makes a startling discovery

that "something" is coming down the road! "Is it a Buick?" we may ask, and get a reply that he can't tell yet because it is too far away. "Then, is it a car?" we counter. Why should we be interested in such a trivial notion as whether it is a car or not, if we are only interested in whether it is a Buick? If it isn't a car, then it can't possibly be a Buick, for all Buicks are cars, as is obvious in figure 1.18. This sentence, put into symbolic form, is $\sim q \rightarrow \sim p$. It has the same implication as our original statement, $p \rightarrow q$, and is called the *contrapositive* form of $p \rightarrow q$. It is a very convenient device in mathematical proofs.

From this we see that it is quite necessary for "it" to be a car before we consider calling it a Buick. Now, let's tackle the question about "p only if q," which states that p can occur only if q takes place or happens, thus making it necessary for q to take place or be true before we even need consider the truth or falsity of p. Since q is the necessary element in "If p, then q," and also in "p only if q," they must carry the same meaning and are therefore equivalent. In comparison, we say that p is sufficient information to conclude that q is true. For, if we know that "it" is a Buick, then "it" must be a car (from figure 1.18), since we have built our discussion on the fact that all Buicks are cars.

We now have the following "control" components by which our computer can react:

Symbols	Name	Use	Translation
		LOGIC	
p,q,r ...	Variables	Represent sentences	the sentence itself
$\sim$	Negation	Opposite sense	"not"
$\cap$	Conjunction	Connect simple sentences	"and"
$\cup$	Disjunction	Connect simple sentences	"or"
$\rightarrow$	Conditional	Connect simple sentences	"if p, then q" "p only if q" "p is a sufficient condition that q" "q is a necessary condition for p" "q if p" "q provided that p" "not p or q" "q follows from p" "p implies q" "if not q then not p"
$\longleftrightarrow$	Equivalent	Connector	"if and only if"

Symbols	Name	Use	Translation
SETS			
$P, Q, R \ldots$	Sets	Represent defined, finite groups	solution sets
$P \subseteq Q$	Subsets	Relate sets	each element of P is an element of Q
$P_c, Q_c, R_c \ldots$	Complement	Represent all other elements, not in $P, Q,$ or $R \ldots$	all elements not P
$P \cap Q$	Intersection	Members with common bond	"and"
$P \cup Q$	Union	Combine sets	"or"

VENN DIAGRAMS

| Set | Complement | Subset | Intersection | Union |

PROBLEM SET 1.4

1. Write each of the following English sentences in symbolic form where:

   p: It is a duck.

   q: It is a bird.

   (a) If it is a duck, then it is a bird.
   (b) If it is a bird, then it is a duck.
   (c) If it is not a duck, then it is not a bird.
   (d) If it is not a bird, then it is not a duck.
   (e) If it is a bird, it is not a duck.
   (f) It is a bird only if it is a duck.
   (g) Being a duck is a sufficient condition for being a bird.

(h) A necessary condition for being a bird is to be a duck. *if*   *then - necessary*

(i) To be a bird, it is necessary to be a duck.

(j) Being a duck is necessary for being a bird.

(k) It is a duck provided it is a bird.

(l) A sufficient condition for not being a duck is that of not being a bird.

2. Classify each of the statements in problem 1 above as either "true" or "false."

3. Construct the Venn diagram for the symbolic statement $q \rightarrow p$.

4. Given the compound statement $p \rightarrow q$ as follows, "If the sun in shining, then it is not cloudy," translate each of the following into English statements and determine which have the same meaning as the original statement.

     (a) $q \rightarrow p$ (b) $\sim p \rightarrow \sim q$ (c) $\sim q \rightarrow \sim p$

1.5. Truth Tables

In our discussion in previous sections, we have found that two simple statements or clauses, p and q, can be compounded many ways, but in every case each clause has one of two values. Either it is T for true or F for false. Then, when two simple sentences are taken together, there are four distinct cases of the compound statement to consider. That is, in one situation we may find that both the first clause and the second clause are true. For the other three cases we have TF, FT, and FF, as discussed. These combinations can be diagrammed as a simple table, figure 1.19.

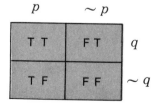

Figure 1.19

A more formal and less cumbersome pattern used to analyze a compound statement is called a *truth table*. The truth table presents a form of logic circuits, and its uses extend far beyond pure mathematics. Using symbols of Boolean algebra (George Boole, 1815–1864), for example, all possible combinations of values for electrical circuits can be investigated. Truth table logic was a great aid in building electronic digital computers.

For now, however, we shall confine ourselves simply to building truth tables themselves. First we place our TF values beneath their represented clauses, as in figure 1.20.

	p	q	
case 1	T	T	
case 2	T	F	
case 3	F	T	
case 4	F	F	

Figure 1.20

The first two columns in our truth table show all possible ways of connecting the two simple parts with regard to their truth or falsity. Then a compound statement, such as $p \cap q$, is placed to the right of the simple parts, as in figure 1.21.

p	q	$p \cap q$
T	T	
T	F	
F	T	
F	F	

Figure 1.21

The table is read across, line by line. The second line, case 2, would mean that we know that statement p is true and that q is false. Knowing these facts, then, we are to decide whether a compound statement is true. For example, let us dissect the compound statement, "It is my opinion *and* it is true," then investigate its truth table.

p: It is my opinion.

q: It is true.

We know that the truth of a compound statement depends upon the truth of its parts; then, for the connector "and," both parts must be true for the compound statement to be true. The truth table is shown in figure 1.22. The compound $p \cap q$ is false under the conditions as stated in case 2 because q is known to be false. The last two cases are also false, for p is false in case 3, and both p and q are false in case 4.

p	q	$p \cap q$
T	T	T
T	F	F
F	T	F
F	F	F

Figure 1.22

For the compound statement, "It is my opinion, *or* it is true," the truth table is shown in figure 1.23. A compound statement with the connector "or" is true in every case except when *both* clauses are false, and our table is consistent with this notion.

p	q	$p \cup q$
T	T	T
T	F	T
F	T	T
F	F	F

Figure 1.23

Should our compound statement be, "*If* it is my opinion, *then* it is true," or $p \rightarrow q$, we would have the truth table of figure 1.24.

	p	q	p → q
case 1	T	T	T
case 2	T	F	F
case 3	F	T	T
case 4	F	F	T

Figure 1.24

Our discussion of "If . . . , then . . . " tells us that the only false argument is case 2, where *p* is true and *q* is false (see figure 1.16). Thus, if *it is my opinion* and yet *it is indeed known not to be true,* as case 2 signifies, then the compound statement is false.

Let's look at a more complicated compound statement, $p \cap (\sim q)$. These symbols may represent a compound statement, such as, "It is cloudy and it is not raining," where:

p: It is cloudy.

q: It is raining.

The statement may be read, "It is cloudy, *but* it is not raining." First, we construct the basic columns for *p* and *q*, then place the statement to be analyzed, as in figure 1.25.

p	q	p ∩ (∼ q)
T	T	
T	F	
F	T	
F	F	

Figure 1.25

We may wish to dissect our sentence into parts so that we can calculate any possible column directly from the basic columns. Recalling the meaning of our connectors, we perform these operations step by step.

We rewrite the column under p to make it readily available. The $(\sim q)$ column, then, is the negation of q in all cases.

p	q	p	$\cap$ $(\sim q)$
T	T	T	
T	F	T	
F	T	F	
F	F	F	
		Step 1	

Figure 1.26

p	q	p	$\cap$ $(\sim q)$
T	T	T	F
T	F	T	T
F	T	F	F
F	F	F	T
			Step 2

Figure 1.27

We can now finish the table by looking at the various TF's for the two clauses. They are T ∩ F, T ∩ T, F ∩ F, F ∩ T. By recalling the meaning of ∩ — *both* simple parts must be true for the compound to be true — we can put in step 3, the truth values for $p \cap (\sim q)$ (see figure 1.28). We see that the only case where our compound statement is true is case 2, satisfying the conditions that it is cloudy and it is not raining.

p	q	p	$\cap$	$(\sim q)$
T	T		F	
T	F		T	
F	T		F	
F	F		F	
			Step 3	

Figure 1.28

Let's take a step deeper into the darkness and rummage about for the truth column for, "If that's the way it is, then that's the way it is or I'm a monkey's uncle." First we let a different letter represent each of the simple clauses and then rewrite the statement in symbolic form:

p: I'm a monkey's uncle.

q: That's the way it is.

Then the symbolic form of the statement is:

$$q \rightarrow (q \cup p)$$

We can now set up the table with the statement more or less separated into parts as in figure 1.29.

p	q	$q \rightarrow (q \cup p)$
T	T	
T	F	
F	T	
F	F	

Figure 1.29

Now, by parts, we can write the truth columns for each to complete figure 1.30.

p	q	q	$\rightarrow$	$(q \cup p)$
T	T	T	T	T
T	F	F	T	T
F	T	T	T	T
F	F	F	T	F
		Step 1	Step 3	Step 2

Figure 1.30

Another example consists of three simple statements which are put together to form a single compound statement. "If I have no homework and I get paid, then I am going to the Islands this weekend." We define:

p: I have homework.

q: I get paid.

r: I am going to the Islands this weekend.

The symbolic statement is:

$$(\sim p \cap q) \to r$$

Now we have three simple parts with which we can find eight possible combinations with regard to the truth or falsity of each. The first clause can be true half the time and false half the time. We list these possibilities in figure 1.31. The second statement can be true in half of the first statement's true instances and false in the rest, as in figure 1.32. Also, the third statement is true for each of half of the second statement's trues and, again, false the rest of the time. Figure 1.33 shows all eight ways of combining the three clauses.

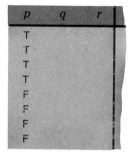

Figure 1.31

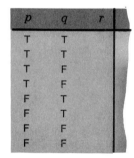

Figure 1.32

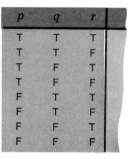

Figure 1.33

By placing our symbolic statement in its position, we are ready to operate, keeping in mind the definitions of the connectors (see figure 1.34).

p	q	r	(∼ p	∩	q)	→	r
T	T	T	F	F	T	T	T
T	T	F	F	F	T	T	F
T	F	T	F	F	F	T	T
T	F	F	F	F	F	T	F
F	T	T	T	T	T	T	T
F	T	F	T	T	T	F	F
F	F	T	T	F	F	T	T
F	F	F	T	F	F	T	F
STEPS			1	3	2	5	4

Figure 1.34

The compound statement is true in every case except for the sixth, which states that "I have no homework, I get paid, and I am not going to the Islands this weekend."

If we have understood all this, we should now shout, "Eureka!" and take a coffee break.

PROBLEM SET 1.5

1. Complete the following truth tables.

p	q	$\sim p \cap q$	$q \to p$	$\sim p \to (\sim q)$	$(\sim p \cap q) \to p$
T	T				
T	F				
F	T				
F	F				

2. Construct truth tables for each of the following:

   (a) $\sim p \cap (\sim q)$

   (b) $\sim [\sim p \cap (\sim q)]$

   (c) $\sim (p \cup q)$

   (d) $\sim p \cup q$

   (e) $(\sim p \cup q) \to p$

   (f) $\sim p \to \sim (\sim p \cap q)$

   (g) $(\sim p \to p) \cup (\sim q)$

   (h) $p \cup (\sim p \cap q)$

   (i) $(p \cup q) \cap r$

   (j) $p \cup (q \cap r)$

   (k) $(p \cup q) \cap (p \cup r)$

3. In problem number 2, compare those statements that have identical truth columns for the last step only. Compare also with statements that have been worked out in this section (figures 1.22, 1.23, 1.24, 1.28, 1.30).

4. Under what conditions is each of the following compounds true? (*Hint:* Use truth tables.)

   (a) If Miami is in Florida, then $3 + 2 = 7$.

   (b) If $3 + 2 = 7$, then Miami is in Florida.

   (c) $3 + 2 \neq 7$ only if Miami is in Florida.

   (d) If $3 + 2 \neq 7$, then Miami is not in Florida.

(e) If we don't go to the beach this summer, then we are not going to the mountains next winter.

(f) If you don't eat your spinach and liver, you can't go out and play.

(g) $(2 + 5 = 7) \rightarrow (5 + 5 = 5)$

(h) $(2 + 5 = 7) \cap (5 + 5 = 5)$

(i) $(2 + 5 = 7) \cup (5 + 5 = 5)$

(j) $(p \rightarrow q) \cap (q \rightarrow r)$

(k) $p \rightarrow r$ (Solve on the same table as 4(j) and compare values.)

1.6. Consistent, Contrary, and Contradictory Statements

There is a certain story about Eulathus, a Greek lad during the fifth century B.C. He wanted to become a lawyer, but had neither the means to finance nor the willingness to pay for an education. Protagoras, a specialist in the art of pleading before juries, knew of the sharp wit of Eulathus, and made a contract to tutor him with the agreement that Eulathus would pay his tuition when he won his first case. Eulathus finished his course, but delayed going into practice for such a time that Protagoras tired of waiting for his fee. He brought suit against his former student.

Protagoras' strategy was simple: "If Eulathus loses, then by the order of the court he must pay me; if he wins, then by the term of our contract he must pay me. Eulathus must either lose or win; therefore he must pay me."

It seemed to be a bad day for Eulathus, but he had learned his lessons well. He countered with an argument that seemed as logical — if not more so: "If I win, by the order of the court I shall not have to pay Protagoras; if I lose, then by the terms of the contract I shall not have to pay for I shall not have won my first case. I must either win or lose, therefore I do not have to pay Protagoras!"

And so goes the fruit of discord between individuals — which, we assume, has existed since Adam and Eve had their disagreement about the apple. Certainly, two sides of an argument, if they are contrary — or contradictory — can't both be logical.

When we speak of something or some statement as being logical, what we really mean is that it is logically true. So now if we can determine the meaning of a statement being logically true, we shall have some output from our untransistorized, human computers. It may be easier to accomplish this chore by illustrations. In figure 1.30 we see that in step 3 (the solution column) the compound statement $q \rightarrow (q \cup p)$ is true for every case and thus, "If that's the way it is, then that's the way it is, or I'm a monkey's uncle" is a *logically true statement*.

Let's take another statement and test for its logical potency.

$$p \cup \sim (p \cap q)$$

All we need do is to derive the truth table and if the final step produces all T's then the statement is logically true. The statement is logically true, as shown in step 4 of figure 1.35.

p	q	p	$\cup$	$\sim$	$(p \cap q)$
T	T	T	T	F	T
T	F	T	T	T	F
F	T	F	T	T	F
F	F	F	T	T	F
STEPS		1	4	3	2

Figure 1.35

Often we find ourselves in a heated argument and make statements that are not accepted as truths by our adversary. We may start off on common grounds — basic ideas — at the onset, but be gradually led in different directions in our thinking; there may be only one valid conclusion. When an argument based on a set of propositions is logically true (true in every case), it is said to be valid; if an argument is not logically true (false in at least one case), then it is a fallacy. If, then, when we thrash out a truth table for an argument and find it is logically true, then the argument (which is actually a statement) is also valid, and vice versa. For example, one argument goes like this:

"I will pass mathematics only if I study, but I didn't study, so I didn't pass mathematics."

A second argument might be:

> "If I don't study, then I will fail mathematics, and
> I did fail mathematics; therefore I didn't study."

Now, we can bag two birds with one stone. By determining the truth value of each statement, we can test each statement for validity. We can also compare the solution set column of one to that of the other. If they are identical, then we say that the statements are *equivalent* or have the same meaning. Or, if p is true whenever q is true, and if p is false whenever q is false, then p is equivalent to q and we write $p \leftrightarrow q$.

Let's construct truth tables and draw our conclusions. First:

p: I will pass mathematics.

q: I study.

Then statement 1 is:

$$[(p \rightarrow q) \cap (\sim q)] \rightarrow (\sim p)$$

Statement 2 is:

$$\{[\sim q \rightarrow (\sim p)] \cap (\sim p)\} \rightarrow (\sim q)$$

With two simple statements compounded we have four possible cases to consider, as shown in figure 1.36. The final result, or solution set, for statement 1 is the column for step 5, T T T T. That for statement 2 is column 7, T T F T. We see that statement 1 is logically true or that it is a valid argument; statement 2 is a fallacy, for the final column contains an F. Now, since the two compound statements have different truth values, they are not equivalent. In general, open statements (those containing pronouns) are *equivalent* if they have the same truth sets. At this point you may wish to check back through truth tables already established and check for equivalent statements. The two statements $p \rightarrow q$ and $\sim p \cup q$ are equivalent, and one form may be substituted for the other in any work requiring the use of truth tables (see figure 1.37).

		statement one					statement two						
p	q	$[(p \to q)$	$\cap$	$(\sim q)]$	$\to$	$(\sim p)$	$\{[\sim q$	$\to$	$(\sim p)]$	$\cap$	$(\sim p)\}$	$\to$	$(\sim q)$
T	T	T	F	F	T	F	F	T	F	F	F	T	F
T	F	F	F	F	T	F	T	F	F	F	F	T	T
F	T	T	T	T	T	T	F	T	T	T	T	F	F
F	F	T	T	T	T	T	T	T	T	T	T	T	T
STEPS		1	3	2	5	4	1	3	2	5	4	7	6

Figure 1.36

p	q	$(p \to q)$	$\longleftrightarrow$	$(\sim p \cup q)$
T	T	T	T	T
T	F	F	T	F
F	T	T	T	T
F	F	T	T	T

Figure 1.37

The statement $x \leqslant 7$ is equivalent to $7 \geqslant x$, and also equivalent to $2 + x \leqslant 7 + 2$, since any value for x in one statement is also a value that satisfies the other two statements.

Let's take another pair of statements.

p: Today is Wednesday.

q: Today is Friday.

Now, obviously, "Today" can't possibly be Wednesday and Friday at the same time! If it's true that today is Wednesday, then it cannot be true that today is Friday; on the other hand, if it's really Friday, then it isn't Wednesday. But, what if today happens to be Sunday? Then it is neither Wednesday nor Friday and both of the given statements are false. We say that p and q are *contrary* statements. A logical truth set for p and q would be

p	q	
T	F	if today is Wednesday,
F	T	if today is Friday,
F	F	if it is any other day of the week.

Figure 1.38

Looking at the two statements,

p: Today is Wednesday.

q: Today is not Wednesday.

we can write,

$\sim p$: Today is not Wednesday.

Our truth table is

p	q	$\sim p \longleftrightarrow q$	
T	F	F	F
F	T	T	T

Figure 1.39

and we say that p and $\sim p$ are contradictory statements, since p is true whenever q is false and p is false whenever q is true; q and $\sim p$ are equivalent.

As an example, let's compare truth tables for $p \cup q$ and $\sim p \cap (\sim q)$, as in figure 1.40. In cases 1, 2, and 3, $p \cup q$ is true, while $\sim p \cap (\sim q)$ is false; but in case 4, $p \cup q$ is false and $\sim p \cap (\sim q)$ is true; thus the two statements are said to be *contradictory*. The idea of contradictory statements is important to mathematicians in proving theorems by using the style of "coming in the back door." The method is to show that a stated hypothesis logically leads to a false conclusion; then the assumed hypothesis must be false. Some classical theorems proven by this method are that there is an infinite set of prime numbers, that the empty set is a subset of any set, and that $\sqrt{2}$ is not rational.

p	q	$p \cup q$		$\sim p$	$\cap$	$(\sim q)$
T	T	T		F	F	F
T	F	T		F	F	T
F	T	T		T	F	F
F	F	F		T	T	T

Figure 1.40

As a final example of valid reasoning, let's consider the following situation in which most unwary students, at one time or another, find themselves.

You are taking a true-false exam consisting of five statements. You know from past experience that there will be more true than false answers and that there will not be any three alike in a row. In looking over the exam, you are completely thunderstruck by the statements. You know that the first and last are contradictories and that there is a *single* correct solution set, provided that you have answered statement number 2 correctly.

QUESTION			ANSWER			
1		T	T	F	F	F
2	T	T	T	T	T	T
3			F		T	F
4			T		F	T
5		F	F	T	T	T
STEP	a	b	c	d	e	f

Figure 1.41

Suppose that the answer to statement 2 is "true" (see figure 1.41, step a). Then, if the first one is T, the last must be F (contradictory), as in step b. Now, since there must be more T's than F's, with no three alike in a row, statements 3 and 4 must be F, T, respectively, as in step c. This seems to be the logical answer, except by the same reasoning we can find another list of TF's that will satisfy these conditions. Suppose that we had called statement 1 "false." Then the last is true, as in step d. Again, 3 and 4 must have opposite answers so that we don't have three in a row with the same value (if both T) and so there won't be more F than T (if both F). We can assign either pair of values TF or FT to statements 3 and 4 and not contradict the given conditions, as in steps e and f. The paradox is that we have three different solution sets when there should be only one. (See steps c, e, and f.) In comparing these three solution sets, we find that for each of the five statements, excluding statement 2, there is at least one T and one F. (Check horizontally.) The truth sets for statements 1, 3, 4, and 5 are inconsistent. Statement 2 in each solution set is true. In the event that we compare solution sets for two or more statements and verify that they are all true for the same case, we say that the truth sets are consistently true and the statements are *consistent* under the given conditions. But this may be the root of our trouble. We were investigating the test answers on the premise that statement 2 was true. Now conduct the search on the assumption that we know that the second statement is false, and that the first and last are opposites. If number 1 is false, then the last three are true, for we must have more T's than F's. But this makes three T's in a row, which is wrong. Right? Thus number 1 is true and 5 is false, as in figure 1.42, step a. Then 3 and 4 are both true, for any other combination will present too many F's. The solution, then, is TFTTF, as in step b, and we get an A for the exam and for logic.

QUESTION	ANSWER	
1	T	T
2	F	F
3		T
4		T
5	F	F
STEP	a	b

Figure 1.42

What appears logical to one person may be illogical to another. There is an episode concerning the woman who was asked why she didn't do her traveling by airplane. "Indeed not," she said. "If God had intended for me to fly He would have given me wings." And then she paid for her train fare.

PROBLEM SET 1.6

1. Determine which of the following are logically true.

(a) $p \cup \sim (p \cap q)$

(b) $p \to (p \cup q)$

(c) $[p \rightarrow (\sim q)] \rightarrow [q \rightarrow (\sim p)]$

(d) $[p \cup (p \cap q)] \leftrightarrow p$

(e) $(p \cap q) \cap \sim (p \cup q)$

2. Classify each of the following sets of statements as consistent, contrary, contradictory, and/or equivalent. (All contradictory statements are necessarily contrary.)

(a) It is a chair. It is a piece of furniture. — *consistent*

(b) It is a chair. It is a sofa. — *contrary*

(c) It is a chair. It is not a chair. — *contradictory*

(d) The tree is a palm. The tree is not an oak.

(e) It is a dog. It is a cat.

(f) It is a dog. It is a canine. It is a mammal. It has fur.

(g) $x \leqslant 5.$ $5 - 2 \geqslant x - 2.$

(h) The number is positive. The number is negative. *contrary*

(i) The number is positive. The number is not positive.

(j) $p \cup (p \cap q).$ $p.$

(k) $x + 3 = 7 - x.$ $x - 7 = -x - 3.$

(l) $(p \cap q) \cap \sim (p \cap q).$ $[(p \rightarrow q) \cap q] \rightarrow q.$ *contradictory*

(m) Tony is 17 years old. Tony is 18 years old.

3. Test each of the following arguments and state whether it is valid or a fallacy.

(a) $[(\sim p \rightarrow q) \cap p] \rightarrow (\sim q).$

(b) $\{[\sim p \rightarrow (\sim q)] \cap q\} \rightarrow p.$

(c) $\{(p \rightarrow q) \cap [r \rightarrow (\sim q)]\} \rightarrow [r \rightarrow (\sim p)].$

(d) $[(p \rightarrow q) \cap (\sim q)] \rightarrow (\sim p).$

4. Consider the following statement, "If it is an aba, then it is a daba." Classify each of the following arguments as "valid" or "fallacy."

(a) It is a daba. Therefore it is an aba.

(b) It is not an aba. Therefore it is not a daba.

(c) It is not a daba. Therefore it is not an aba.

(d) It is not true that it is an aba and it is not a daba.

5. For the following statement, "No college professor is wealthy. Some poets are wealthy," determine which of the conclusions are valid.

   (a) Poets who are wealthy are not college professors.

   (b) Some poets are college professors.

   (c) Poets who are not wealthy are college professors.

   (d) Some poets are not college professors.

6. Write the following paragraphs in symbolic form; relate the sentences with appropriate symbols.

   (a) On your sweetheart's birthday, you will send her flowers. Either it's her birthday or you are going fishing. You did not send her flowers today. Therefore you went fishing.

   (b) If I work, I can't study. Either I work or I pass science. I passed science. So, I studied.

   (c) All doctors are wealthy. Artists are temperamental. No temperamental person is wealthy. Then, no artist is wealthy.

   (d) Children are illogical. No one is disliked who can play football. Illogical people are disliked. Thus, children cannot play football.

7. For each of the paragraphs in problem 6, above, determine whether each has a valid conclusion or is a fallacy.

8. If the replacement set for n is $\{1, 2, 3, 4, 5, 6, 7\}$, determine:

   (a) The truth set for the open statement $n < 6$.

   (b) The truth set that forms a contradiction of $n < 6$.

   (c) The truth set for the open statement $n > 6$.

   (d) The truth set for the open statement $n \not< 6$ (read "n is not less than 6").

   (e) Which of the statements above are contrary? Contradictory?

9. Test the validity of each conclusion to the following argument: All timid creatures are bunnies. Some timid creatures are dumb. Some freshmen are timid creatures. Therefore,

   (a) Some bunnies are dumb.

   (b) Some freshmen are bunnies.

   (c) Some freshmen are dumb bunnies.

10. Mr. Outdoors has three daughters: Niki, Vicki, and Deanna. One is yachting at Naples, a second is at the Doral Country Club, and the third is at Wimbledon. One is playing tennis, one is yachting, and the other is playing golf. Niki is not at Naples, Deanna is not at Doral Club, and the daughter who plays golf is not at Wimbledon. If the yachting enthusiast is not Deanna, who is playing golf, and where?

1.7. Computers

It has been said that the development of electronic digital computers has had a greater impact on the intellectual and practical achievements of mankind than the invention of the printing press. Perhaps this is true, although it is hard to believe than man could ever have reached his capacity to create these supplementary "brains" without generations of book-stored knowledge behind him. On the other hand, scientific transcribers, working like medieval monks, could have generated on paper all the information required to lift a spacecraft off a launching pad — but the split-second calculations of computers are required to bring it home again.

Man has long had calculating devices. The first "computer" consisted of his fingers and, as we shall see in the next chapter, his counting on his fingers led to our whole decimal number system. Later, he used piles of sticks or pebbles or shells — whatever was handy where he lived — to denote his concepts of quantity. As he progressed, his devices became more mechanical and sophisticated. Around 3000 B.C., someone, no one knows who, invented the abacus, a calculating device so successful that it is still used in many parts of the world for basic computation. There are varieties of abacuses (or, more properly, abaci), but the one most familiar to most people is the Chinese suan-pan, illustrated in figure 1.43. Like all such devices, it operates by sliding beads, representing various amounts, along rods. As a "one" bead is moved over, it represents the number one, as the next "one" bead is slid over, the total represents two, etc. As certain aggregate levels, such as five, are reached, other beads are used. In figure 1.43, the abacus is set to represent the number 19,635.

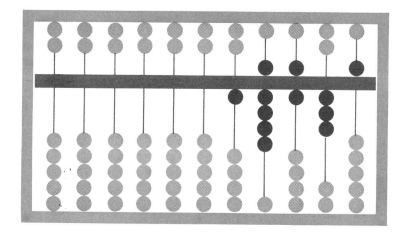

Figure 1.43 A Chinese suan-pan abacus. Each bead above the crossbar represents five of the different orders (ones, tens, hundreds, etc.). Beads from top and bottom are pushed to the middle when they are used.

The Japanese commonly use a similar device, called a soroban. In 1947, Kiyoshi Matsuzake, of the Japanese Ministry of Communications, used his soroban to beat Private Tom Wood of the U.S. Army, armed with a modern electric calculator, in four out of five problem categories.

In 1642, Blaise Pascal, at the age of nineteen, built a calculating machine that operated much like the odometer of today's automobile. It was a gear-driven computer that added eight columns of numbers by dialing a series of wheels bearing digits, zero to nine, around the circumference. A ratchet device advanced a wheel one digit when the wheel to its right made one complete revolution, thereby accomplishing the carrying of tens automatically for the first time.

Pascal's ratchet machine, ingenious as it was for the times, could only add. In 1671, the German mathematician Leibniz developed the first machine that could automatically multiply and divide correctly and use applied formal logic, constructing tables of syllogisms.

But the first really modern calculating machine was developed by the Englishman Charles Babbage (1792-1871). In 1822 he designed the "Analytical Engine," which won for him the first gold medal of the Royal Astronomical Society. This machine, based on the same general principles as today's electronic computers, could tabulate the values of any function and print the result. The building of the machine was financed by the British government, because of possible use by the Admiralty. However, expenses ran far higher than expected, and the project was never completed. The Analytical Engine was consigned to the Kensington Museum.

In 1890, Dr. Herman Hollerith of the U.S. Census Office devised an electrical clock-like counting device to "read" punched cards on which were recorded a person's name, age, sex, address, and other vital statistics needed for the 1890 census. His ideas enabled the government to tabulate the data more than twice as fast as it had been handled in the 1880 census, even though the population was up 25%. Without some sort of mechanization, the census data would have become obsolete before it could have been analyzed.

The punched card is still used extensively today. It is probably the most common way of storing information for computers — despite the fact that it must not be bent, folded, spindled, or mutilated. Almost all of us have seen punched cards in one form or another, usually in the form of requests for payment. The standard punched card is made out of light cardboard, and contains eighty columns. There are twelve rows where punches may be made to represent specific numbers, letters, and symbols. Ten of the rows are numbered, zero through nine. A single punch in any column in one of these rows represents the value of that row. Thus, a hole punched in row nine represents the value nine. Letters and symbols use combinations of the numeric rows and the other three "zone" rows. Notice in figure 1.44 how the letters of the alphabet are coded in "numeric" order with zone punches to distinguish them from numbers.

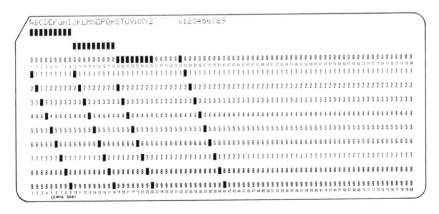

Figure 1.44 Alphabet and digits

As man's mechanical computational capabilities advanced, so did his desire for bigger and better devices. He was never quite satisfied. The grass was always greener . . . or, maybe, the more he could do with his improving computational equipment, the more computational grass he could see. Finally, in 1946, the speed of electronics was applied to the principles developed through centuries of calculating devices, and the first modern electronic digital computer was built. ENIAC, a 30-ton, 150-kilowatt monster, was developed for the U.S. Army. Problems encountered during the Second World War had demonstrated the need to solve rapidly problems involving vast quantities of information. For example, all the possibilities involved in decoding secret messages could much more easily have been stored in a computer's memory than in a man's — or several men's. The routine but vital information required for supply and communications constituted an immense store of information which had to be manipulated quickly and upon which decisions had to be made rapidly.

Although ENIAC itself turned out to miss the war, the need for computers had been demonstrated. Once man got used to his new brainchild, he continued to invent and discover problems of justifiable magnitude, until, today, computers have found their place in almost every conceivable discipline, from medicine to meteorology.

Despite their capabilities and publicity, however, computers are nothing more than basic problem solvers spiced up with the latest technology. Like any other problem solver, including human beings, they have five basic components: input, storage, computation, output, and control.

Suppose you should be given the following problem: Add two and two. (This is probably the easiest problem you'll encounter in this course, so make the most of it!) What do you do to solve it?

First, you must read or hear the problem and write it down: $2 + 2 = ?$ This is input. The 2 and the 2 are what you have to work with, or *data* (from the Latin word meaning "things"), the plus sign denotes the arithmetic operation of addition, the equals sign implies that you will need an answer on the right to match the expression on the left, and the question mark, for the moment, represents that answer, or output. Notice that there are two kinds of information in your input, even for such a simple problem. First there is the data, or information to be manipulated; second there are instructions (in this case, add and give a sum) which define what is to be done with the data. Electronic computers also require these two types of input — data and instructions, or a program.

Once you have written your program and data down, they are stored on the paper. Computer storage units, or memories, are generally made up of miniature ferromagnetic "donuts," called magnetic cores, which can be polarized in different directions to represent different numbers, letters, and symbols. Each location in computer storage has a unique address, so information can be found when needed.

When you work a problem, you do the arithmetic and logic in your head, either all at once or step by step, depending on the complexity of the problem. The computer also has an arithmetic/logical unit, where it carries out every problem, no matter how easy, operation by operation, as defined by the program.

Your output is the answer you write on the paper or put on the blackboard. The computer's output can be punched cards, magnetic tape, telephone signals, or printed reports (which spew out of the system printer at speeds of 1100 lines per minute and faster).

The crucial element of either problem-solving system, human or electronic, is the control unit. With you, it is your brain, figuring out and coordinating all the steps required for solution. With the computer, it is the control unit, which ties together the other components — input, storage, arithmetic/logical, and output — in following program instructions and producing a result. It is this control unit which distinguishes electronic computers from all previous calculating devices. Once the program is stored in memory and the start button is pushed, human intervention is no longer necessary in the *logical* execution of the problem. It is true that an operator might have to produce a deck of cards for the computer to eat, or load a magnetic tape for it to read, but he does not have to look at intermediate results of a solution and say, "Well, um-m-m . . . why don't we try this?"

And so, these wonderful conglomerations of transistors and switches and nuts and bolts gained the dubious and frightening reputation of being "giant brains," capable of wiping out all mankind. The image has been strengthened by Madison Avenue, but it is primarily due to this fundamental decision-making, self-controlling capability of computers. Not too many people know — or really care — that each element of that self-control must be carefully considered by a human programmer and specifically included in his instructions to the machine.

The programmer's job is to tell the computer what to do, from beginning to end of a specified problem. He must decide what input he needs, and in which form it would be most useful. He must define each arithmetic and logical operation to be performed by the computer and, in the case of logical decisions, which alternatives to take under which circumstances. For example, suppose you were a programmer and you wanted to know how many 18-year-old blonde girls attended your school, Slippery Stone State College. Suppose, further, that you had access to a deck of punched cards, one for each student in the college, each of which contained the following information: (a) name, (b) sex, (c) age, (d) eye color, (e) hair color, (f) weight, and (g) telephone number. A typical card might look like the one in figure 1.45.

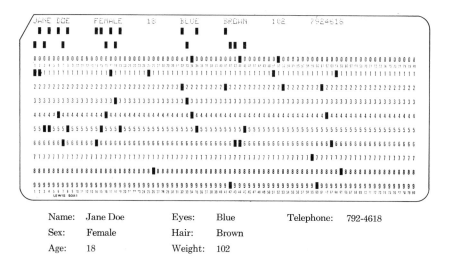

Name:	Jane Doe	Eyes:	Blue	Telephone:	792-4618
Sex:	Female	Hair:	Brown		
Age:	18	Weight:	102		

Figure 1.45

There is a great deal of information in each card, and most of it, as a matter of fact, you are not interested in, at least for purposes of this particular program. It might be nice to go back and get it on a second-round effort. But for now, all you want is 18-year-old blonde girls.

The computer will have to perform the following steps:

1. Read student's card.

2. Find sex, age, and hair-color fields.

3. Is it a girl?

4. If so, is she 18 years old?

5. If so, is she a blonde?

6. If so, add her to the total.

7. Read the next card . . .

This makes things appear very simple, but there's a lot left out of that little list. What if it isn't a girl? What if she isn't 18? What if she's 18, but not blonde? What if you've read the last card — how do you stop the machine?

To write down all these alternatives in words would be a waste of time for you as a programmer. Furthermore, unless you knew the exact number of cards, you couldn't even do it, for you would have to repeat the whole series of steps for each card. It would be easier to tabulate the whole business by hand.

To avoid these problems, and to logically depict a problem and the steps of its solution, a programmer uses a block diagram, or *flowchart*. Each box represents a logical step in the solution process. Usually, different shapes represent different types of operations — input/output, arithmetic, decision-making, etc. Figure 1.46 is a flowchart to find all the 18-year-old blonde girls at Slippery Stone State College. We use round "boxes" for input and output operations, rectangular ones for computation, diamond-shaped ones for decision-making, or logical, oper- ations, and oval ones for terminal steps (you must always tell a computer when to stop and go). Notice that there is always more than one exit from a decision box; you must specify what the computer is to do when the answer is "yes," and what it is to do when the answer is "no."

Once you have your flowchart, you translate the boxes into specific instructions to the computer. There are many programming languages that have been written so that people can communicate with computers (which, being electronic devices, tend not to speak ordinary human languages). The language you use depends upon several factors: which ones the particular computer you're using can understand, which ones you can understand, and which one is the most efficient for the type of problem you are trying to solve.

When the instructions are written, you have a program. This is then fed into the system (usually by punched cards), and you're ready

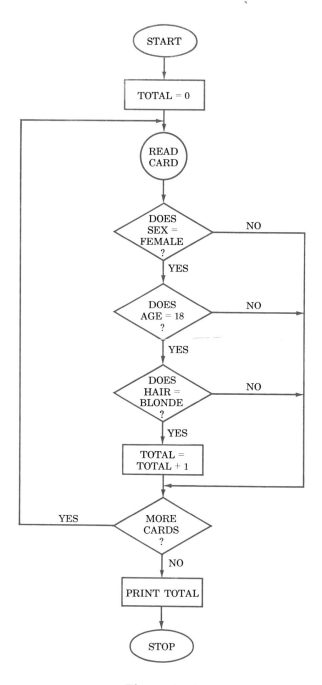

Figure 1.46

to go. Just push the start button and let her rip . . . and the computer will solve your problem just up to the first point where you left something out. Suppose you left a "no" exit off of your "Is she a blonde?" instruction. With the first nonblonde, the computer will come to a grinding halt, and there it will sit until you come to its rescue by correcting your programming and resubmitting it to the system.

Program testing and correcting can take at least as much time as the original analysis and coding. This whole chapter may, hopefully, have illustrated the ease with which we can make logical mistakes. We don't always catch our own, but the computer does.

But that's the programmer's problem. It is up to us just to recognize that the problem does exist and that, despite reports to the contrary, "giant brains" are really no more than brainless but efficient (and rather expensive) beasts of computational burden.

PROBLEM SET 1.7

1. Prepare a flowchart for each of the following situations:

   (a) Sharpening a pencil.

   (b) Getting up in the morning.

   (c) Preparing an egg for breakfast.

   (d) Making a dress.

   (e) Multiplying the sum of the first ten decimal digits by 5.

   (f) Finding the average of 50 given numbers.

   (g) Making a peanut butter and jelly sandwich.

   (h) Changing a wheel on an automobile.

   (i) Barbecuing a steak.

2. Invent a situation and prepare a flowchart for its solution.

3. Using a deck of punched cards mentioned in this section, a programmer wants to know how many blue-eyed girls between the ages of 16 and 20 years attend Slippery Stone State College. Set up a flowchart which can be used to find these girls.

Chapter 2

NUMBERS: PEBBLES, FINGERS, SYMBOLS

2.1 Numeral Systems

One of man's earliest tools was the idea of number. He needed some way to keep track of the quantity of his belongings. Of course, if his pickings consisted of only two or three sheep, it was a relatively easy task to determine if he had the correct number. This could be accomplished by mere observation. For the affluent, however, it was a more difficult chore. If, for example, a man owned 15 sheep, it would try one's patience to tell by observation alone if one was missing. A more systematic method would be necessary.

One such method would be to keep a set of small pebbles, with one pebble for each sheep. As long as there was a one-to-one correspondence between the set of pebbles and the set of sheep, he could feel confident that he had the correct number of sheep. If, however, in performing the one-to-one matching, he ran out of sheep before he did pebbles, he would know that the number of missing sheep would correspond to the number of unmatched pebbles. On the other hand, if sheep kept entering the corral *after* all the counting stones had been taken in hand, the pebble packer would be overjoyed, but subject to a direct frontal attack from the neighboring chief whose flock came in that many too few. One can appreciate the fact that keeping track of 2,000 sheep by the "pebble method" would become a weighty problem. Man soon discovered that

56

he could keep track of large quantities by making tally marks in the sand or on clay tablets. This certainly was an improvement over carrying a pebble for each item.

Since the time of early man, many numeral systems have been devised, each serving the needs of the particular culture involved. An example of a fairly primitive system, but one which showed some ingenuity, is the Egyptian system, which evolved many centuries B.C.

A single-stroke tally mark is made for each item up to ten. To simplify matters, once ten items are counted a new symbol is used to designate a set of ten articles. The following are some of the symbols used by the Egyptians.

Tally Mark . . . . one

Heelbone . . . . ten

Coil of Rope . . . . one hundred

Lotus Flower . . . . one thousand

Bent Line . . . . ten thousand

Figure 2.1

Combinations of these symbols were used to represent various numbers.

Figure 2.2

We refer to the Egyptian system as an additive system, since it is the values rather than the positions of the symbols which are important.

The number 235 could be represented by ⑥⑥∩ ∩ ∩|||||
as well as by ∩||⑥∩|⑥∩||.

Our numeral system, Hindu-Arabic, is a positional as well as additive system. Here position *is* important. There are ten symbols in the system:

$$0, 1, 2, 3, 4, 5, 6, 7, 8, 9$$

The position of the symbol 3 in a numeral tells us whether we are considering 3 items, 30 items, 300 items, etc. The symbol represents a different quantity in each different position. When we read a numeral such as 2834, the digit at the far right represents the number of (1's) that we have (in this example, we have four (1's)). The next digit to the left (in this case, 3) tells us how many (10's) we have. Moving one more position to the left, we find how many ten (10's) or (100's) we have. One more place to the left gives us the number of (1000's). The value of each position represents ten times the value of the position to its immediate right.

$$\underline{2} \quad \underline{8} \quad \underline{3} \quad \underline{4}$$

thousands hundreds tens ones

The number 2834 could be written as a sum:

$$2834 = 2000 + 800 + 30 + 4$$
$$= 2(1000) + 8(100) + 3(10) + 4(1)$$

REMARK: You may have forgotten, or never remembered, that we can eliminate the good old-fashioned multiplication symbol $\times$ from between two numbers, such as 2×3, by replacing the $\times$ with a dot, $2 \cdot 3$, or by enclosing one of the numbers in parentheses, $2(3)$, or by enclosing both of the numbers in parentheses, $(2)(3)$.

In counting, we start with the (1's) position, and when we have ten items we group them as one unit and write a 1 in the (10's) position. Thus, ten would be written

$$10 = 1 \text{ ten} \quad \text{and } 0 \text{ ones}$$
$$= 1(10) + 0(1)$$

We continue to count using these two positions until we have ten (10's). We then group these as one unit and write a 1 in the (100's) position.

$$\underline{1} \quad \underline{0} \quad \underline{0} = 1(100) + 0(10) + 0(1)$$

hundreds *tens* *ones*

Since we are always grouping in (10's), we say our number system is based on 10, or, simply, base 10.

PROBLEM SET 2.1

1. Change each of the following from Egyptian to Hindu-Arabic form.

(a) $\lceil \, \mathbb{Q} \, \cap \, | \, |$

(b) $\stackrel{\circ}{\underline{\lambda}} \, \mathbb{Q} \, \mathbb{Q} \, \mathbb{Q} \, \cap \, | \, | \, | \, | \, |$

(c) $\cap \, \cap \, \cap \, \cap \, \stackrel{\circ}{\underline{\lambda}} \, |$

(d) $\lceil \, \lceil \, \lceil \, \stackrel{\circ}{\underline{\lambda}} \, \stackrel{\circ}{\underline{\lambda}} \, \stackrel{\circ}{\underline{\lambda}} \, \stackrel{\circ}{\underline{\lambda}} \, \mathbb{Q} \, \mathbb{Q} \, | \, | \, |$

2. Change each of the following to Egyptian representation.

   (a)   137   (b)   1,352

   (c) 5,729   (d) 23,491

3. See if you can recall the Roman numeral system. Write each of the following Roman numerals in Hindu-Arabic form.

   (a) LXVI   (b) XLVII

   (c) DCCXLI   (d) MCMLXIX

4. Change each of the following to Roman number symbols.

   (a)   19   (b)   98

   (c) 411   (d) 1271

5. Which is larger, LXXXVIII or C?

6. Multiply XXXII times LXIV without changing to "ordinary" number symbols.

7. The numerals 27 and 72 are both composed of the same two digits, 2 and 7. Explain why they do not represent the same number. Will interchanging the digits of any two-digit number always result in a different two-digit number?

8. The amount of time it takes for each of two contestants to finish a certain auto race is 4 hours, 8 minutes, 15 seconds, and 3 hours, 53 minutes, 27 seconds, respectively. How long had the two drivers been competing collectively, and what is the difference in their times?

2.2. Number Bases

Why our numeral system developed on base 10 is not certain, but the reason probably is connected to the fact that man has ten fingers on his hands. There certainly is no reason to become smug or narrow-minded about using base 10. Any other base, such as 2, 5, or 7, might serve just as well.

Let us consider a numeral system using base 7. We use seven symbols. Since we are familiar with them, let us use the symbols 0, 1, 2, 3, 4, 5, 6. In base 10 we grouped items in (10's). In base 7, we group in (7's). Thus, when we have counted seven items, we represent this by placing a 1 in the (7's) position and a 0 in the (1's) position. Hence, 7 (base 10) = 10 (base seven).

In order to distinguish bases, we can use a subscript for all bases. If a subscript is not used, the number is base 10. The subscript will indicate the base being used. Thus, 25_7 means two (7's) and five (1's), or

$$2(7) + 5(1) = 19$$

Other examples are:

$$341_7 = 3(49) \ + 4(7) \ + 1(1)$$
$$2453_7 = 2(343) + 4(49) + 5(7) + 3(1)$$

Each position represents seven of the units at its immediate right.

$$31{,}542_7 = \underline{3} \quad \underline{1} \quad \underline{5} \quad \underline{4} \quad \underline{2}$$

seven (343's) = (2401's)

seven (49's) = (343's)

seven (7's) = (49's)

(7's)

(1's)

To change a numeral from base 7 to base 10, we merely expand the number as we have in the previous examples and find the total of the indicated sum.

$$341_7 = 3(49) \ + 4(7) \ + 1(1)$$
$$= 147 \ \ \ + 28 \ \ \ + 1$$
$$= 176$$

$$2453_7 = 2(343) + 4(49) + 5(7) + 3(1)$$
$$= 686 \quad + 196 \quad + 35 \quad + 3$$
$$= 920$$

It may be interesting and important to know that changing a number from base 10 to base 7 can be simplified if we first set up an outline of the various positions that will be used in the number. As an example, let us change 235 to a base 7 number. First set up an outline in base seven as follows:

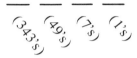

We really only need three positions, since the value of the fourth position to the left is 343, which is larger than our number, 235.

We start with the largest group of items and subtract as many as possible from 235. The largest such group is (49's) and, dividing, we can squeeze four 49's out of 235. We place a 4 in the (49's) position.

$$\underline{\hphantom{4}4\hphantom{4}} \quad \underline{\hphantom{xx}} \quad \underline{\hphantom{xx}}$$
$$(49's) \quad (7's) \quad (1's)$$

After removing four (49's), or 196, from 235, we have a remainder of 39. Next we try for the righthand neighbor group of (7's) and salvage five (7's) from 39. Anchor a 5 in the (7's) position.

$$\underline{\hphantom{4}4\hphantom{4}} \quad \underline{\hphantom{4}5\hphantom{4}} \quad \underline{\hphantom{xx}}$$
$$(49's) \quad (7's) \quad (1's)$$

Removing five (7's), or 35, from 39, we have a remainder of four (1's). A 4 in the (1's) position completes the number in base 7.

$$\underline{\hphantom{4}4\hphantom{4}} \quad \underline{\hphantom{4}5\hphantom{4}} \quad \underline{\hphantom{4}4\hphantom{4}}$$
$$(49's) \quad (7's) \quad (1's)$$

Eureka! $235 = 454_7$.

Let's perform some operations with numbers in base 7. Study the following examples carefully.

Example 1   Add 34_7 to 25_7.

Solution
$$
\begin{aligned}
25_7 &= 2\,(7) + 5\,(1) \\
+\ 34_7 &= 3\,(7) + 4\,(1) \\
\hline
&\ \ 5\,(7) + 9\,(1)
\end{aligned}
$$

but $9\,(1) = 1\,(7) + 2\,(1)$

so we can write $5\,(7) + 9\,(1) = 5\,(7) + 1\,(7) + 2\,(1)$

$$= 6\,(7) + 2\,(1)$$

$$= 62_7$$

Now that we have struggled over a tough one, let's try a few more and see if they become easier. All problems of this type are alike except for a change in digits.

Example 2   Add 435_7 to 234_7.

Solution
$$
\begin{aligned}
234_7 &= 2\,(49) + 3\,(7) + 4\,(1) \\
+\ 435_7 &= 4\,(49) + 3\,(7) + 5\,(1) \\
\hline
&\ \ 6\,(49) + 6\,(7) + 9\,(1)
\end{aligned}
$$

but $9\,(1) = 1\,(7) + 2\,(1)$

so the sum is $6\,(49) + 6\,(7) + 1\,(7) + 2\,(1)$

but this is $6\,(49) + 7\,(7) + 2\,(1)$

and $7\,(7) = 1\,(49) + 0\,(7)$

therefore, we have $6\,(49) + 1\,(49) + 0\,(7) + 2\,(1)$

which equals $7\,(49) + 0\,(7) + 2\,(1)$

again, $7\,(49) = 1\,(343) + 0\,(49)$

so we have $1\ (343) + 0\ (49) + 0\ (7) + 2\ (1)$

we can now indicate our final answer:

$$234_7 + 435_7 = 1002_7$$

Example 3   Subtract 13_7 from 54_7.

$$\begin{array}{r} 54_7 \\ -\ 13_7 \\ \hline \end{array}$$

Solution   This subtraction problem brings about no situations other than those we have already confronted in base 10, so we shall go directly about our business. 3 from 4 leaves 1, and we write

$$\begin{array}{r} 54_7 \\ -\ 13_7 \\ \hline 1_7 \end{array}$$

5 minus 1 is 4, and our problem is finished.

$$\begin{array}{r} 54_7 \\ -\ 13_7 \\ \hline 41_7 \end{array}$$

Nothing to it! Let's try subtraction again.

Example 4   Subtract 36_7 from 65_7.

$$\begin{array}{r} 65_7 \\ -36_7 \\ \hline \end{array}$$

Solution

$$\begin{aligned} 65_7 &= \quad\ \ 6\ (7) + 5\ (1) \\ -36_7 &= -\ [3\ (7) + 6\ (1)] \end{aligned}$$

Immediately we run into a dilemma, for we can't take 6 (1's) from 5 (1's). Therefore, we have two approaches to the answer. First, we may remain static, shed a few tears, and wait for someone to give us the answer. Second, we can become dynamic, go to the (7's) place, and borrow something. In this age of loans and credit cards this should present no challenge. Since 6 (7) is equal to 5 (7) + 1 (7), or in a more useful form, 5 (7) + 7 (1). Upon borrowing, 6 (7) + 5 (1) will look something like this:

$$5 (7) + 7 (1) + 5 (1)$$

or
$$5 (7) + 12 (1)$$

thus
$$\begin{array}{r} 5 (7) + 12 (1) \\ - [3 (7) + 6 (1)] \\ \hline \end{array}$$

equals
$$2 (7) + \cdot 6 (1)$$

or
$$26_7$$

Example 5 Multiply 326_7 by 32_7.

Solution

The procedures of multiplication are the same in base 7, or any other number base, as they are in base 10. First, we multiply 346_7 by 2_7. We immediately run into a stone wall, for $2_7 \times 6_7 = 12_7$. Remember that the amount "twelve" exists in every base; the difficulty arises in writing the number in digit form. Twelve in base 7 notation is $1(7) + 5 (1)$. There, we place the 5 in the (1's) column and carry the 1 to the (7's) column.

$$\begin{array}{r} 346_7 \\ \times 32_7 \\ \hline 15_7 \end{array}$$

By placing our digits in their respective places, our product by 2_7 will look like this:

$$\begin{array}{r} 346_7 \\ \times 2_7 \\ \hline 15_7 = 2_7 \times 6_7 \\ 11_7 = 2_7 \times 4_7 \\ 6_7 = 2_7 \times 3_7 \end{array}$$

Now, if we can do our carrying and adding mentally as we go along, the partial product will condense to

$$\begin{array}{r} 346_7 \\ \times 2_7 \\ \hline 1025_7 \end{array}$$

Now we are ready to multiply by the next digit.

$$346_7$$
$$\times \quad 32_7$$
$$1025_7 = 2_7 \times 346_7$$
$$24_7 = 3_7 \times 6_7$$
$$15_7 = 3_7 \times 4_7$$
$$12_7 = 3_7 \times 3_7$$

Here again, if some of the adding and carrying can be done in the mind —it takes practice—the picture is:

$$346_7$$
$$\times \quad 32_7$$
$$1025_7$$
$$1404_7$$
$$\overline{15065_7}$$

After becoming fortified by at least a hazy understanding of the process, you may wish to avoid using the expanded form and perform the operation more compactly, as you did in the more familiar base 10. Follow through each of the following examples, but cautiously—they may require some thought.

Example 6   Find the sum of 254_7 and 465_7.

Solution
$$254_7$$
$$+ \quad 465_7$$
$$\overline{1052_7}$$

Example 7   Subtract 256_7 from 534_7.

Solution
$$534_7$$
$$- \quad 256_7$$
$$\overline{245_7}$$

Example 8   Multiply 524_7 by 14_7.

Solution

$$\begin{array}{r}
524_7 \\
\times \quad 14_7 \\
\hline
3032_7 \\
524_7 \\
\hline
11302_7
\end{array}$$

PROBLEM SET 2.2

1. Change each of the following to base 10 (decimal notation).

   (a) 235_7 (b) 146_7 (c) 1524_7

   (d) 234_5 (e) 3213_4 (f) 2011_3

   (g) 756_8 (h) 110101_2 (i) 1101011_2

2. Change each of the following to base 7.

   (a) 598   (b) 2013   (c) 425_6

3. Change each of the following to base 5.

   (a) 238   (b) 1827   (c) 257_8

4. Change each of the following to base 2 (binary notation).

   (a) 43   (b) 256   (c) 2041_5

   (d) 99   (e) 270   (f) 1000

5. Perform the indicated operations.

   (a) $\begin{array}{r} 324_5 \\ + 143_5 \\ \hline \end{array}$
   (b) $\begin{array}{r} 632_7 \\ - 453_7 \\ \hline \end{array}$
   (c) $\begin{array}{r} 231_4 \\ \times 23_4 \\ \hline \end{array}$

   (d) $\begin{array}{r} 275_8 \\ + 703_8 \\ \hline \end{array}$
   (e) $\begin{array}{r} 2021_3 \\ - 212_3 \\ \hline \end{array}$
   (f) $437_8 + 253_8 + 176_8$

   (g) $\begin{array}{r} 11011_2 \\ + 10101_2 \\ \hline \end{array}$
   (h) $\begin{array}{r} 11011_2 \\ - 10110_2 \\ \hline \end{array}$
   (i) $\begin{array}{r} 10011_2 \\ \times 111_2 \\ \hline \end{array}$

6. Determine the following amounts. What base seems to be implied in each?

   (a) $\begin{array}{l} 5 \text{ gross } 3 \text{ dozen } 1 \text{ unit} \\ + 4 \text{ gross } 6 \text{ dozen } 5 \text{ units} \\ \hline \end{array}$
   (b) $\begin{array}{l} 3 \text{ gross } 8 \text{ dozen } 7 \text{ units} \\ + 2 \text{ gross } 3 \text{ dozen } 5 \text{ units} \\ \hline \end{array}$

(c)   2 feet 5 inches   (d)   3 hours 6 min. 8 seconds
       + 6 feet 9 inches   − 1 hour 7 min. 9 seconds

7. Try to establish what base is being used in the following problem and translate it to base 10. On May 103, 30340 a man worked 22 hours at a pay rate
   of 12 dollars per hour. On June 32, he worked 24 hours at 10 dollars per
   hour. He therefore worked a total of 101 hours. What were his total earnings?

8. Write 1970 in base 8 and then in base 2 notation. Place your new numbers
   one under the other and compare. See if you can find some simple way of
   converting from base 8 to base 2 and back without going through decimal
   notation. (*Hint:* Starting from the right, place each base 8 digit with each
   triple of base 2 digits.)

9. After stopping and thinking about this whole business for awhile, you may
   want to growl and flex your mental muscles on this one: We have a system
   with 26 symbols, each digit a letter of the alphabet. Thus we are working
   in base 26. a = 0, b = 1, c = 2, d = 3, . . ., z = 25. In this system, how
   much is one + two, one + one? Which represents the largest number:
   hundred, thousand, or million?

Hint: one = o   n   e
               (676's) (26's) (1's)

2.3. The Natural Numbers

Probably the first and most important set of numbers with which we
battled in our early school years, or anywhere else, was the set of *natural
numbers* {1, 2, 3, 4, . . .}. We begin now to peek at some of their properties, the first being that each has a unique value. For those who have
not peered into ancient mathematics before, the experience may create

an irresistible urge to make other pilgrimages. We need some way to link our elements to each other. For this reason, we form the following definitions:

$$1 + 1 = 2$$
$$2 + 1 = 3$$
$$3 + 1 = 4$$
$$4 + 1 = 5$$
$$5 + 1 = 6$$
$$6 + 1 = 7$$
$$7 + 1 = 8$$
$$8 + 1 = 9$$
$$9 + 1 = 10$$

etc.

If we let these definitions collectively define the operation of addition, then we can find the result of adding 1 to any other number.

From our experience with these natural numbers, we should be able to list a few of their properties for addition. One such property is that it does not matter which number is written first. That is, $3 + 5$ represents the same sum as $5 + 3$, and $2 + 9$ has the same sum as $9 + 2$. In general, we say that

$$a + b = b + a$$

where a and b are natural numbers. This is called the *Commutative Property of Addition*. Notice, the only difference between the left and the right side of the problem is the change of position of the numbers with reference to the addition symbol.

To show that this property holds for all pairs of natural numbers, we would need to take them all, two by two, and lead them through the pattern. Mathematicians shorten the work with a gimmick called mathematical induction. Another quick visible indication that the Commutative Property of Addition holds for the natural numbers is to construct an addition table of the digits 1 through 9 and then draw a diagonal from the operation symbol to the opposite corner (from upper left to lower right). If the two halves formed have the same numbers in the same relative position on either side of the diagonal, then the table is said to be symmetric about this diagonal and the operation is commutative.

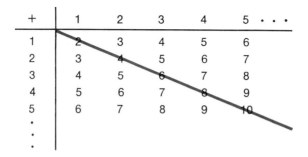

Figure 2.3

Now, suppose that we are asked to find the sum of three numbers, like $2 + 5 + 4$. Innocently, we can add only two numbers simultaneously, and so the question arises, do we add the 2 and 5 and then add that sum to 4,

$$(2 + 5) + 4 = 7 + 4 = 11$$

or do we add 2 to the sum of 5 and 4 as

$$2 + (5 + 4) = 2 + 9 = 11$$

We see by the results that in this example it makes no difference which numbers we added first. From experience, we know that in general it does not matter which pair is added first; the result will be the same. We can then state

$$(a + b) + c = a + (b + c)$$

where a, b, and c are natural numbers. This property is the *Associative Property of Addition*.

> *REMARK: In the Commutative Property the numbers actually traded places, whereas in the Associative Property the numbers remain fixed and the punctuation—the parentheses—has moved about a different pair of numbers. We can do very little in mathematics without the Commutative and Associative Properties, so they are developed early in the game.*

"Daddy, 28 plus (36 plus 49) equals (28 plus 36)
plus what--using the associative principle?"

If we accept the definition of addition from this section, along with the Commutative and Associative Properties of Addition, we can prove the rest of the addition table. Suppose we are asked to prove that $3 + 2 = 5$. The proof follows.

1. $3 + 2 = 3 + (1 + 1)$	1. Definition $1 + 1 = 2$
2. $\quad = (3 + 1) + 1$	2. Associative Property of Addition
3. $\quad = 4 + 1$	3. Definition $3 + 1 = 4$
4. $\quad = 5$	4. Definition $4 + 1 = 5$

Again, we show that $3 + 3 = 6$.

1. $3 + 3 = 3 + (2 + 1)$	1. Definition $2 + 1 = 3$
2. $\quad = (3 + 2) + 1$	2. Associative Property of Addition

3. $= 5 + 1$ 3. We have already proved that
                                             $3 + 2 = 5$

4. $= 6$ 4. Definition $5 + 1 = 6$

All other entries in the addition table could be similarly proved.

We shall wave our magical wand of induction and take for granted that all such addition proofs have been made. Now we know all sums such as $9 + 7$, $8 + 9$, and even $123 + 98$! (Incidentally, we say that for each pair of natural numbers the sum is unique.)

Another familiar operation with the natural numbers is multiplication. The knotty point of issue now is whether this set of natural numbers follows the same rituals in multiplication that it does in addition. Perhaps we are familiar with the era of flashcards and multiplication tables, when teachers and people who wrote textbooks presumed that we had become computers who were required to conjure up solutions for $6 \cdot 7$, $9 \cdot 6$, and $8 \cdot 9$ instantaneously upon demand. Had we made the profound observation at that time that $9 \cdot 7$ and $7 \cdot 9$ claim the same simple solution, our struggle would have been mere child's play. After we had learned that $5 \cdot 9$ was just another name for 45, when we got to the (9's), we would have already known that $9 \cdot 5$ was also 45; that $8 \cdot 7 = 7 \cdot 8$; and, in general, if a and b represent any natural numbers whatsoever,

$$a \cdot b = b \cdot a$$

or simply $$ab = ba$$

Voila! The *Commutative Property of Multiplication!*

Ab initio, we have pursued only products of two numbers. But there are times when we are confronted by an indicated product of three numbers, or four, or . . . well, to become more specific, we note that $(2 \cdot 5) \cdot 7 = 10 \cdot 7$, where $2 \cdot 5$ is defined as 10 in our cache of values. Thus, the problem has been reduced to two elements and we can eliminate the whole affair by taking $10 \cdot 7 = 70$. But let's tarry for a moment. We have arbitrarily chosen as our first step to multiply the pair of numbers 2 and 5. Suppose we wished to multiply 5 and 7 first. Does $2 \cdot (5 \cdot 7)$ represent 70 just as $(2 \cdot 5) \cdot 7$ does? Once more from our repertory of facts, $5 \cdot 7$ is 35 and $2 \cdot (5 \cdot 7) = 2 \cdot 35$, which in turn is our friendly fellow, 70.

At first it may seem awkward, but we state that if a, b, and c represent any natural numbers, then

$$(ab)\, c = a\,(bc)$$

This is the *Associative Property of Multiplication.*

Another observation is that $2 \cdot 1 = 2$, $3 \cdot 1 = 3$, $4 \cdot 1 = 4$, and in general $a \cdot 1 = a$, where a represents any natural number. The natural number 1 is called the *Multiplicative Identity.*

One other property is worthy of mention here. Suppose we are asked to simplify the expression $3(2 + 5)$, which says, "multiply the sum of 2 and 5 by 3." One solution would be $3(2 + 5) = 3(7) = 21$. We note, however, that the same result could be obtained in a slightly different way. We could do this as follows: $3(2 + 5) = 3(2) + 3(5) = 6 + 15 = 21$. Let's try another example.

$$2(3 + 7) = 2(10) = 20$$

or

$$2(3 + 7) = 2(3) + 2(7) = 6 + 14 = 20$$

A few more examples should begin to convince us that these two methods should always lead to the same result. In general, if a, b, and c are proxies for natural numbers, then

$$a(b + c) = ab + ac$$

This is called the *Distributive Property of Multiplication over Addition.* We shall refer to it simply as the Distributive Property.

With these properties we can now completely develop the multiplication table. An example will illustrate how this can be done. Let us prove that $3 \cdot 2 = 6$. We do this as follows:

1. $3 \cdot 2 = 3(1 + 1)$ 1. Definition $2 = 1 + 1$

2. $= 3(1) + 3(1)$ 2. Distributive Property

3. $= 3 + 3$ 3. Multiplicative Identity

4. $= 6$ 4. We have already proved that $3 + 3 = 6$.

This example shows a relationship between multiplication and addition. In fact, we can see that a multiplication problem is nothing more than a problem in addition. Thus, multiplication is often referred to as "repeated addition."

A most commonplace and obvious property is so commanding that it may lead us directly into other number sets or the empty set for solutions. It is the property of *closure*. If any two natural numbers are added, our sum will always be a unique natural number. The same is true for multiplication. The set of natural numbers is said to be *closed* under the operations of addition and multiplication. Usually, when we define an operation on a set of numbers, we *assume* the closure property exists under that operation.

Another operation which we met in the elementary grades, and a first cousin to the operation of addition, is subtraction. We were asked to solve such problems as $7 - 3 = ?$ The problem is read "seven minus three equals question mark," but what we are really looking for is a number that could be added to 3 and would give 7 as a result. In other words, the problem could be restated as $3 + ? = 7$, which is an addition statement. One more time, qualifying a, b, and c as members of our natural numbers and given the subtraction problem $a - b = c$, we are asked to find the number c that could be added to b and give us the sum a. The result defines the operation of subtraction.

$$a - b = c \rightarrow b + c = a$$

$$c + b = a \rightarrow a - c = b$$

Now consider the statement $3 - 5 = ?$ As we have seen, the statement is equivalent to $5 + ? = 3$. Ridiculous! There is no natural number which we could add to 5 and obtain a sum of 3. The solution set, then, for $3 - 5$ is the empty set—if we are held to selecting an answer from the natural numbers. One such example is enough to let us state that if we subtract any two natural numbers, we do not always obtain a natural number as a result, and this set is *not* closed under the operation of subtraction.

Suppose we decide to require that every subtraction problem have an answer. We will have to invent some new numbers and, therefore, will no longer be dealing with just the natural numbers. Such a set of numbers, the integers, will be considered in Section 2.5.

PROBLEM SET 2.3

1. How large is a million? Would you care to guess how many bottles of cold drinks are consumed in the United States in one year? (*Hint:* Use someone as an average, maybe yourself, and approximate the number of people to be something like 200,000,000.) Have you ever heard of a googol? Googolplex? You may wish to do some more research on large numbers. Check other resource material.

2. Which sum is the greater, that of the figures on the left, or on the right?

987654321	123456789
87654321	12345678
7654321	1234567
654321	123456
54321	12345
4321	1234
321	123
21	12
1	1

3. How many one-digit numbers are there in the set discussed in this section? How many two-digit numbers? Can you form a general rule?

4. Prove the following statements:

   (a) $2 + 2 = 4$ (b) $2 + 3 = 5$ (c) $3 + 4 = 7$

   (d) $2 \cdot 2 = 4$ (e) $3 \cdot 3 = 9$ (f) $3 \cdot 4 = 12$

5. Use the distributive property to simplify the following:

   (a) $3(1 + 2)$ (b) $5(2 + 3)$ (c) $4(2 + 7)$

   (d) $6(10 + 3)$ (e) $(2 + 3)5$ (f) $(a + b)(c + d)$

   REMARK: At times the distributive property may be used to simplify multiplication. If we are asked to multiply $7 \cdot 14$, we may rewrite the problem as $7(10 + 4)$. We then use the distributive property to finish the problem.

   $$7(10 + 4) = 7 \cdot 10 + 7 \cdot 4 = 70 + 28 = 98$$

6. Use this technique to perform the following multiplications:

    (a) $3 \cdot 16$ (b) $6 \cdot 17$

    (c) $8 \cdot 23$ (d) $4 \cdot 67$

    (e) Using the pattern in Problem 5 (f), find $33 \cdot 27$.

7. Find the missing digits which are represented by question marks in the following multiplication problem. Use the given digits for a guide.

$$\begin{array}{r} ??5 \\ 1?? \\ \hline 2??5 \\ 13?0 \\ ??? \\ \hline 4?77? \end{array}$$

8. Perform the following subtractions where possible. Indicate where there is no answer in the set of natural numbers.

    (a) $7 - 2$ (b) $23 - 17$ (c) $85 - 29$

    (d) $17 - 71$ (e) $25 - 25$ (f) $93 - 99$

9. Consider the operation of division. Is the set of natural numbers closed under the operation? Explain.

10. Using knowledge gained in this section, turn back to problem set 2.1 and solve problem 6 again. Use the fact that the Roman numeral system is an additive and subtractive system (i.e., $VI = V + I$ and $IV = V - I$), and also the Commutative, Associative, and Distributive Properties.

11. Consider the set operations of union and intersection.

    (a) Is each commutative (i.e., does $A \cup B = B \cup A$)?

    (b) Is each associative?

    (c) Do they possess identity elements?

    (d) Is union distributive over intersection?

    (e) Is intersection distributive over union?

2.4. Prime Numbers

We now add a pinch of spice and a dash of confusion to our naturals and proclaim that any natural number may be expressed as a product of two or more natural numbers! For example, 42 may be expressed as $2 \cdot 21$; $35 = 5 \cdot 7$; $49 = 7 \cdot 7$; and $56 = 2 \cdot 28$. One might ask about a number such as 13. Our reply would be $13 = 1 \cdot 13$, and, in fact, $1 = 1 \cdot 1$. The numbers that are multiplied together to form the product are called *factors* of the product. Obviously, then, 2 and 21 are factors of 42. We should now be going in full pursuit to see if there are any other factors of 42. It turns out that 6 and 7 are factors, as well as 3 and 14. We see that there are several factors of 42, including 1 and 42.

Returning to the number 13, upon scrutiny we see that it has only two different factors, 1 and 13. This certainly isn't why 13 is unlucky for so many people; if it were, there would be infinitely many unlucky numbers, for we can find an infinite amount of numbers that have only two different factors. The numbers 7, 11, 23, and 107 are just a few examples. A special name is given to the set of natural numbers which have exactly two distinct (different) factors. They are called *prime numbers,* and the only factors for these prime numbers are the numbers themselves and the unit number, 1.

The first ten prime numbers are 2, 3, 5, 7, 11, 13, 17, 19, 23, and 29. Why isn't 1 included as a prime number? We notice that 2 is the only even prime number. Why?

Remember the element 42 that had several factors? We could express 42 as $2 \cdot 21$. Notice that the factor 2 is a prime number, but 21 is not. We could express 21 as $3 \cdot 7$. Both factors of 21 are prime numbers. Therefore, we say that $42 = 2 \cdot 3 \cdot 7$. Each factor is a prime number and we say that 42 is factored into *prime factors.*

For those mathematical addicts who are persistent enough to seek the other factors of 42 mentioned earlier, we lead into a proclamation exemplified by the following:

$$42 = 2 \cdot 21 = 2 \cdot 3 \cdot 7 \qquad \text{as shown}$$
$$42 = 6 \cdot 7 \; = (2 \cdot 3) \cdot 7 \qquad \text{factors of 6}$$
$$ = 2 \cdot 3 \cdot 7 \qquad \text{why?}$$
$$42 = 3 \cdot 14 = 3 \cdot (2 \cdot 7) \qquad \text{factors of 14}$$
$$ = (3 \cdot 2) \cdot 7 \qquad \text{why?}$$

$$= (2 \cdot 3) \cdot 7 \qquad \text{why?}$$
$$= 2 \cdot 3 \cdot 7 \qquad \text{why?}$$

PROCLAMATION: Every natural number can be written as a product of prime factors in one and only one way, disregarding order!

Let us try factoring some other numbers into prime factors.

Example 1   Factor 770 into prime factors.

Solution   For a systematic approach to the solution, first try the smallest prime number as a factor. 2 is a factor of 770, i.e., $770 = 2 \cdot 385$. Now try to factor 385. Again we try 2 as a factor, but we see it is not a factor. We try the next largest prime number. 3 is not a factor of 385, so we try 5. Since 5 is a factor of 385, we may write $770 = 2 \cdot 385 = 2 \cdot 5 \cdot 77$. Now try to factor 77. By the process of elimination, 2, 3, and 5 are not factors of 77, so we try 7, which is a factor. Now we have $770 = 2 \cdot 385 = 2 \cdot 5 \cdot 77 = 2 \cdot 5 \cdot 7 \cdot 11$. Next we try to factor 11, but it is a prime number and we are finished. Thus, $770 = 2 \cdot 5 \cdot 7 \cdot 11$ in the prime factored form.

Example 2   Factor 504 into prime factors.

Solution   Again starting with 2, we obtain $504 = 2 \cdot 252$. Trying 2 again yields $504 = 2 \cdot 252 = 2 \cdot 2 \cdot 126$. We see that 2 is a factor of 126, and thus write $504 = 2 \cdot 2 \cdot 126 = 2 \cdot 2 \cdot 2 \cdot 63$. We try 2 once more, but it is not a factor of 63. We try 3, and obtain $504 = 2 \cdot 2 \cdot 2 \cdot 63 = 2 \cdot 2 \cdot 2 \cdot 3 \cdot 21$. Trying 3 for the second time, we get $504 = 2 \cdot 2 \cdot 2 \cdot 3 \cdot 3 \cdot 7$. Since 7 is a prime number, we have completed the prime factorization of 504.

Example 3   Express 167 in prime factors.

Solution   Starting with 2 and then trying larger primes, we see that there are no primes which are factors of 167. Thus 167 is itself a prime number.

Example 3 brings up an interesting question. What is the largest number we need to try before we can conclude that 167 is prime? Do we have to try all prime numbers smaller than 167? We know that $167 +$

$2 = 169 = 13 \cdot 13$. Then, when we have tried all primes up to 13 without success, can we conclude that 167 is prime? If any prime number 13 or larger is a factor of 167, the other factor must also be 13 or larger, since we have already tried all primes less than 13. Then the product would be greater than 167. If we do not find a factor by the time we have reached that prime which, when multiplied by itself, produces a larger number than the one we are trying to factor, we may conclude that our original number is not factorable into primes and is therefore a prime number itself.

PROBLEM SET 2.4

1. The following represent prime factorization of numbers. Find the numbers.

   (a) $2 \cdot 3 \cdot 7 \cdot 13$ (b) $3 \cdot 3 \cdot 5 \cdot 7 \cdot 11$

   (c) $3 \cdot 5 \cdot 103$ (d) $2^3 \cdot 3^2 \cdot 23$

2. Factor the following into prime factors. If they are already prime, indicate so.

   (a) 30   (b) 426

   (c) 29   (d) 396

   (e) 243   (f) 187

   (g) 819   (h) 391

3. The prime numbers 3 and 5 are called twin primes since they differ by 2. Find all pairs of twin primes less than 100.

4. (a) In the third century B.C., Eratosthenes devised a simple way to identify primes. He listed all numbers from 2 up to a given number. (We will use the numbers 2 through 40 as an example.) He concluded that 2 is a prime, but every second number thereafter is not prime since it would have 2 as a factor. He would therefore cross out every second number after 2. Now 3 is a prime, but every third number thereafter has a factor of 3 and consequently is not prime. Each of these numbers was crossed out. 5 is a prime, but every fifth number thereafter may be eliminated by the same type of reasoning. This process is continued. How far do we have to continue? The comment after example 3 tells us in this case we may stop searching after removing all multiples of 5 since 7 is the next prime and $7 \cdot 7 = 49$.

This leaves us with the prime numbers 2, 3, 5, 7, 11, 13, 17, 19, 23, 29, 31, 37. Instead of crossing out the numbers, Eratosthenes punched the numbers out with a sharp instrument, hence his method became known as the "sieve of Eratosthenes."

$$
\begin{array}{cccccccccc}
2 & 3 & \cancel{4} & 5 & \cancel{6} & 7 & \cancel{8} & \cancel{9} & \cancel{10} \\
11 & \cancel{12} & 13 & \cancel{14} & \cancel{15} & \cancel{16} & 17 & \cancel{18} & 19 & \cancel{20} \\
\cancel{21} & \cancel{22} & 23 & \cancel{24} & \cancel{25} & \cancel{26} & \cancel{27} & \cancel{28} & 29 & \cancel{30} \\
31 & \cancel{32} & \cancel{33} & \cancel{34} & \cancel{35} & \cancel{36} & 37 & \cancel{38} & \cancel{39} & \cancel{40}
\end{array}
$$

Use the sieve of Eratosthenes to find all prime numbers less than 150.

(b) Another arrangement of the numbers produces a sieve which presents a definite semisymmetric (whatever that means) pattern of primes. It can be constructed by writing the natural numbers in multiples of six and drawing straight vertical and diagonal lines in appropriate places, striking out all numbers that are not prime.

$$
\begin{array}{cccccc}
 & 2 & 3 & 4 & 5 & 6 \\
7 & 8 & 9 & 10 & 11 & 12 \\
\cdot & \cdot & \cdot & \cdot & \cdot & \cdot \\
\cdot & \cdot & \cdot & \cdot & \cdot & \cdot \\
\cdot & \cdot & \cdot & \cdot & \cdot & \cdot
\end{array}
$$

5. Determine the largest prime numbers that we need to consider in order to guarantee prime factorization of the following numbers.

    (a) 89   (b) 301   (c) 151

    (d) 429   (e) 1024   (f) 111,111

6. "Every even number greater than 2 may be expressed as a sum of two prime numbers." For example, $8 = 3 + 5$. This statement is called Goldbach's conjecture (1742 A.D.). It is called a conjecture because, although the statement seems to be true, it has never been proven. Show that Goldbach's conjecture is valid for all even numbers from 50 to 100.

2.5. The Integers

To begin with, we need a place to start; this sounds like double talk, but what we really need is the name for the starting place. Call it zero. Zero is defined to be a number that can be added to any given number and yield a sum which is the given number itself. For example,

$$2 + 0 = 2, \quad 19 + 0 = 19, \quad 6 + 0 = 6$$

In general we say that

$$a + 0 = a$$

and that *zero is the identity element for addition.*

The set $\{\ldots, -3, -2, -1, 0, 1, 2, 3, \ldots\}$ is called the set of *integers*. The word is derived from two Latin words meaning "not a fraction" or, in other words, a "whole." The set of natural numbers is included in this set of elements and is often referred to as the set of *positive integers*. We call the set of numbers $\{-1, -2, -3, \ldots\}$ the set of *negative integers*. Thus, the set of integers is:

$$\{1, 2, 3, \ldots\} \cup \{0\} \cup \{-1, -2, -3, \ldots\}$$

We define the negative integers as follows: The number -1 is the number which, when added to 1, will yield 0 (i.e., $1 + (-1) = 0$). The number -2 added to 2 begets the identity element for addition, 0. Thus, with very little effort, we conclude that for any natural number a there exists a number $-a$ such that

$$a + (-a) = 0$$

In particular, the numbers a and $-a$ are *inverses* of each other.

Often it is helpful to picture the integers set out on the *number line,* an almost perfect model for mathematicians. Draw a line, choose any point on the line and label it 0, then measure successive equal intervals to the right and to the left of 0. The endpoints of the intervals to the right of 0 are labeled with the positive integers. Those to the left of 0 are labeled with the negative integers, as in figure 2.4.

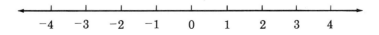

Figure 2.4

With this model, the order of the integers should become clear. When we write $4 > 2$ (read "4 is greater than 2"), we mean the number 4 is to the right of the number 2 on the number line. We could say

$$3 > 0, \quad 2 > -4, \quad -2 > -3, \ldots$$

On the other hand, when we write $-4 < 1$ (read "-4 is less than 1"), we mean that -4 is to the left of 1 on the line.

Let's keep swimming with the tide and fish out some of the properties of integers. At this point we should emphasize that our approach will be consistent with the theme of the book; that is, we will develop these properties by the use of patterns rather than by trying to drown the reader with sophisticated proofs. It should be noted, however, that each of these properties may be established by means of a rigorous mathematical proof. The interested student is encouraged to consult almost any new algebra text for such proofs.

In the operation of addition of integers, much of the chore has been completed for us. We have already discussed the addition of positive integers in the preceding section on natural numbers. Our first question, then, is, "What is the result of adding two negative integers?" Let's look at a few examples.

Example 1   Add: $-3 + (-2)$.

Solution   We know from the definition of negative numbers that

$$3 + (-3) = 0 \text{ and } 2 + (-2) = 0$$

It follows, then, that

$$[3 + (-3)] + [2 + (-2)] = 0 \text{ or that } 0 + 0 = 0$$

After rearranging terms, we have

$$(3 + 2) + [(-3) + (-2)] = 0$$

and then

$$5 + [(-3) + (-2)] = 0$$

Looking at the last expression, we know that the number that must be added to 5 to yield 0 is -5. Therefore,

$$(-3) + (-2) = -5$$

Example 2   Add: $-4 + (-5)$.

REMARK: Without the parentheses around the second negative integer, there are two side-by-side symbols, which presents some confusion. The parentheses are just for clarity.

Solution   Following Example 1, we can say that

$$4 + (-4) = 0 \text{ and } 5 + (-5) = 0$$
$$[4 + (-4)] + [5 + (-5) = 0] \ (0 + 0 = 0)$$

by rearranging, $(4 + 5) + [(-4) + (-5)] = 0$

or $9 + [(-4) + (-5)] = 0$

and $9 + (-9) = 0$

so we conclude that $(-4) + (-5) = -9$

A few examples of this type lead us to suspect that

$$-a + (-b) = -(a + b)$$

Our final (at long last) consideration in addition of integers consists of adding a positive and a negative integer.

Example 3   Add: $5 + (-3)$.

Solution   Since we know now that $3 + (-3) = 0$, we begin by expressing

$$5 = 2 + 3$$

Consequently, $5 + (-3)$ can be written

$$2 + 3 + (-3)$$

But this can be simplified further as

$$2 + 0$$

but this is equal to 2, so our solution can be stated as

$$5 + (-3) = 2 + 3 + (-3) = 2 + 0 = 2$$

Example 4   Add: $9 + (-5)$.

Solution   Following the same pattern as example 3, we have

$$9 + (-5) = 4 + 5 + (-5) = 4 + 0 = 4$$

Example 5   Add: $3 + (-7)$.

Solution $3 + (-7) = 3 + (-3) + (-4) = 0 + (-4) = -4$

Example 6   Add: $-8 + 3$.

Solution $-8 + 3 = (-5) + (-3) + 3 = -5 + 0 = -5$

We now concern ourselves with multiplication of the integers. In Section 2.3 we have already discussed multiplication of two positive integers (naturals). From that discussion we could write the following statements.

$$4 \cdot 2 = 8$$
$$3 \cdot 2 = 6$$
$$2 \cdot 2 = 4$$
$$1 \cdot 2 = 2$$

Notice what is happening to the product by holding one of the factors the same and decreasing the other (the multiplier) by one. Each successive product is diminished by two. Now if we take another step and decrease our multiplier by one, our multiplier becomes 0. What should the product of $0 \cdot 2$ be, so that it will follow the pattern of being two less than the previous product? Maybe we are not expected to guess the result, but it seems reasonable that it should be 0, that is, two less than 2. Logically, then, to fit the pattern we should have $0 \cdot 2 = 0$. This, of course, should be no surprise to anyone who knows his multiplication tables, although it may tease memories of those who have forgotten. In fact, we know that any number a multiplied by 0 equals 0.

$$0 \cdot a = 0$$

Shuffling this new statement into our list, it now becomes

$$4 \cdot 2 = 8$$

$$3 \cdot 2 = 6$$

$$2 \cdot 2 = 4$$

$$1 \cdot 2 = 2$$

$$0 \cdot 2 = 0$$

If we continue to decrease the multiplier by one, we arrive at -1 as the next new multiplier. What should the product of $-1 \cdot 2$ be in order to follow the pattern above of being two less than the preceding product? Use the number line to help you if you have trouble visualizing the answer. Congratulations if you arrived at -2 for your answer; if not, don't be a sore loser, but keep trying.

Continuing with this pattern, we can get other results, such as:

$$0 \cdot 2 = 0$$

$$-1 \cdot 2 = -2$$

$$-2 \cdot 2 = -4$$

$$-3 \cdot 2 = -6$$

Enough examples, then, would lead us to believe that, if a and b are natural numbers,

$$-a \cdot b = -(ab) \quad \text{or} \quad a \cdot (-b) = -(ab)$$

Consider the following statements.

$$3 \cdot (-2) = -6$$

$$2 \cdot (-2) = -4$$

$$1 \cdot (-2) = -2$$

Here we see that by maintaining -2 as one of the factors and again decreasing the other by one, the product increases by two. To fit the continuing pattern, then, the next statement should be

$$0 \cdot (-2) = 0$$

and this is consistent with our definition of multiplying by 0. If we decrease the multiplier by one again, obtaining -1 as the newest multiplier, our product of $-1 \cdot (-2)$ should be 2 in order to fit the pattern. Other results follow.

$$0 \cdot (-2) = 0$$
$$-1 \cdot (-2) = 2$$
$$-2 \cdot (-2) = 4$$
$$-3 \cdot (-2) = 6$$

Thus we have the rule of thumb that if a and b are natural numbers, then

$$-a \cdot (-b) = ab$$

We have seen in this pattern why it makes sense that a negative number multiplied by another negative number produces a positive number. This seems to be one of the big mysteries for algebra students. Caution is again given here: *we have not proved* that a "negative times a negative is a positive." We have merely shown that it is not nonsensical. Proof of this is left for investigation by the more adventuresome.

In Section 2.3 we mentioned that there was no natural number which would serve as a solution of $3 - 5 = ?$ If we change the statement to an equivalent form involving addition we obtain $5 + ? = 3$. We can see now that this sentence would have a solution in the set of integers because we would add -2 to 5 and obtain 3 as a sum. A simple method for obtaining the same result follows: Rather than subtract a number, add the inverse of the number. Therefore, $3 - 5 = ?$ is equivalent to $3 + (-5) = ?$

We can now handle expressions of this kind in the same way as our earlier addition of integers. Thus,

$$3 - 5 = 3 + (-5) = 3 + (-3) + (-2) = 0 + (-2) = -2$$

Consider the following examples.

Example 7   Subtract: $8 - 12$.

Solution Our first step is to change the operation from subtraction to addition, using inverses.

$$8 - 12 = 8 + (-12)$$

Now continue as in addition of integers.

$$8 + (-12) = 8 + (-8) + (-4) = 0 + (-4) = -4$$

Example 8 Subtract: $-4 - 7$.

Solution $-4 - 7 = -4 + (-7) = -(4 + 7) = -11$

Example 9 Subtract: $3 - (-5)$.

Solution $3 - (-5) = 3 + (5) = 8$

As we work various subtraction problems, it is evident that each of them has an integer as a solution. We conclude, then, that the set of integers is closed under the operation of subtraction. The reader should also convince himself (and everyone else that he meets) that all the properties discussed in Section 2.3 which held for the natural numbers also will hold for the integers. These include the Commutative and Associative Properties for addition and multiplication, and the Distributive Property.

PROBLEM SET 2.5

1. Use the methods employed in examples 1-6 of this section to perform the following additions.

   (a) $-3 + (-9)$ (b) $-12 + (-71)$

   (c) $-173 + (-2417)$ (d) $47 + (-10)$

   (e) $23 + (-58)$ (f) $-13 + 41$

   (g) $-27 + 16$ (h) $-38 + (-103)$

   (i) $69 + (-95)$ (j) $-163 + (-147)$

2. Multiply the following integers.

    (a) $15 \cdot (-7)$ (b) $8 \cdot (-23)$

    (c) $-24 \cdot (14)$ (d) $-6 \cdot 57$

    (e) $-4 \cdot (-7)$ (f) $-13 \cdot (-21)$

    (g) $16 \cdot 54$ (h) $-36 \cdot 0$

    (i) $-61 \cdot (-1)$ (j) $-3 \cdot (-2) \cdot (-7)$

3. Use the methods of examples 7-9 to perform the following subtractions.

    (a) $28 - 17$ (b) $13 - 17$ (c) $17 - 28$

    (d) $-32 - 19$ (e) $-16 - 42$ (f) $15 - (-7)$

    (g) $21 - (-30)$ (h) $-6 - (-3)$ (i) $-14 - (-71)$

    (j) $-27 - (-27)$ (k) $1 - (-1) - 1$ (l) $-1 - 1 - (-1)$

4. Replace the question marks with one of the three symbols, $>$, $<$, or $=$, whichever is proper.

    (a) 17 ? 6 (b) -2 ? 1

    (c) -14 ? -100 (d) -5 ? 5

    (e) 213 ? -321 (f) $2 \cdot (-7)$? $-5 \cdot (-2)$

    (g) $6 + (-9)$? $-1 + (-2)$ (h) $-8 + (-5)$? $6 + 7$

    (i) $17 - 43$? $25 - 14$ (j) $-81 - (-12)$? $-42 - 27$

5. If the sum of two numbers is zero, the numbers are said to be *additive inverses* of each other. As an example, 5 is called the additive inverse of -5, and vice versa. State the additive inverse of each of the following.

    (a) 17 (b) -31

    (c) $13 + (-46)$ (d) $-21 + (-33)$

    (e) $16 - (-12)$ (f) 0

    (g) $14 - 30$ (h) $-19 - (-23)$

6. Mt. Everest is 29,141 feet high and is the highest point on earth. The Marianas Trench in the Western Pacific is the greatest known depth and is 35,800 feet deep. Using appropriate integers, find the total distance from "top to bottom."

7. An elevator started at the 14th floor, descended 7 floors, rose 3 floors, rose 2 floors, and dropped 13 floors. Where is the elevator? If there are 14 feet between floors, how far did the elevator travel?

8. Archimedes, one of the three greatest of all mathematicians, was born in 287 B.C. and died in 212 B.C. How many years did he live?

9. On the first hand of a card game you lost 35 points. How many points are needed for you to have a score of 69 at the end of the second hand? For a score of 72 after the third?

2.6. Odd and Even Integers

Any integer can be classified as either even or odd. An integer is considered to be even if it can be expressed as a product of 2 and any other integer. In symbols we say that an *even integer* is of the form $2 \cdot n$ or $2n$, where n stands for any integer. Thus 8 and -14 are examples of even integers, since $8 = 2(4)$ and $-14 = 2(-7)$.

An *odd integer* is an integer which is not even. It can be expressed as $2n + 1$, where n is any integer. Examples of odd integers are 15 and -23, since $15 = 2(7) + 1$ and $-23 = 2(-12) + 1$.

If we multiply two even integers, such as 6 and 8 or 4 and 10, we see that the result is also an even integer (48 and 40, respectively). The more examples we try, the more convinced we should become that the product of even integers will always be even. Of course, since we have not tried all possibilities, we cannot be certain this will always be true. If we can show, however, that the product of *any* two even integers is even, then we can be certain that this will be true for any *specific* even integers. Since any even integer can be put in the form of 2 times an integer, let us consider two even integers which we will indicate as $2a$ and $2b$, where a and b are integers. We form the product $(2a)(2b)$, which is equal to $2(2ab)$.

If we let $2ab = c$, we know that c is an integer, since the product of integers is an integer (closure, remember?). Therefore,

$$(2a)(2b) = 2(2ab) = 2c$$

which is an even integer. We decree that the product of two even integers is an even integer.

Consider now the product of two odd integers. By way of examples such as $7 \cdot 5 = 35$ and $3 \cdot 9 = 27$, it appears that the product of odd integers is also an odd integer. Let us take the two general odd integers and find their product. The expressions $2a + 1$ and $2b + 1$ represent odd integers. We form their product:

$$(2a + 1)(2b + 1)$$

Using the distributive property, we may write

$$(2a + 1)(2b + 1) = (2a + 1)(2b) + (2a + 1)(1)$$

In the words of Laplace (1749-1827), "Il est aise à voir,"

$$(2a + 1)(2b) + (2a + 1)(1) = 2b(2a + 1) + 2a + 1 \qquad \text{why?}$$
$$= 2[b(2a + 1) + a] + 1 \qquad \text{why?}$$

Now, $b(2a + 1) + a$ is an integer which we can call c. Then,

$$2[b(2a + 1) + a] + 1 = 2c + 1$$

which represents an odd integer. Our good judgement is that the product of two odd integers is always odd.

If you still have some breath left, you may want to ask about the sum of two even integers or two odd integers. We leave as exercises the proofs of the answers to these queries. The student should not panic, however, at the thought of writing these proofs. We have left the more difficult ones behind us already.

PROBLEM SET 2.6

1. Simplify each of the following where necessary and classify as either an even or odd integer. Express each in the form $2n$ or $2n + 1$, using the proper value for n.

    (a) 19   (b) -34

    (c) -297 (d) $-38 - 112$

    (e) $-31(-52)$ (f) $-17 - (-15)$

    (g) 1   (h) $-14(-12 - 3)$

    (i) 0   (j) $37 + (-12) - 26$

2. Using a few specific examples, guess whether the sum of two even integers is even or odd. Using the two general even integers, show that this will always be the case.

3. Will the result of adding two odd integers be even or odd? Prove that this will always be the case.

4. Show that the sum of an even integer and an odd integer will always be odd.

5. Show that the product of an even integer and an odd integer will always be even.

2.7. The Rational Numbers

A number which can be put in the form a/b, where a and b are integers and $b \neq 0$, is called a *rational number*. It is sometimes referred to as a *quotient of two integers* (written $a \div b$) and, even more commonly, as a *fraction*. The integer that is represented by a is called the *numerator* and the integer for b is the *denominator*. It is very important that we emphasize that b cannot equal zero in this rational form. For example, if a represents any integer and $b = 0$ we are faced with the misproportioned "number," $\dfrac{a}{0}$. If $\dfrac{a}{0}$ is equal to a particular number n, then we can write

$$\frac{a}{0} = n, \text{ or } a = n \cdot 0, \text{ or } a = 0$$

for we know that 0 times any number is 0. But this says that any integer is equal to zero. Impossible! We have backed ourselves into a corner and shall ease out of this ticklish predicament by simply stating that if 0 is the denominator, the number is undefined.

We can see that the set of integers is included in the set of rational numbers for they can be expressed as $\dfrac{a}{1}$ where a is an integer.

There is more than one way to represent a rational number. For example, $\frac{2}{3}$ can also be written as $\frac{4}{6}$, $\frac{6}{9}$, $\frac{8}{12}$, etc. We see there are infinitely many ways of expressing this number. The form $\frac{2}{3}$ is called the *reduced form* of the others. There is a rule we use in arithmetic which says, $\dfrac{a \cdot x}{b \cdot x} = \dfrac{a}{b}$. This called the *Fundamental Principle of Fractions*. From this we can reduce $\frac{4}{6}$ by first factoring the 4 and 6 into prime factors. $\dfrac{4}{6} = \dfrac{2 \cdot 2}{3 \cdot 2}$. We now can use the rule and obtain $\dfrac{4}{6} = \dfrac{2 \cdot 2}{3 \cdot 2} =$

$\frac{2}{3}$. Often it is helpful to cross out the common factors in both numerator and denominator. Thus, $\frac{4}{6} = \frac{2 \cdot \cancel{2}}{3 \cdot \cancel{2}} = \frac{2}{3}$.

Example 1   Reduce $\frac{15}{35}$.

Solution $\frac{15}{35} = \frac{3 \cdot \cancel{5}}{7 \cdot \cancel{5}} = \frac{3}{7}$

Example 2   Reduce $\frac{126}{330}$.

Solution $\frac{126}{330} = \frac{7 \cdot 3 \cdot \cancel{3} \cdot \cancel{2}}{11 \cdot 5 \cdot \cancel{3} \cdot \cancel{2}} = \frac{7 \cdot 3}{11 \cdot 5} = \frac{21}{55}$

Let us now consider the operations on rational numbers. If we wish to add two rational numbers with the same denominator, we simply add the numerators. That is, to add $\frac{3}{8} + \frac{2}{8}$,

$$\frac{3}{8} + \frac{2}{8} = \frac{3 + 2}{8} = \frac{5}{8}$$

NOTE: If you are wondering why we didn't add the denominators, making the problem

$$\frac{3}{8} + \frac{2}{8} = \frac{3 + 2}{8 + 8} = \frac{5}{16}$$

consider adding $\frac{8}{2}$ and $\frac{4}{2}$. If we add both numerators and denominators, we would have

$$\frac{8}{2} + \frac{4}{2} = \frac{8 + 4}{2 + 2} = \frac{12}{4} = 3$$

but $\frac{8}{2} + \frac{4}{2} = 4 + 2 = 6$

or $\frac{8}{2} + \frac{4}{2} = \frac{8 + 4}{2} = \frac{12}{2} = 6.$

Now suppose we are asked to add $\frac{2}{3} + \frac{1}{5}$. Before we can add them, we must first obtain a common denominator. We see the common denominator is 15 and, using our previous rule, we can write:

$$\frac{2}{3} = \frac{2 \cdot 5}{3 \cdot 5} \text{ and } \frac{1}{5} = \frac{1 \cdot 3}{5 \cdot 3}$$

Therefore, $\quad \dfrac{2}{3} + \dfrac{1}{5} = \dfrac{2 \cdot 5}{3 \cdot 5} + \dfrac{1 \cdot 3}{5 \cdot 3} = \dfrac{10}{15} + \dfrac{3}{15} = \dfrac{13}{15}$

Example 3 Add $\dfrac{3}{7} + \dfrac{2}{5}$.

Solution $\qquad \dfrac{3}{7} + \dfrac{2}{5} = \dfrac{3 \cdot 5}{7 \cdot 5} + \dfrac{2 \cdot 7}{5 \cdot 7} = \dfrac{15}{35} + \dfrac{14}{35} = \dfrac{29}{35}$

Example 4 Add $\dfrac{2}{15} + \dfrac{3}{10}$.

Solution We first rewrite the expression with the denominators in factored form.

$$\frac{2}{15} + \frac{3}{10} = \frac{2}{3 \cdot 5} + \frac{3}{2 \cdot 5}$$

For the denominators to be equal, we need a 2 in the first denominator and a 3 in the second. Thus,

$$\frac{2}{15} + \frac{3}{10} = \frac{2 \cdot 2}{3 \cdot 5 \cdot 2} + \frac{3 \cdot 3}{2 \cdot 5 \cdot 3} = \frac{4}{30} + \frac{9}{30} = \frac{13}{30}$$

Example 5 Add $\dfrac{35}{36} + \dfrac{11}{30}$.

Solution $\qquad \dfrac{35}{36} + \dfrac{11}{30} = \dfrac{35}{2 \cdot 2 \cdot 3 \cdot 3} + \dfrac{11}{2 \cdot 3 \cdot 5}$

$$= \frac{35 \cdot 5}{2 \cdot 2 \cdot 3 \cdot 3 \cdot 5} + \frac{11 \cdot 2 \cdot 3}{2 \cdot 3 \cdot 5 \cdot 2 \cdot 3}$$

$$= \frac{175}{180} + \frac{66}{180} + \frac{241}{180}$$

The answer in example 5 can be written in a different form. That is,

$$\frac{241}{180} = \frac{180}{180} + \frac{61}{180}$$

$$= 1 + \frac{61}{180}$$

$$= 1 \frac{61}{180}$$

Subtraction of rational numbers is similar to that of subtraction of integers. We can rewrite a subtraction statement such as $\frac{2}{3} - \frac{1}{5}$ as the addition statement $\frac{2}{3} + (-\frac{1}{5})$. At this point it is advantageous to rewrite the terms with a common denominator. Thus, $\frac{2}{3} + (-\frac{1}{5})$ can be written as $\frac{2 \cdot 5}{3 \cdot 5} + \left(-\frac{1 \cdot 3}{5 \cdot 3}\right)$ or $\frac{10}{15} + \left(-\frac{3}{15}\right)$. Combining terms, we obtain

$$\frac{10}{15} + \left(-\frac{3}{15}\right) = \frac{7}{15} + \frac{3}{15} + \left(-\frac{3}{15}\right) = \frac{7}{15} + 0 = \frac{7}{15}$$

Example 6   Subtract $\frac{2}{7} - \frac{3}{5}$.

Solution   We rewrite and obtain $\frac{2}{7} + \left(-\frac{3}{5}\right)$

which is equivalent to $\frac{2 \cdot 5}{7 \cdot 5} + \left(-\frac{3 \cdot 7}{5 \cdot 7}\right)$

then

$$\frac{2 \cdot 5}{7 \cdot 5} + \left(-\frac{3 \cdot 7}{5 \cdot 7}\right) = \frac{10}{35} + \left(-\frac{21}{35}\right) = \frac{10}{35} + \left(-\frac{10}{35}\right) + \left(-\frac{11}{35}\right)$$

$$= 0 + \left(-\frac{11}{35}\right)$$

$$= -\frac{11}{35}$$

Multiplication of two rational numbers can be very simple. We multiply numerators to obtain the numerator of the product and multiply denominators to obtain the denominator of the product. Thus,

$$\frac{2}{3} \cdot \frac{5}{7} = \frac{2 \cdot 5}{3 \cdot 7} = \frac{10}{21}$$

Sometimes we may be able to reduce or simplify the expression before actually multiplying the factors, as in the next example.

Example 7   Multiply $\dfrac{6}{35} \cdot \dfrac{10}{33}$.

Solution $\dfrac{6}{35} \cdot \dfrac{10}{33} = \dfrac{2 \cdot 3}{5 \cdot 7} \cdot \dfrac{2 \cdot 5}{3 \cdot 11} = \dfrac{2 \cdot 3 \cdot 2 \cdot 5}{5 \cdot 7 \cdot 3 \cdot 11} = \cdots$

At this point we can see that both the numerator and denominator of this product contain, and therefore can be divided by, the factor $3 \cdot 5$. Write $\dfrac{2 \cdot 3 \cdot 2 \cdot 5}{5 \cdot 7 \cdot 3 \cdot 11} = \dfrac{2 \cdot 2}{7 \cdot 11}$ and, in reduced form, $\dfrac{4}{77}$.

Example 8   Multiply $\dfrac{21}{70} \cdot 4\dfrac{2}{7}$.

Solution   First, we should write $4\frac{2}{7}$ in the form $\dfrac{a}{b}$.

Thus $4\dfrac{2}{7} = 4 + \dfrac{2}{7} = \dfrac{4}{1} + \dfrac{2}{7} = \dfrac{4 \cdot 7}{1 \cdot 7} + \dfrac{2}{7} = \dfrac{28}{7} + \dfrac{2}{7} = \dfrac{30}{7}$

Then $\dfrac{21}{70} \cdot 4\dfrac{2}{7} = \dfrac{21}{70} \cdot \dfrac{30}{7} = \dfrac{3 \cdot 7}{2 \cdot 5 \cdot 7} \cdot \dfrac{2 \cdot 3 \cdot 5}{7}$

$$= \frac{3 \cdot \overset{1}{\cancel{7}} \cdot \overset{1}{\cancel{2}} \cdot 3 \cdot \overset{1}{\cancel{5}}}{\underset{1}{\cancel{2}} \cdot \underset{1}{\cancel{5}} \cdot \underset{1}{\cancel{7}} \cdot 7} = \frac{3 \cdot 3}{7} = \frac{9}{7} = \frac{7}{7} + \frac{2}{7} = 1\frac{2}{7}$$

In arithmetic we learned a rule for the division of fractions which most of us may still recall. It went something like this, "Invert the fraction you are dividing by and then multiply." Thus, a problem such as $\frac{5}{11} \div \frac{2}{3}$ would become $\frac{5}{11} \cdot \frac{3}{2} = \frac{15}{22}$. Such a rule quickly gives us the answer to the problem, but it does not answer why we invert and multiply. Look at the problem again.

$\frac{5}{11} \div \frac{2}{3}$ means $\dfrac{\frac{5}{11}}{\frac{2}{3}}$ (or a less meaningful $\frac{2}{3} \overline{\smash{)}\,\frac{5}{11}}$).

We have what is called (for what it's worth) a *complex fraction*. It is a fraction whose numerator and/or denominator are fractions. For the number to make more sense, we wish to make the denominator of this complex fraction equal to 1, for $\dfrac{a}{1} = a$. Therefore, in this example, we should multiply the denominator by $\frac{3}{2}$. The rule says, however, that if we multiply the denominator by $\frac{3}{2}$, we must also multiply the numerator by the same number.

Hence, $\dfrac{\frac{5}{11}}{\frac{2}{3}} = \dfrac{\frac{5}{11} \cdot \frac{3}{2}}{\frac{2}{3} \cdot \frac{3}{2}} = \dfrac{\frac{15}{22}}{1} = \dfrac{15}{22}$

Let's look at another example to see the pattern.

Example 9   Divide: $\dfrac{7}{15} \div 2\dfrac{1}{10}$.

Solution $\dfrac{7}{15} \div 2\dfrac{1}{10} = \dfrac{7}{15} \div \dfrac{21}{10}$

$$= \dfrac{\frac{7}{15}}{\frac{21}{10}} = \dfrac{\frac{7}{15} \cdot \frac{10}{21}}{\frac{21}{10} \cdot \frac{10}{21}} = \dfrac{7}{3 \cdot 5} \cdot \dfrac{2 \cdot 5}{3 \cdot 7}$$

$$= \dfrac{\overset{1}{\cancel{7}} \cdot 2 \cdot \overset{1}{\cancel{5}}}{3 \cdot \underset{1}{\cancel{5}} \cdot 3 \cdot \underset{1}{\cancel{7}}}$$

$$= \dfrac{2}{9}$$

Check this last example by using the "invert and multiply" rule. It should be noted that the set of nonzero rational numbers is closed under division. This is the first set of numbers that we have discussed which exhibits this closure property.

PROBLEM SET 2.7

1. Write four different representations in the form $\frac{a}{b}$ for each of the following numbers.

    (a) $\frac{2}{3}$ (b) $\frac{21}{66}$ (c) $-\frac{16}{18}$ (d) 1   (e) 0

    (f) $\frac{-3}{2}$ (g) $\frac{-3}{-5}$ (h) $\frac{5}{-3}$ (i) $\frac{-12}{15}$ (j) $\frac{a}{b}$

2. Reduce the following to lowest terms.

    (a) $\frac{10}{15}$ (b) $\frac{30}{231}$ (c) $\frac{84}{126}$ (d) $\frac{5049}{5814}$

3. Perform the indicated operation for each of the following.

(a) $\dfrac{3}{5} + \dfrac{2}{7}$

(b) $\dfrac{5}{9} - \dfrac{2}{7}$

(c) $\dfrac{7}{33} - \dfrac{10}{42}$

(d) $\dfrac{21}{55} + \dfrac{6}{35}$

(e) $\dfrac{3}{7} \cdot \dfrac{5}{9}$

(f) $\dfrac{6}{35} + \dfrac{15}{14}$

(g) $\dfrac{14}{165} - \dfrac{22}{105}$

(h) $\dfrac{45}{77} \cdot \dfrac{11}{75}$

(i) $\dfrac{7}{25} - 4\dfrac{1}{5}$

(j) $\dfrac{119}{330} + \dfrac{42}{935}$

4. Perform the following divisions by the method employed in example 9. Check each by the "invert and multiply" method.

(a) $\dfrac{2}{7} \div \dfrac{3}{5}$

(b) $\dfrac{6}{35} \div \dfrac{15}{14}$

(c) $\dfrac{3}{14} \div \dfrac{5}{7}$

(d) $\dfrac{7}{25} \div 4\dfrac{1}{5}$

(e) $\dfrac{10}{-21} \div \dfrac{-15}{14}$

(f) $\dfrac{a}{b} \div \dfrac{c}{c}$

5. Replace the question mark in each of the following statements with the appropriate symbol $>$, $<$, or $=$.

(a) $\dfrac{3}{5} \ ? \ \dfrac{2}{3}$

(b) $\dfrac{7}{9} \ ? \ \dfrac{17}{15}$

(c) $\dfrac{12}{13} \ ? \ \dfrac{84}{91}$

(d) $\dfrac{212}{413} \ ? \ \dfrac{121}{257}$

6. Perform the indicated operations for each of the following:

(a) $\dfrac{-4}{9} \div \left(\dfrac{35}{18} \div \dfrac{-10}{3} \right)$

(b) $\dfrac{-4}{9} - \dfrac{35}{18} - \dfrac{-10}{3}$

(c) $\dfrac{-4}{9} \cdot \dfrac{35}{18} \cdot \dfrac{-10}{3}$

(d) $\dfrac{a}{b} \div \dfrac{c}{d} \cdot \dfrac{n}{r}$

7. An electronic machine sorts cards for the computer operator at 480 cards per minute. At this rate, how long will it take to sort 3600 cards? Express your answer in reduced rational form.

2.8. The Real Numbers

The Greeks were so enchanted with rational numbers that they thought they could explain the geometry of the universe with them. They hoped to express any measurement with a rational number. Then up popped the devil. A problem was introduced which dashed their hopes so badly that they turned their attention away from geometric measurements and returned to studying geometry as a relationship of forms.

The problem involved a right triangle (a triangle that has one of its angles equal to 90°). Pythagoras had proved a formula for the relationship between the legs and the hypotenuse (longest side opposite the 90° angle of a right triangle). If the legs of a right triangle are represented by a and b and the hypotenuse is c (figure 2.5), the relationship is $a^2 + b^2 = c^2$.

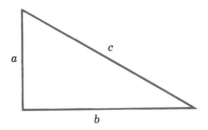

Figure 2.5

If the legs are 3 and 4, then the hypotenuse c is found by $c^2 = 3^2 + 4^2 = 9 + 16 = 25$. From the expression $c^2 = 25$, we are looking for a value of c such that $c \cdot c = 25$. We represent this by the expression $c = \pm \sqrt{25}$ (read "c equals positive or negative square root of 25"). There are two values of c which, when multiplied by themselves, yield 25. They are 5 and -5. Since we are talking about a length we are only interested in the positive value of c. Therefore $c = 5$.

When only the positive square root of a number n is desired, we write ($\sqrt{}$). Notice that there is no positive or negative sign in front of the radical sign, but a positive sign is understood. Thus, $\sqrt{25} = 5$, $\sqrt{4} = 2$, $\sqrt{16} = 4$, and $\sqrt{225} = 15$.

All was well until someone introduced the problem where both sides of the right triangle were equal. If, for example, each side is 1 unit in length (figure 2.6), then

$$c^2 = 1^2 + 1^2 = 2$$
$$\text{and } c = \sqrt{2}$$

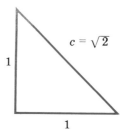

Figure 2.6

We can find no rational number for c such that $c \cdot c = 2$. There-fore $\sqrt{2}$ is not a rational number and cannot be expressed in the form $\frac{a}{b}$ where a and b are integers, $b \neq 0$, This is not the only example of a nonrational number. Others are $\sqrt{3}$, $\sqrt{5}$, $\sqrt{23}$, etc. We also find that we cannot express the ratio of the circumference of a circle to its diameter as a rational number. We use a number designated by the Greek letter π (pi). Many other numbers of this type have been found. In fact, it can be shown that there are more numbers of this type than there are rational numbers. It appears, then, that we have a new set of numbers. We call this set the *irrational numbers*. Notice that the set of rational numbers and the set of irrational numbers are *disjoint sets*. That is, if a number is rational, it cannot also be irrational, and vice versa. The union of these two sets is called the set of *real numbers*.

If a real number can be put in the form $\frac{a}{b}$ where a and b are integers, $b \neq 0$, then it is rational. If it cannot be put in that form, then it is irrational.

There is another way to distinguish a rational number from an irrational number. In the seventeenth century, John Napier introduced the decimal as we use it today. The number in the first position to the right of the decimal point stands for how many $\frac{1}{10}$'s we have. Thus, .3 means $\frac{3}{10}$. The number in the second position stands for how many $\frac{1}{100}$'s. Hence, .05 $= \frac{5}{100}$. The next position stands for $\frac{1}{1000}$'s, etc. We see then that

$$.357 = \frac{3}{10} + \frac{5}{100} + \frac{7}{1000} = \frac{300}{1000} + \frac{50}{1000} + \frac{7}{1000} = \frac{357}{1000}$$

Example 1   Change .2109 to a fraction.

Solution $.2109 = \frac{2}{10} + \frac{1}{100} + \frac{0}{1000} + \frac{9}{10,000}$

$$= \frac{2,000}{10,000} + \frac{100}{10,000} + \frac{0}{10,000} + \frac{9}{10,000}$$

$$= \frac{2109}{10,000}$$

It appears that the only digits in the decimal number .357 are 3, 5, and 7. Those in .2109 are 2, 1, 0, and 9. It should be understood, though, that if we wished to add another digit to the right beyond the 7 or 9 (or numbers of this nature) it would have to be a 0, then another 0, etc. That is, an infinite number of zeros can be added to the right of our decimal number without changing its value. To put it bluntly, decimals such as .3, .217, and .013579 are referred to as *repeating zero decimals* or *terminating decimals*. But what about decimals such as .3333 . . . or .272727 . . . ? These decimals repeat non-zero digits endlessly and are called *repeating non-zero decimals*. To aid in compactness of writing a decimal such as .3333 . . . , we use a more convenient notation. We place a bar over the 3 (in this case) to indicate it continues to repeat forever and ever. Thus we write $.\overline{3}$. The decimal .272727 . . . would appear as $.\overline{27}$. We have seen in example 1 that a repeating zero decimal can be expressed as a fraction and is therefore a rational number. The question that naturally arises is that of whether a repeating non-zero decimal is also a rational number. If it is, then it can be put in fraction form. Let us see if we can put $.\overline{3}$ in the form of a fraction. We can write

$$.\overline{3} = (.\overline{3})\,\frac{(10-1)}{9}$$

(notice $\frac{10-1}{9}$ is actually a different form of 1). We apply the distributive property in the numerator and obtain

$$\overline{.3} = (\overline{.3})\frac{(10-1)}{9} = \frac{\overline{.3}\,(10) - \overline{.3}\,(1)}{9} = \frac{3.\overline{3} - \overline{.3}}{9} = \frac{3}{9} = \frac{1}{3}$$

Let's look at another example of this type.

Example 2   Change $\overline{.6}$ to a quotient of integers.

Solution

$$\overline{.6} = (\overline{.6})\frac{(10-1)}{9} = \frac{\overline{.6}\,(10) - \overline{.6}\,(1)}{9} = \frac{6.\overline{6} - \overline{.6}}{9} = \frac{6}{9} = \frac{2}{3}$$

The decimal $\overline{.27}$ has two repeating digits. Instead of multiplying by $\frac{(10-1)}{9}$, we will use $\frac{(100-1)}{99}$. This is a necessary bit of trickery in order to place the decimal point in the correct position. The reader is urged to convince himself that $\frac{(10-1)}{9}$ will not work. Thus,

$$\overline{.27} = (\overline{.27})\frac{(100-1)}{99} = \frac{\overline{.27}\,(100) - \overline{.27}\,(1)}{99} = \frac{27.\overline{27} - \overline{.27}}{99} = \frac{27}{99} = \frac{3}{11}$$

Example 3   Express $\overline{.63}$ as a quotient of integers.

Solution

$$\overline{.63} = (\overline{.63})\frac{(100-1)}{99} = \frac{\overline{.63}\,(100) - \overline{.63}\,(1)}{99} = \frac{63.\overline{63} - \overline{.63}}{99} = \frac{63}{99} = \frac{7}{11}$$

Example 4   Express $\overline{.345}$ as a quotient of integers.

Solution

$$\overline{.345} = (\overline{.345})\frac{(1000-1)}{999} = \frac{\overline{.345}\,(1000) - \overline{.345}\,(1)}{999} = \frac{345.\overline{345} - \overline{.345}}{999}$$

$$= \frac{345}{999} = \frac{115}{333}$$

In example 4 we again used a different form of one to multiply the decimal. The correct form to use is very easy to determine. Notice that the number of repeating digits agrees with the number of nines in the denominator of the fraction.

Thus, if there is only one repeating digit, we multiply by $\dfrac{(10-1)}{9}$. If there are four repeating digits, we multiply by $\dfrac{(10,000-1)}{9999}$, etc.

Example 5   Express $1.3\overline{521}$ as a quotient of integers.

Solution   There are two repeating digits. Thus,

$$1.35\overline{21} = (1.35\overline{21})\frac{(100-1)}{99} = \frac{1.35\overline{21}\,(100) - 1.35\overline{21}\,(1)}{99}$$

$$= \frac{135.\overline{21} - 1.35\overline{21}}{99} = \frac{135.21\overline{21} - 1.35\overline{21}}{99}$$

$$= \frac{133.86}{99}$$

We do not have a quotient of integers, since 133.86 is not an integer. Thus, we must multiply numerator and denominator by 100 to get rid of the decimals.

$$\frac{133.86}{99} = \frac{133.86\,(100)}{99\,(100)} = \frac{13386}{9900}$$

We have seen that a repeating zero decimal (terminating) or repeating nondecimal can be expressed as a quotient of integers. These types of decimals are therefore rational numbers. We claim that a nonrepeating decimal cannot be expressed as a quotient of integers and is, therefore, an irrational number. Numbers such as $2.718281828459045\ldots$, $1.4142\ldots$, $3.14159\ldots$, $2.010010001\ldots$ are examples of nonrepeating decimals and are, therefore, irrational numbers.

It is a relatively simple process to change a number in rational form to a decimal. We merely divide the numerator by the denominator. Thus $\frac{1}{2} = .5$, $\frac{1}{4} = .25$, $\frac{1}{3} = .\overline{3}$, etc.

It should be mentioned here that all the properties which hold for the integers and rational numbers also hold for the real numbers.

PROBLEM SET 2.8

1. Classify each of the following numbers as rational or irrational.

    (a) 365   (b) 42.91

    (c) $37.3\overline{12}$ (d) 4.12015 . . .

    (e) $^{37}\!/_{59}$ (f) π

    (g) $\sqrt{23}$ (h) 169

2. Express each of the following as a decimal.

    (a) $\frac{1}{5}$ (b) $^{7}\!/_{33}$

    (c) $^{36}\!/_{111}$ (d) $\frac{1}{7}$

    (e) $5\frac{1}{6}$ (f) $^{4}\!/_{13}$

3. Express each of the following numbers as a quotient of integers.

    (a) .3   (b) 42.71

    (c) $.\overline{5}$ (d) .35

    (e) $2.\overline{17}$ (f) $.\overline{129}$

    (g) $3.21\overline{63}$ (h) $.1\overline{41273}$

4. Explain why $\sqrt{2} = 1.41421$ . . . cannot be expressed as a quotient of integers by the method used in examples 2 - 5.

5. Using the method employed in examples 2 - 5, show that .999 . . . = 1.000 . . . .

6. Express $\dfrac{137174210}{111111111}$ as a decimal.

2.9. The Complex Numbers

At this point we might feel confident that the set of real numbers includes all the numbers that we would possibly need. Such is not the case, however, as we shall illustrate with the following problem. Consider the statement:

$$a^2 = -1$$

We are asked to find a number a such that when it is multiplied by itself the product will be -1, that is, $a \cdot a = -1$ or $a = \sqrt{-1}$. If a is a real number it is positive, negative or zero. If it is zero, then $a^2 = 0$. The only choices left, then, are that it is positive or negative, but we know from the properties of real numbers that the product of two positives is positive and the product of two negatives is positive. We must conclude then that there is no real number a such that $a = \sqrt{-1}$. Other examples of non-real numbers are $\sqrt{-5}$, $\sqrt{-9}$, $\sqrt{-100}$, etc. In general, the square root of a negative number is not a real number. This set of numbers is called the set of *imaginary numbers*.

When a real number is combined with an imaginary number, such as $3 + \sqrt{-7}$, we call the result a *complex number*.

Any imaginary number can be expressed as the product of a real number and $\sqrt{-1}$. For example, $\sqrt{-4} = \sqrt{4\,(-1)} = \sqrt{4}\,\sqrt{-1} = 2\,\sqrt{-1}$. To simplify notation, mathematicians have agreed to substitute the letter i for $\sqrt{-1}$. Therefore, $2\,\sqrt{-1} = 2\,i$.

Example 1 Express $\sqrt{-5}$ in the form bi, where b is a real number.

Solution $\sqrt{-5} = \sqrt{5\,(-1)} = \sqrt{5}\,\sqrt{-1} = \sqrt{5}\,i$

We see from this that any complex number may be written in the form $a + bi$, where a and b are real numbers.

Example 2 Express $3 + \sqrt{-7}$ in the form $a + bi$.

Solution $3 + \sqrt{-7} = 3 + \sqrt{7\,(-1)} = 3 + \sqrt{7}\,\sqrt{-1} = 3 + \sqrt{7}\,i$

A close look at the form of a complex number (i.e., $a + bi$) shows us that the set of real numbers is really a special case of the complex numbers, where $b = 0$. We can also see that if $a = 0$, we obtain the set of imaginary numbers.

At the time of their discovery, complex numbers served as nothing more than a mathematical amusement. Today, however, they play a major role in modern physics and other important scientific areas.

PROBLEM SET 2.9

1. Classify each of the following numbers as imaginary, real and/or complex.

    (a) 2.93   (b) $\sqrt{25}$

    (c) $-\sqrt{36}$ (d) $8i$

    (e) $\sqrt{-49}$ (f) $-7-12i$

    (g) $6+0i$ (h) $0+7i$

    (i) $0+0i$

2. Express each of the following in the form bi where b is a real number.

    (a) $\sqrt{-7}$ (b) $\sqrt{-125}$ (c) $\sqrt{-8}$

3. Express each of the following in the form $a+bi$, where a and b are real numbers.

    (a) $\sqrt{5}$ (b) $\sqrt{-64}$ (c) $-7+\sqrt{-50}$

Chapter 3
ALGEBRA

3.1. The Real Number Line

In Chapter 2 we introduced the concept of a number line, where we positioned the set of integers at equal intervals along a straight line (figure 3.1).

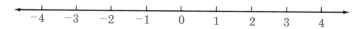

Figure 3.1

Each integer corresponds to a specific point on the line. We can think of each point as being a certain distance from the point named 0. Thus the point which corresponds to 2 is two units to the right of 0. The point which corresponds to —3 is three units to the left of 0, etc.

Since each point on the line represents a particular distance from 0, there must be a point that is ½ unit from 0, another which is ⅞ units from 0, another which is —⅝ units from 0, etc. We can see that we could match every rational number with a point on the number line (figure 3.2).

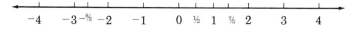

Figure 3.2

Now, have we completed our task of giving every point on the number line a name? (Remember that each point represents a distance from

0.) If we were inspired by the traumatic experience of the Pythagoreans (Section 2.8), we recall their discovery that all distances cannot be measured in rational units. Therefore, there must be a point on the line which is $\sqrt{2}$ units from 0, another which is π units from 0, another which is $-\sqrt{5}$ units from 0, etc. Thus each irrational number corresponds to a point on the number line (figure 3.3).

Figure 3.3

We can now label every point on the number line with either a rational number (including the integers) or an irrational number. These two sets, remember, constitute the real numbers; hence we call the line the *real number line*.

The arrows on each end of the line indicate that, no matter which point you may choose to think of as the "last" one, you could crawl out on the line just a little farther to another point, and from that point you can crawl out just a little bit more. In fact, the number line might be said to have the "crawling out property."

We can represent a particular number on the number line by making a heavy solid dot at that point. Thus, we may represent, or "graph," the number -2 as in figure 3.4.

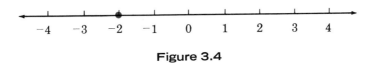

Figure 3.4

The following examples illustrate graphing numbers on the number line.

Example 1 Graph all integers between -3 and 2.

Solution

Notice the word "between" implies that -3 and 2 are not included.

Example 2   Graph all real numbers between —3 and 2.

Solution

In this example we include all numbers (integers, rational, and irrational) on the line between —3 and 2, but again do not include —3 and 2. We indicate this by making a "hollow" dot at these points.

Example 3   Graph all real numbers greater than 1.

Solution

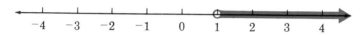

The arrow indicates the solid dark line extends to the right indefinately. The phrase "greater than 1" implies that 1 is not included.

PROBLEM SET 3.1

Graph the following sets of numbers.

1. All integers between —4 and 3.

2. All odd integers between —5 and 3.

3. All even integers from —6 to 2, inclusive.

4. All real numbers between 2 and 7.

5. All nonnegative, nonpositive integers.

6. All real numbers greater than —5.

7. All real numbers greater than or equal to 0 and less than or equal to 4.

8. All real numbers greater that 3 or less than 1.

9. All real numbers greater than or equal to —2 and less than 3.

10. All real numbers greater than 2 and less than -3.

11. Graph the following on the same number line and state the result of the union of the two sets, i.e., $A \cup B$.

$A = \{x \mid x < 7\}$

$B = \{x \mid x > 7\}$

12. Graph each of the following on the number line and state the result of the intersection of the two sets, i.e., $A \cap B$.

$A = \{x \mid x \leq 7\}$

$B = \{x \mid x \geq 2\}$

3.2. Open Sentences

Today is Friday.

A whale is a mammal.

$5 + 3 = 12$.

Bosstick was the first president of the United States.

Each of the above statements is a sentence which can be classified as either true or false. Now consider the sentence

$$x + 5 = 9$$

This sentence is neither true nor false until we replace x with a number. Such a sentence is called an *open sentence* or *conditional equation*. Any real number may be substituted for x. Depending on which value of x is used, the sentence will then either be true or false. Since x may take on various values, we call it a *variable*. The set of numbers that can be substituted for x which make the sentence true is called the *solution set* or *truth set*. In the above example, of course, there is only one value which makes the sentence true. The solution set is therefore $\{4\}$.

Example 1   Find the solution set for $x^2 = 16$ where x is any real number.

Solution   There are two real numbers which satisfy this sentence, 4 and -4. Therefore the solution set is $\{-4,4\}$.

Example 2   Find the truth set for $-1 < x < 5$ where x is an integer.

Solution   There are five integers which satisfy the condition, $\{0,1,2,3,4\}$.

Example 3   Find the solution set for $x \cdot 0 = 1$ where x is a real number.

Solution   Since the product of zero and any number is zero, there are no real numbers that we may substitute for x and have a true statement. Our solution set is therefore empty, ϕ.

Example 2 was an open sentence involving inequalities, while examples 1 and 3 were concerned with equalities. Sentences which involve only equalities are called *equations*.

Finding the solution set of an equation such as

$$x + 3 = 8$$

is relatively easy since we can find a value for x which will satisfy the expression merely by inspection. Solving an equation such as $3x - 2 = x + 6$ by inspection is possible, but more difficult. There are two principles that we may apply to systematically solve equations of this type.

Principle 1   The same expression may be added to or subtracted from each side of an equation.

Principle 2   We may multiply or divide each side of an equation by the same expression. (Dividing by zero is not allowed.)

We will now use these principles in finding the solution set to the previously mentioned equation, $3x - 2 = x + 6$.

Principle 1 allows us to add 2 to each side. We choose to add 2 since the left side of the equation will become $3x - 2 + 2 = 3x$, and we are trying to eliminate everything except the groups of x's from one side of the equation.

$$3x - 2 + 2 = x + 6 + 2$$

which simplifies to

$$3x = x + 8$$

Using principle 1 again, we subtract x from each side obtaining

$$2x = 8$$

Now, dividing each side by 2 or multiplying both sides by the multiplicative inverse (reciprocal) of 2, i.e., ½, we finally arrive at

$$x = 4$$

Example 4   Solve $2x + 3 = 4x - 7$.

Solution   We first subtract 3 from each side, getting

$$2x = 4x - 10$$

Subtracting $4x$ from each side yields

$$-2x = -10$$

Finally, dividing each side by -2, we have

$$x = 5$$

One rut most beginning algebra students fall into is that they feel or believe that in solving equations the variable, x, must always be placed to the left of the equals sign. This is not the case, for if we accept the *symmetric property of equality,* if $a = b$, then $b = a$, when our solution arrives in the form $4 = x$ then we can also accept that $x = 4$. Therefore, if we wish to work back-end-to and foremost-end-backward, it is perfectly acceptable. If we had wished, in example 4 we could have first added 7 to each side, leaving

$$2x + 10 = 4x$$

Then, upon subtracting $2x$ from each side, we have

$$10 = 2x$$

and finally, dividing each side by 2 (here is the big difference), we end up with

$$5 = x$$

Example 5   Solve: $\frac{2}{3}x - 2 = 4$.

Solution   Adding 2 to each side, we obtain $\frac{2}{3}x = 6$. We now multiply each side by $\frac{3}{2}$ in order to obtain $1 \cdot x$ or x. Thus,

$$\frac{3}{2} \cdot \frac{2}{3}x = \frac{3}{2} \cdot 6$$

which simplifies to

$$x = 9$$

PROBLEM SET 3.2

Find the solution set for each of the following open sentences. (Unless otherwise stated, the set of possible solutions is the set of real numbers.)

1. $x + 2 = 4$

2. $x - 3 = 7$

3. $3 < x < 8$ (x is an integer)

4. $-3 \le x \le 5$ (x is an integer)

5. $12 \le x < 20$ (x is an integer)

6. $7 < y \le 8$ (y is an integer)

7. $2 < y < 3$ (y is an integer)

8. $2x = 12$

9. $3a = 27$

10. $3s + 1 = 10$

11. $2v = v + 3$

12. $x = x + 1$

13. $5x - 3 = 2x + 6$

14. $x + 3 = x + 3$

15. $2b + 7 = 4b - 5$

16. $3x - 1 = 9$

17. $5c + 2 = 13$

18. $3h - 2 = h + 5$

19. $x = x - 5$

20. $x^2 = -25$

21. $t^2 = 169$

22. $2x - 3 = 5x - 9$

23. $6x + 2 = 8x + 16$

24. $4k - 1 = 3k - 5$

25. $m - 7 = m - 7$

26. $9x + 3 = 2x - 18$

27. $7x - 5 = 10x - 6$

3.3. Linear Equations

In the preceding section, we considered open sentences containing one variable. Consider the following open sentence.

$$2x + 3y = 8$$

We notice that this is an equation in two variables. Any equation which can be put in the form

$$Ax + By = C$$

where A, B, and C represent real numbers, is called a *linear equation*.

Returning now to the equation $2x + 3y = 8$, we wish to find a value to substitute for x and a value for y which will make the statement true. By inspection we see that if $x = 1$ and $y = 2$,

$$2(1) + 3(2) = 8$$

we obtain a true statement. That is, therefore, a solution. Instead of writing the solution as $x = 1$ and $y = 2$ we may write it in the more compact form $(1,2)$, where we agree that the first number represents the value for x and the second the value for y. The expression $(1,2)$ is called an *ordered pair*. It is so named because the order of the numbers is important. The ordered pair $(1,2)$, which means $x = 1$ and $y = 2$, is a solution to our equation, but $(2,1)$, which means $x = 2$ and $y = 1$, is not a solution since

$$2(2) + 3(1) \neq 8$$

A question we may ponder at this point concerns the ordered pair $(1,2)$; is it the only solution to the above equation? Further inspection, possibly by trial and error, yields $(4,0)$ as another solution. We also find $(7,-2)$, $(-2,4)$, and $(0,\frac{8}{3})$ are solutions. We begin to suspect that there are many solutions.

In fact, if we substitute any real number for one of the variables, we can solve the equation for the other variable by the techniques established in Section 3.2. Thus we may determine infinitely many ordered pairs in the solution set of this equation.

Example 1   Find two solutions other than those already mentioned for

$$2x + 3y = 8$$

Solution

(a) Select any value for x, say $x = 2$. Then
$$2(2) + 3y = 8$$
or $$4 + 3y = 8$$

Subtracting 4 from each side gives
$$3y = 4$$

Dividing each side by 3 yields
$$y = \tfrac{4}{3}$$

Thus $(2, \tfrac{4}{3})$ is a solution.

(b) Let $$x = 3$$

Then $$2(3) + 3y = 8$$
or $$6 + 3y = 8$$

Subtracting 6 from each side gives
$$3y = 2$$

Dividing each side by 3 yields
$$y = \tfrac{2}{3}$$

Thus $(3, \tfrac{2}{3})$ is a solution.

Example 2   Find four solutions for $5x - 2y = 10$.

Solution

(a) Let $$y = 0$$

Then $$5x - 2(0) = 10$$
or $$5x = 10$$

Dividing each side by 5 gives

$$x = 2$$

Thus $(2,0)$ is a solution.

(b) Let $\qquad x = 0$

Then $\qquad 5(0) - 2y = 10$

or $\qquad -2y = 10$

Dividing each side by -2 yields

$$y = -5$$

Thus $(0,-5)$ is a solution.

(c) Let $\qquad y = 5$

Then $\qquad 5x - 2(5) = 10$

or $\qquad 5x - 10 = 10$

Adding 10 to each side gives

$$5x = 20$$

Dividing each side by 5 yields

$$x = 4$$

Thus $(4,5)$ is a solution.

(d) Let $\qquad x = 1$

Then $\qquad 5(1) - 2y = 10$

or $\qquad 5 - 2y = 10$

Subtracting 5 from each side gives

$$-2y = 5$$

Dividing each side by -2 yields

$$y = -\tfrac{5}{2}$$

Thus $(1, -\frac{5}{2})$ is a solution.

Example 3   Find several solutions for

$$-2x + 3y = 12$$

Solution   Possibly a more orderly approach, but certainly no more accurate, to finding a solution set for a given equation would be to solve the existing form explicitly for one of the unknowns, say y. Then an equivalent equation for

$$-2x + 3y = 12$$

is

$$3y = 12 + 2x \text{ (by adding } 2x - \text{the inverse of } -2x$$

to both sides of the equation).

Then
$$y = \frac{12 + 2x}{3}$$

by dividing both sides by 3.

In this form all that is required is to substitute number values for x and then simplify. A neat table may also help us to keep track of individual ordered pairs.

x	y

$$\text{Substituting in } y = \frac{12 + 2(x)}{3}$$

				x	y
if $x = 0$	$y = \dfrac{12 + 2(0)}{3}$	$= \dfrac{12 + 0}{3}$	$= \dfrac{12}{3} = 4$	0	4
if $x = 3$	$y = \dfrac{12 + 2(3)}{3}$	$= \dfrac{12 + 6}{3}$	$= \dfrac{18}{3} = 6$	3	6
if $x = -3$	$y = \dfrac{12 + 2(-3)}{3}$	$= \dfrac{12 - 6}{3}$	$= \dfrac{6}{3} = 2$	-3	2
if $x = -6$	$y = \dfrac{12 + 2(-6)}{3}$	$= \dfrac{12 - 12}{3}$	$= \dfrac{0}{3} = 0$	-6	0

Frequently, if we are cautious in our choice of values for substitutions, we can find solutions which are integers rather than fractions. You will note in example 2 we used wise choices in parts (a), (b), and (c). In part (d) if we had used $x = -2$ rather than $x = 1$ we would have obtained the ordered pair $(-2, -10)$ as a solution rather than $(1, -\frac{5}{2})$. Granted, both of these are solutions, and one is just as valid as the other. In the next section, however, we will want to find solutions which contain integers, since they will be easier and more accurate to graph.

PROBLEM SET 3.3

Find five solutions for each of the following equations.

1. $x = y$ 2. $x + y = 5$ 3. $x = 3y$

4. $x - y = 7$ 5. $x = -y$ 6. $x + 5y = 20$

7. $2x + 3y = 6$ 8. $5x - 2y = 12$ 9. $3x = 5y + 4$

10. $7x - 9y = 63$ 11. $13x - y = 24$ 12. $3x + 3y = 0$

13. $x = -4$ 14. $y = 2$ 15. $y = 0$

3.4. Graphing Equations

The directions given by Blackbeard's treasure map may have read, "From the large dead oak tree take 20 paces east and then 8 paces north." This may be a way of locating the burying place of a pirate's treasure. It is reasonable that any spot could have been chosen as a burying place and then marked by a certain number of paces east or west of the oak tree, followed by a certain number of paces north or south. Each spot would have its own set of directions which would be different from those given for any other spot.

In the 17th century, the French mathematician and philosopher René Descartes devised a method of locating any point on a plane. His method was very similar to that used by the pirates in the above example. He used two number lines placed *perpendicular* to each other. That is, the intersection of the two lines forms four 90° angles.

We have already discussed the horizontal number line in an east-west direction with positive numbers to the right, or east, and the negative numbers to the left, or west. Likewise, we can construct a vertical number line passing through the point 0, stepping off our desired positive numbers upward to the north (as in map reading) and the negative numbers downward or south (see figure 3.5).

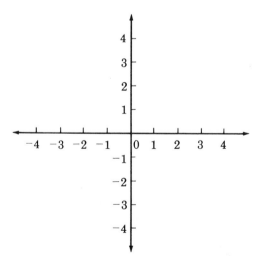

Figure 3.5

If we use the intersection of the two lines as a starting point (origin), we can get to any point on the plane by moving first to the right or left along the horizontal line and then up or down in the vertical direction. For example, the point indicated in figure 3.6 can be reached by moving three units to the right followed by two units up. This point could be labeled with the ordered pair (3,2), where it is understood that the first number represents the horizontal distance and the second number represents the vertical distance. These two numbers are called the *coordinates* of the point.

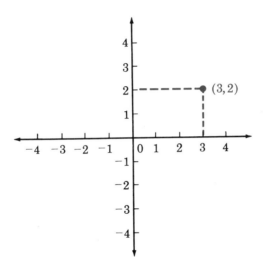

Figure 3.6

We can see that every point on the plane can be labeled with an ordered pair, and, conversely, every ordered pair corresponds to a point on the plane. There is a one-to-one correspondence between the set of ordered pairs and the set of points on a plane. In honor of Descartes, we call this system the *Cartesian coordinate* system.

NOTE: Memory is not always how much you remember, but what you may select to forget. If we can throw away some of the chaff, then the fundamentals become more meaningful. Thus, in plotting ordered pairs, concentrate on the two positive directions east and north; then, by necessity, movement west and south will be negative.

Example 1   Locate the point represented by the ordered pair $(2,-3)$.

Solution   The first number tells us to move two units to the right. The second number indicates that we should move three units down.

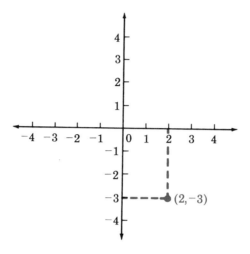

Example 2   Plot the point represented by $(-3,2)$.

Solution   The first number requires us to move three units to the left, and the second number takes two units upward.

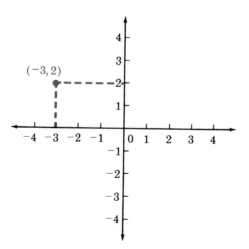

We now return to the equation

$$2x + 3y = 8$$

which we have discussed in Section 3.3. Recall that we found there were infinitely many ordered pairs which satisfied this equation. In the present section we have seen that each ordered pair represents a point on the plane. It would be interesting to locate the points on the plane which are represented by the solutions to this equation. Of course, we cannot locate all points, but we can locate enough to see the pattern of what the graph of the points looks like. We know from Section 3.3 that $(1,2)$, $(4,0)$, $(7,-2)$, $(-2,4)$, $(0,\%)$, $(2,\%)$, and $(3,\%)$ are solutions. We plot these points in figure 3.7.

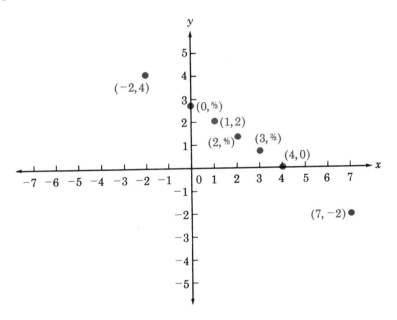

Figure 3.7

If we should get bold and connect these points with line segments, it becomes apparent that we have a straight line. If we were to find other points we would discover that they too are on this line. In fact, all solutions of this equation represent points on this line and every point on the line represents a solution of the equation.

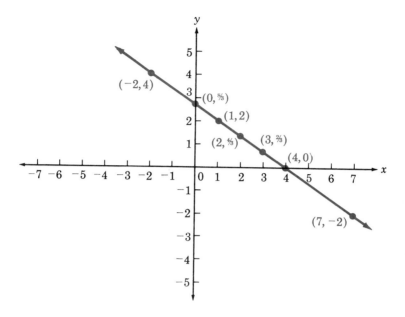

Figure 3.8

The graph of the solution set of any equation of the form

$$Ax + By = C$$

will be a straight line. This is why these equations are referred to as *linear equations*. Since this type of equation has a graph which is a straight line it is relatively easy to draw. After a moment's thought, we should agree that we need only two points to draw a line. Hence, we need only find two solutions for a given linear equation. To be on the safe side, however, it is usually desirable to find a third solution as a check to make sure that all the points are on that same line. If any one point is not, then we will look for an error in determining our solutions.

Example 3   Draw the graph of $3x - 2y = 6$.

Solution   We first find three solutions.

(a) Let $$x = 0$$

Then $$3(0) - 2y = 6$$

or $\qquad\qquad\qquad\qquad\qquad\qquad -2y = 6$

which becomes $\qquad\qquad\qquad\qquad\quad y = -3$

Thus $(0,-3)$ is a solution.

(b) Let $\qquad\qquad\qquad\qquad\qquad\qquad y = 0$

Then $\qquad\qquad\qquad\qquad\quad 3x - 2(0) = 6$

or $\qquad\qquad\qquad\qquad\qquad\qquad 3x = 6$

which becomes $\qquad\qquad\qquad\qquad\quad x = 2$

Thus $(2,0)$ is a solution.

(c) Let $\qquad\qquad\qquad\qquad\qquad\qquad y = 3$

Then $\qquad\qquad\qquad\qquad\quad 3x - 2(3) = 6$

or $\qquad\qquad\qquad\qquad\qquad 3x - 6 = 6$

Adding 6 to each side, we obtain $\qquad\quad 3x = 12$

which results in $\qquad\qquad\qquad\qquad\quad x = 4$

Thus $(4,3)$ is a solution.

We now plot these three points and draw the line which contains them.

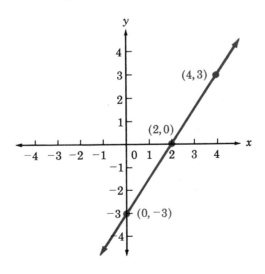

Not all equations have graphs which are straight lines. Consider the following example.

Example 4   Graph: $y = x^2 + 2x + 1$.

Solution   We can find several solutions of this equation by choosing various values for x and solving for y.

(a) Let $x = -3$

Then $y = (-3)^2 + 2(-3) + 1$
$$= 9 - 6 + 1$$
$$= 4$$

Thus $(-3,4)$ is a solution.

(b) Let $x = -2$

Then $y = (-2)^2 + 2(-2) + 1$
$$= 4 - 4 + 1$$
$$= 1$$

Thus $(-2,1)$ is a solution.

(c) Let $x = -1$

Then $y = (-1)^2 + 2(-1) + 1$
$$= 1 - 2 + 1$$
$$= 0$$

Thus $(-1,0)$ is a solution.

(d) Let $x = 0$

Then $y = (0)^2 + 2(0) + 1$
$$= 0 + 0 + 1$$
$$= 1$$

Thus $(0,1)$ is a solution.

(e) Let $\qquad\qquad\qquad\qquad x = 1$

Then $\qquad\qquad\qquad\qquad y = (1)^2 + 2(1) + 1$
$$= 1 + 2 + 1$$
$$= 4$$

Thus $(1,4)$ is a solution.

We now plot these points and connect them with a smooth continuous curve.

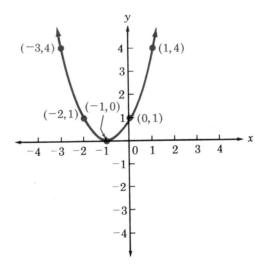

In the above example we can see that more than two points are needed to draw the graph. Such a curve is called a *parabola*. If the reader is adventurous he might try to graph an equation such as $x^2 + y^2 = 25$, which is a circle, or $x^2 + 4y^2 = 36$, which is an ellipse.

The work we have done in this section represents some of the fundamentals of a field of mathematics known as analytic geometry.

PROBLEM SET 3.4

1. Plot and label the points represented by the following ordered pairs.

   (a) $(1,5)$ (b) $(6,2)$ (c) $(2,-7)$ (d) $(0,3)$

   (e) $(-2,-3)$ (f) $(0,0)$ (g) $(\frac{1}{2},3)$ (h) $(-3,5)$

2. Using graph paper and a convenient unit length, plot each of the following points and connect them with straight line segments. (Connect the first point to the second, the second to the third . . . to the first.)

   (a) $(4,1)$, $(1,1)$, $(0,4)$, $(-1,1)$, $(-4,1)$, $(-1\frac{1}{2},-\frac{1}{2})$, $(-2\frac{1}{2},-3)$, $(0,-1\frac{1}{2})$, $(2\frac{1}{2},-3)$, $(1\frac{1}{2},-\frac{1}{2})$

   (b) $(-3,-4)$, $(2,-1)$, $(1,-5)$

3. Graph each of the 15 equations given in Problem Set 3.3.

4. Graph the parabola $y = x^2$.

5. Graph the parabola $y = x^2 - 3x + 2$.

6. Graph the parabola $x = y^2 + 2y + 1$.

7. Graph $x + y = 7$ and $3x + 2y = 18$ on the same coordinate system. Label the coordinates of the point which is the intersection of these two lines. Notice that this ordered pair is a solution of both equations.

8. Graph each of the following equations on the same coordinate system. Do you see any pattern of symmetry? How many points do the three equations have in common? Where are they?

   (a) $2x + 3y = 6$ (b) $3x + 2y = 6$ (c) $y = x$

9. Graph each of the following equations on the same coordinate system. Is there anything exciting about the picture? How many points do the two equations have in common?

   (a) $-3x + 4y = 12$ (b) $-3x + 4y = 24$

10. Graph both of the following equations on the same set of axes. How many points do they have in common?

    (a) $3x + y = 2$ (b) $4y = 8 - 12x$

REMARK: It may be wise to stuff in a statement at this time to tie together some of the notation from preceding chapters with current material. In graphing we have mentioned, and then taken for granted, that we are concerned with the solution *set of each equation. Occasionally the solution set is empty or becomes so complicated to describe that the equation itself is the best way to state the set. In example 3, the solution set of the equation* $3x - 2y = 6$ *may be written*

$$\{(x,y)\,|\,3x - 2y = 6\}$$

to emphasize the fact that we are seeking all the ordered pairs that will satisfy the given equation. It means, "Find the set of all the ordered pairs that will make the equation $3x - 2y = 6$ *be a true statement."*

3.5. Graphing Inequalities

We have discussed the graphing of inequalities such as $x < 3$ and $x \geqslant -5$ in Section 3.2. We now turn our attention to such sentences involving two variables. Consider the open sentence

$$2x + y < 4$$

If we try to find ordered pairs which satisfy this statement, we soon become convinced that we could never find them all. In other words, there are an infinite number of solutions. Examples are $(0,1)$, $(1,0)$, $(-3,-1)$, $(3,-3)$, $(-3,2)$, $(-4,-2)$, $(0,3)$, $(0,2)$, $(1,1)$, $(-1,4)$, $(-1,-3)$. Graphing these points on a coordinate system (figure 3.9) indicates that we do not obtain a straight line from this type of sentence as we did in the equations from Section 3.4.

As we continue to plot points, we see that all of them are situated to the left and below the line $2x + y = 4$, which is shown as a dashed line in figure 3.9. In fact, all points in this "half-plane" satisfy the condition $2x + y < 4$. If we were asked to locate all points satisfying $2x + y \leq 4$, we would include all points in the half-plane, as well as all points on the line $2x + y = 4$, and to indicate that the line is included, we would draw it as a solid line as in figure 3.10.

We therefore see that a systematic method for graphing a sentence such as $2x + y < 4$ is to first locate the line $2x + y = 4$. The next step

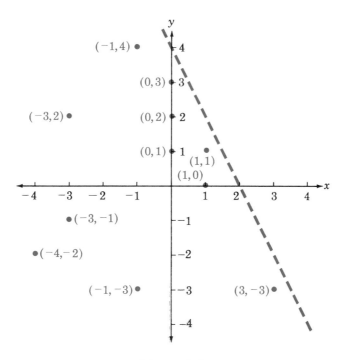

Figure 3.9

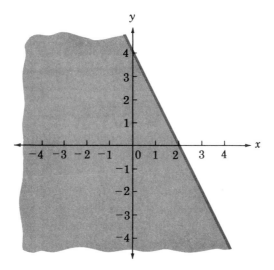

Figure 3.10

is to "test" a point on either side of the line. If the point satisfies the condition, then every point in that half-plane must satisfy the same condition. If, on the other hand, it does not satisfy the condition, then the correct region must be on the other side of the line. We offer the following examples to help clarify our discussion.

Example 1   Graph $3x - 2y > 6$.

Solution   We first draw as a dashed line the graph of the equation $3x - 2y = 6$. Next we test a point on one side of the line. A convenient point is $(0,0)$.

$$3(0) - 2(0) = 0$$

Since 0 is not greater than 6, this point does not satisfy the condition; therefore the points which do satisfy it are on the other side of the line. Our graph is thus:

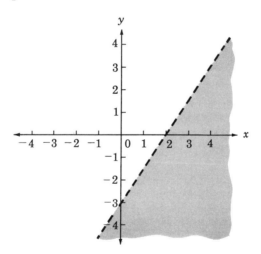

Example 2   Graph the points which satisfy *both* of the following conditions: $2x + y < 4$ and $3x - 2y > 6.$

Solution   We draw both graphs on the same set of coordinates. The intersection of the two regions is the desired result, since it contains points which satisfy both conditions.

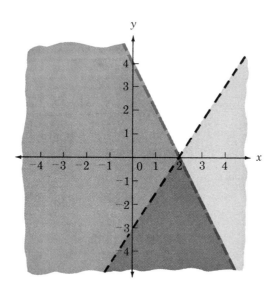

PROBLEM SET 3.5

Graph each of the following.

1. $x + y > 0$

2. $x - y < 0$

3. $2x + 3y < 6$

4. $x + 4y > 4$

5. $2x - y > 8$

6. $x - 3y < 6$

7. $x + y < 3$
   $2x - y > 4$

8. $3x - y < -3$
   $2x - 3y > -6$

9. $x \geqslant 0$
   $y \geqslant 0$
   $2x + 3y \leqslant 4$

3.6 Linear Programming

In problem set 3.5, exercise 9, we graphed a system of linear inequalities whose intersection set is the interior of a *convex polygon*. A region is *convex* if the line segment connecting any two of its points, say P and Q, is entirely contained within the region (figure 3.11).

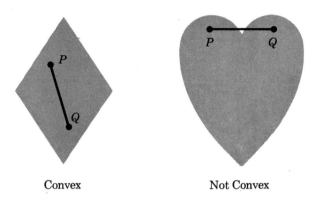

Convex   Not Convex

Figure 3.11

Consider the three inequalities in exercise 9, problem set 3.5.

$$x \geq 0$$

$$y \geq 0$$

$$2x + 3y \leq 4$$

Each inequality determines a half-plane and the figure determined is a right triangle, as shown in figure 3.12. The coordinates of the vertices of the polygen are $A(0,0)$, $B(2,0)$, and $C(0,\frac{4}{3})$. The triangle and its interior represent a convex set.

Now, by substituting ordered pairs from the triangular set into some linear expression of the form

$$k = Ax + By + C$$

where x and y are the same variables as those in the system, we will obtain a line which will pass through the polygon. In particular, there

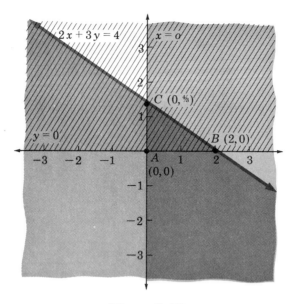

Figure 3.12

will be some value for k that will cause the line to pass through one of the vertices of the polygon. The value of k then will be a maximum value with respect to the convex set. There will be another value that will send a line through another of the vertices which will be a minimum value.

It can be proved (but not now) that this maximum or minimum value occurs at a vertex of the polygon. Thus, to find a maximum or minimum all that is required is to replace x and y with the coordinates of the vertices of the polygon in $Ax + By + C$.

Example 1   Using the convex polygon as shown in figure 3.12, find the maximum and minimum values of the linear equation

$$k = x + y + 1$$

Solution   Substituting from vertices

$A(0,0)$: $k = 1(0) + 1(0) + 1 = 1$

$B(2,0)$: $k = 1(2) + 1(0) + 1 = 3$

$C(0,\frac{4}{3})$: $k = 1(0) + 1(\frac{4}{3}) + 1 = \frac{7}{3}$

Thus, the maximum value of the function is 3 at B and the minimum is 1 at A.

Example 2   Also using figure 3.12, find the maximum and minimum values for

$$k = 4x - 3y + 2$$

Solution   Substituting

$A(0,0):$ $k = 4(0) - 3(0) + 2 = 2$

$B(2,0):$ $k = 4(2) - 3(0) + 2 = 10$

$C(0,\frac{4}{3}):$ $k = 4(0) - 3(\frac{4}{3}) + 2 = -2$

With this function the maximum is 10 at B and the minimum is -2 at C.

Example 3   With the convex polygon of figure 3.12, find the maximum and minimum for

$$k = -2x - 3y + 7$$

Solution   Substituting

$A(0,0):$ $k = -2(0) - 3(0) + 7 = 7$

$B(2,0):$ $k = -2(2) - 3(0) + 7 = 3$

$C(0,\frac{4}{3}):$ $k = -2(0) - 3(\frac{4}{3}) + 7 = 3$

The maximum value is 7 at A and the other two vertices are both minimums, 3.

This process is called *linear programming*. It is used extensively, particularly in business, to solve practical problems where certain limitations are placed upon the variables. The following example illustrates a "real life" application of linear programming.

Example 4   Farmer Zeke Whiffle has a "back 40" where he intends to plant either corn or soybeans. Zeke is allowed to plant not more than 25 acres of corn, which will cost $30.00 per acre for seed and fertilizer and will demand 10 hours of labor per acre at $2.10 per hour. He hopes to get a yield of 125 bushels per acre and sell the corn at $1.00 per bushel. For soybeans, there is no restriction on acreage; seed and fertilizer will cost $25.00 per acre and demand 8 hours labor per acre at $2.10 per hour. Zeke's average yield for soybeans has been 40 bushels per acre and he can sell them on the futures at $2.10 per bushel. How should Farmer Whiffle divide his 40 acres between corn and soybeans to get maximum income?

Solution   Let c equal the number of acres of corn and s equal the number of acres of soybeans. Then,

$$c \geqslant 0 \text{ minimum acres of corn}$$

$$s \geqslant 0 \text{ minimum acres of soybeans}$$

$$c \leqslant 25 \text{ maximum acres of corn}$$

$$s \leqslant 40 \text{ maximum acres of soybeans}$$

$$c + s \leqslant 40 \text{ total corn and soybeans}$$

We can graph the set of inequalities and determine the vertices as follows.

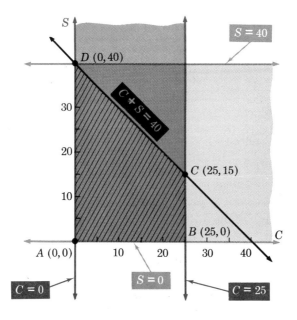

$$A(0,0), B(25,0), C(25,15), D(0,40)$$

The total income, I, is the expected income per acre times the number of acres of each crop, or

$$I = 125c + 84s$$

Substituting the vertices into the function of income we have

at $A = (0,0)$ $I = 125(0) + 84(0) = \$0$

at $B = (25,0)$ $I = 125(25) + 84(0) = \$3125$

at $C = (25,15)$ $I = 125(25) + 84(15) = \$4385$

at $D = (0,40)$ $I = 125(0) + 84(40) = \$3360$

Hence the maximum income is $4385, obtained by planting 25 acres of corn and 15 acres of soybeans; the minimum is, of course, zero from planting nothing at all. Finding the maximum profit is left to the student in exercise 5 of the problem set.

PROBLEM SET 3.6

1. Which of the following sets are convex?

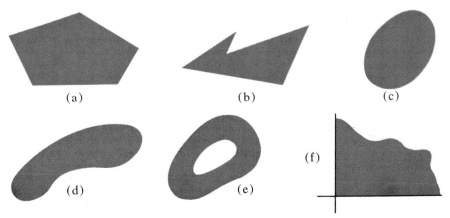

(a)   (b)   (c)

(d)   (e)   (f)

2. Determine the feasible convex regions on the following sets of inequalities.

(a) $x \leqslant 7$ (b) $x \geqslant 1$ (c) $x + 4y \leqslant 12$

     $x \geqslant 0$ $y \geqslant 2$ $3x - 2y \geqslant -6$

     $x \geqslant y$ $5x + 4y \leqslant 20$ $x + y \geqslant -2$

     $y + 2 \geqslant 0$ $3x - y \leqslant 10$

3. Find the coordinates of the vertices of the polygons formed by the inequalities in problem 2.

4. On the graph of the system of inequalities in problem 2, part (a), graph the following linear equations, using $k = -4, 0, 1, 2, 4$, and 7, respectively.

$$x + 2y = k$$

Do any of these lines pass through a vertex of the convex polygon described by the system? If so, is it a maximum or minimum value for that particular linear function?

5. Find the expected maximum profit and the number of acres of each crop in example 4. *Hint:* The profit from any crop equals the income minus the expenses involved.

6. A man has a maximum of $12,000 to invest in two types of bonds. Bond A returns 8% and bond B 10% per year. His investment in bond B must not exceed 50% of his investment in bond A. How much should he invest at each rate in order to obtain a maximum profit?

3.7. Verbal Problems

Problems that tell a story must surely be as old as mathematics itself. They are fun, intriguing, frustrating, and, above everything else, involve the daily situations that we encounter. We are not always willing to solve these problems, however. Some of us put them in a jar for safe-keeping until tomorrow; then the problem doesn't seem so important and tomorrow never comes.

An Egyptian papyrus revealed one of the oldest recorded problems, estimated to have been written around 2200 B.C. Except for a word here and there, it is but little different from one that might appear in any modern algebra textbook:

"A heap and its seventh make 19; how large is the heap?"

One that is quite similar, but slightly more complicated, is dated 1150 A.D. and comes from India:

"Out of a heap of pure lotus flowers, a third part, a fifth part, and a sixth part were offered respectively to the gods Siva, Vishnu, and the Sun; a quarter of the original heap was presented to Bhavani. The remaining six lotuses were given to the venerable preceptor. Tell quickly the whole number of lotus flowers."

Many of our modern-day problems can be solved by using simple arithmetic. Consider, "How many candy bars, at 10¢ each, can you buy for a dollar?" A little mental arithmetic gives us the answer ten. Some problems, however, are too difficult to solve by this method. For example, "Niki has $2.65 in nickels, dimes, and quarters. She has two more dimes than nickels and three more quarters than dimes. How many of each kind of coin does she have?"

Assuredly, one might solve this problem by trial and error and eventually stumble upon the correct answer, but we would rather have a more systematic approach to the solution. Such is the role of algebra.

Before we dive headlong into actual problem solving, we should first gain some practice in translating word phrases to mathematical expressions. Some examples will illustrate this technique.

Example 1   Express the sum of twice a number x and 5.

Solution   Twice a number x may be written as $2x$. Therefore the sum of these two expressions is $2x + 5$.

Example 2   Express three times the sum of $4x$ and 1.

Solution   The wording indicates we are multiplying three times the sum of $4x$ and 1. The sum of $4x$ and 1 is $4x + 1$. Therefore the product is $3(4x + 1)$.

Example 3 Write an expression for the length of a rectangle which is 7 feet longer than the width, which is w feet.

Solution The length is $w + 7$.

Example 4 Express the value of n nickels.

Solution Each nickel is worth 5 cents, so n nickels is worth $5n$ cents.

Example 5 Express the first even integer larger than the even integer x.

Solution The next even integer larger than x is two integers larger than x. Thus the answer is $x + 2$.

After gaining some practice in writing algebraic expressions from verbal phrases, we are ready to progress to problem solving.

One crucial step in solving verbal problems is to correctly translate the words into an algebraic equation. Again, several examples will help illustrate the procedure.

Example 6 The sum of twice a number and 5 is 39. Find the number.

Solution We introduce the letter x to represent the number we are looking for. The sum of twice the number x and 5 can be represented by $2x + 5$ (see example 1).

Thus
$$2x + 5 = 39$$

Solving this equation by processes established in Section 3.2, we obtain
$$x = 17$$

Example 7 Steve is one year older than four times Mike's age. Kelly is three times as old as Steve. If Kelly is 27, how old are Steve and Mike?

Solution Let x represent Mike's age. Then $4x + 1$ represents Steve's age, and $3(4x + 1)$ represents Kelly's age.

Thus
$$3(4x + 1) = 27$$

Solving, we get
$$x = 2$$

and
$$4x + 1 = 9$$

Therefore, Mike is 2 and Steve is 9.

Example 8   The length of a rectangle is 7 feet longer than its width. If the perimeter is 26 feet find the length and width.

Solution   Let w represent the width in feet. Then $w + 7$ represents the length in feet (see example 3). The perimeter is found by adding twice the length and twice the width.

Thus
$$2w + 2(w + 7) = 26$$

Solving, we obtain
$$w = 3$$
$$w + 7 = 10$$

Therefore, the width is 3 feet and the length is 10 feet.

Example 9   Niki has $2.65 in nickels, dimes, and quarters. She has two more dimes than nickels and three more quarters than dimes. How many of each kind of coin does she have?

Solution   Since the type of coin she has the fewest of is nickels, we will let x represent the number of nickels. Then $x + 2$ represents the number of dimes and $(x + 2) + 3$ or $x + 5$ represents the number of quarters. Now the total value of the nickels is $5x$ cents. The total value of the dimes is $10(x + 2)$ cents and the total value of the quarters is $25(x + 5)$ cents. Since the total value of all coins is 265 cents, we can write the equation
$$5x + 10(x + 2) + 25(x + 5) = 265$$

or
$$5x + 10x + 20 + 25x + 125 = 265$$

which simplifies to
$$40x + 145 = 265$$

and, solving, we get
$$x = 3$$
$$x + 2 = 5$$
$$x + 5 = 8$$

Thus Niki has 3 nickels, 5 dimes, and 8 quarters.

Example 10   The sum of two consecutive even integers is 254. Find the integers.

Solution Let x represent the first even integer. We have seen in example 5 that $x + 2$ represents the next even integer.

Then	$x + x + 2 = 254$
or	$2x + 2 = 254$
and	$2x = 252$
hence	$x = 126$
and	$x + 2 = 128$

PROBLEM SET 3.7

Write an algebraic expression for each of the following word phrases.

1. Five more than a number x.

2. Twice a number n.

3. The sum of three times a number x and 8.

4. Nine less than six times a number d.

5. The next odd integer greater than the odd integer x.

6. The sum of x and a number three larger than x.

7. The length of a rectangle is 3 feet longer than twice its width, w.

8. The sum of three consecutive integers if the smallest integer is x.

9. The total value of d dimes and $(d + 4)$ quarters.

10. Two more than three times a number x.

11. A girl's age 18 years from now if her present age is x years.

12. The sum of three numbers if the largest is three times the smallest and the third is 7 larger than the smallest. The smallest is x.

13. Five more than a number is 17. Find the number.

14. Twice a number is 72. Find the number.

15. The sum of three times a number and 8 is 65. Find the number.

16. Nine less than six times a number is 129. Find the number.

17. The sum of two consecutive odd integers is 400. Find the numbers.

18. Mike is 3 years older than Lila. The sum of their ages is 29. How old is each?

19. The length of a rectangle is 3 feet longer than twice the width. If its perimeter is 102 feet, find the dimensions of the rectangle.

20. The sum of three consecutive integers is 84. Find the integers.

21. Janet has $5.05 in dimes, quarters, and half-dollars. If she has four more quarters than dimes and twice as many half-dollars as dimes, how many of each type of coin does she have?

22. Deanna is twice as old as Vicki. Janet is 2 years older than three times Vicki's age. The sum of their ages is 32. How old is each?

23. In 18 years Tom will be three times as old as he is now. How old is Tom?

24. A wire 37 feet in length is cut into three pieces. The longest piece is three times as long as the shortest piece. The third piece is 7 feet longer than the shortest. Find the length of each piece.

Make up a word problem which could be represented by the following algebraic equations.

25. $2x + 3 = 13$

26. $w + (3w - 2) = 26$

27. $5x + 10 (x + 2) + 25 (3x) = 240$

28. Diaphantus, who lived about 200 A.D., is referred to as the father of algebra. Little is known of his life except for a riddle made up by one of his contemporaries which gives us the age at which Diaphantus died. The following is the riddle. Can you solve it?

"Diaphantus' youth lasted one sixth of his life. He grew a beard after one twelfth more. After one seventh more of his life he married. Five years later he had a son. The son lived exactly one half as long as his father and Diaphantus died just four years after his son. All this adds up to the years Diaphantus lived."

Chapter 4
PROBABILITY

Mathematical Patterns

Combinations: An Application
of Pascal's Triangle

Tree Diagrams

Probability

Odds and Expectation

Conditional Probability

4.1. Mathematical Patterns

One of our first encounters with numbers and mathematics may have been when relatives came to visit and Dad said to us, "Tell Uncle Elmer how old you are." After being coaxed a few times, we proudly held up three fingers. But Uncle Elmer wasn't satisfied with this display of fingers and asked, "And how many fingers is that?" By the time this experience had been echoed many times — at least once for each friend and relative — we had learned to associate three fingers with the number 3.

The following year we related four fingers and the digit 4. After still another birthday, we linked all of the fingers on one hand to the digit 5, and so it went. We used one finger to correspond with each year of our existence, and we found that this worked exceedingly well for the first ten years. We could put each of our ten fingers in a one-to-one correspondence with each of the years up to and including age 10. That is, we took the set of fingers to represent the set of the first ten counting numbers.

This method followed a very old pattern. If our prehistoric ancestors did any counting at all, it was done in this fashion — by using fingers to represent "how many." The word *digit* is derived from the Latin word *digitus,* meaning finger or toe. The set of digits {0,1,2,3,4,5,6,7,8,9} is used to write all counting, or natural, numbers.

The set of natural numbers can thus be written by using different arrangements of digits: 5, 39, 1,271, 6,850,774, 1,000,000,000, and on past the googol and the googolplex.

The googol, by the way, is the name of a very large number. It is enormous even compared to Archimedes' calculations (287-212 B.C.)

of the number of grains of sand needed to fill the universe. In his book, *Sand Reckoner,* he estimated 10^{63} grains. The googol is 10^{100} (read "10 to the 100th power") and is the digit 1 followed by 100 zeros. Do you see why we describe the number rather than attempt to write it? But the googol isn't even the largest number, for we have the googolplex, 10^{googol} or $10^{10^{100}}$. One mathematician has reckoned that if you begin at a point on earth with the digit 1 and write a single zero in each inch of space to Mars, then on to Jupiter, and on to each planet out to Pluto, you should have a few zeros of a googolplex left over.

Of course, the pattern of counting numbers is very familiar to you. Here we wish to investigate other patterns, more sophisticated and, we hope, more meaningful in our work in answering the question, "how many?"

For instance, if we were asked to determine how many lines of type there were in this textbook, we could begin on page 1, count the lines that exist on it, carry that total on to page 2, and continue counting until we reached the last line on the last page. This final number would be the *cardinal number* of lines; that is, it would tell us how many. If we did not need the exact number of lines, however, we could lessen the work and time involved by choosing any one page at random. We could count the lines on that page and assume that this number was the average number of lines for all the pages in the book. The total number could then be approximated by multiplying the average, or *mean,* by the number of pages. This might not be as accurate a method as counting every line, but it is expedient. Try to estimate how many names there are in your local telephone directory.

Another type of pattern involving numbers is called a *sequence.* A sequence is an ordered set of numbers. It may be finite or infinite. (A *finite* set is a set whose members can be counted with the counting coming to an end. An *infinite* set is a set which has an unlimited number of members.)

Suppose we begin with the very simple sequence that we have already mentioned.

Example 1   1, 2, 3, . . . , 98, 99, 100. This is the finite sequence of natural numbers from 1 through 100.

Example 2   3, 5, 7, 9, 11, 13. This is the set of odd numbers 3 through 13, inclusive.

Examples 1 and 2 are finite sets; that is, the members can be counted. The three dots in example 1 take the place of the counting numbers that have been omitted but follow the obvious pattern.

Example 3   2, 4, 8, 16, . . . , 2^n, ... This is an infinite set of numbers where each term is of the form 2^n, where n is the number of the term examined; that is, the numeral represented by 2^3 is 8 and is the third element in the set, the numeral for 2^5 is 32 and is the fifth element, and $2^{20} = 1,048,576$, and is the twentieth element. The set 2, 4, 8, 16, . . . , 2^{10} is the set 2^1 to 2^{10}, inclusive, where each term is defined by using 2 as the base for each of the exponents 1, 2, 3, 4, 5, 6, 7, 8, 9, and 10, respectively.

Number of the term	1	2	3	4	5	. . .
	↓	↓	↓	↓	↓	
Exponential form of the term	2^1	2^2	2^3	2^4	2^5	. . .
	↕	↕	↕	↕	↕	
Calculated value of the term	2	4	8	16	32	· · ·

We have already encountered this set in Chapter 1. Recall that when we were considering truth tables of two statements (p,q), we found that there were $2^2 = 4$ ways of putting the two simple statements in compound sentences with p and q being either true or false. In the case of statements (p,q,r), there were 2^3 ways of making compound statements. That is, if a set has n elements, then there are 2^n subsets. We shall deal with this prodigy, 2^n, many times in this chapter. Beware!

Other intriguing number patterns that have been toyed with since at least 1000 B.C. are magic squares. Magic squares use each counting number, 1, 2, . . . , n arranged to fill a square array of an odd number of spaces so that the sum of each row, column, or diagonal is the same.

Example 4   3 by 3 square, sum is 15.

8	1	6
3	5	7
4	9	2

To construct this magic square, we write the numbers consecutively, starting with 1 in the center block of the top row. We always work on a diagonal line moving upward and to the right. When we pass completely out of the box at the top, we begin again at the bottom of the column to the right. If we emerge from the box at the side, we begin in the left-most square in the row immediately above. When we use a number that is multiple of the length of a side of the square (3, in our example above) we go directly to the block immediately below that multiple.

At the age of 10, Carl F. Gauss (1777-1855), called the prince of mathematicians, found a general method for computing the solution to the sum of arithmetic sequences. (An *arithmetic sequence* has each of its terms after the first determined by adding the same fixed number to the preceding term.) He was not the first, but for a young boy to discover this on his own, immediately upon confrontation of the problem, was truly remarkable. Chances are that the following was not the problem he solved, but it will illustrate his method.

Find the sum of

$$1 + 2 + 3 + 4 + 5 + \ldots + 96 + 97 + 98 + 99 + 100$$

Obviously, we could find this sum by adding up all of the elements in the series one by one. However, instead of developing a faint heart and settling for this tedious and unimaginative method, we could follow young Gauss' steps and think of the numbers as being written

$$(1 + 100) + (2 + 99) + (3 + 98) + \ldots + (50 + 51)$$

By taking the numbers in pair — the first with the last, second with the next-to-last, and so on — we will have ½ of 100 numbers in 50 pairs. Every pair has the sum of 101, so we have

$$50 \cdot 101 = 5050$$

From this we write a general formula for the sum of an arithmetic sequence:

$$S = \tfrac{1}{2} n (f + L)$$

where S is the sum, n is the number of terms, f the first term, and L the last term.

The patterns already illustrated and those in the following exercises should help you discover a variety of useful number relationships.

PROBLEM SET 4.1

1. In example 3, what is the 7th term of the sequence? Write the numeral in two different forms.

2. In example 3, what is the sum of the first 7 elements of the sequence?

3. What is the obvious first term of the following pattern?

$$—, —, —, 10, 13, 16, 19, 22, \ldots$$

4. Find the common difference between each consecutive pair of elements in the preceding sequence; find the 15th term.

5. Fill in the blanks with the appropriate numbers. Try to determine a general pattern involved in each sequence that lets you find any single element, write the pattern in the last blank, as in (a).

   (a) $1, 3, 5, \underline{7}, \underline{9}, \ldots, \underline{2^n - 1}, \ldots$

   (b) $1, \frac{1}{2}, —, \frac{1}{4}, —, —, \ldots, —, \ldots$

   (c) $-5, -1, 3, 7, —, —, \ldots, —, \ldots$

   (d) $-\frac{1}{4}, 0, \frac{1}{6}, \frac{2}{7}, \ldots, —, \ldots$

   (e) Write eight consecutive odd numbers whose sum is 64.

6. If d = common difference between each pair of numbers, f = first term, L = last term, and n = the number of terms, and if $L = f + (n - 1) \cdot d$ in an arithmetic sequence, then:

   (a) Find the last term in the arithmetic sequence where the first term is 2, the common difference is 4, and there are twelve terms.

   (b) Find the common difference where the first term is 3, the last term is 12, and there are four terms.

   (c) If the common difference is 3, there are five terms, and the last term is 14, find the first term.

   (d) Find the 25th term of the arithmetic sequence $(2, 5, 8, 11, \ldots)$.

   (e) If the 6th term of a sequence is 27 and the 12th term is 48, find the first term.

7. In example 3, each element after the first is formed by multiplying the preceding term by the same fixed number (common ratio), 2 in this case. This is a *geometric sequence*. Two other examples of geometric sequences are 9, 18, 36, 72, ..., and $\frac{1}{2}, \frac{1}{4}, \frac{1}{8}, \frac{1}{16}, \ldots$. If D = common ratio, F = first term, L = last term, and N = the number of terms, and if $L = F \cdot (D^{N-1})$ in geometric sequence, then:

(a) Find the next three terms of the sequence 1, 4, 16, —, —, —.
Find the last term where $N = 8$.

(b) Find the next two terms in the following sequence: 27, 9, 3, —,
—. Find the last term for $N = 8$.

(c) Find the sixth element, if the first number in a geometric sequence
is 2, and the common ratio is 3.

8. Here is a pattern using symbols other than numbers. You will find this
type of pattern in civil service or aptitude tests.

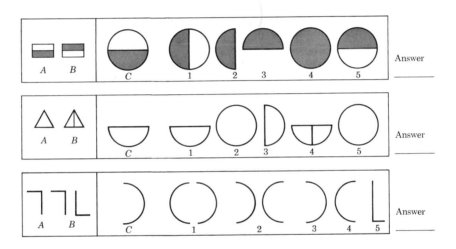

In the panels above, study the change of the patterns from A to B. Find
the rule or rules by which the change is made. Use the same rule to find
the symbol in set 1 through 5 for the change from C.

9. Make a 5 by 5 magic square. The multiples will be 5, 10, 15, ... Find
the sum of each row, column, and diagonal. What is the sum of all the
entries in the square?

10. In problem 6, what is the sum of each sequence?

11. Mr. I. D. Clare has passed on, leaving $15,000 and five children, not
necessarily in that order. Kelly, Jo, Niki, Tony, and Patty (ranked from
the youngest to the oldest) are to receive the total amount, assuming that
there is no inheritance tax, gift tax, lawyer fees, etc. etc. How much will
each get if the money is to be divided so that, starting with the youngest,
Kelly, each gets $250 less than the next?

12. If a ball is dropped from a height of 6 feet and rebounds ⅔ of the distance that it falls, then continues to fall and rebound ⅔ of that height, how far will the ball travel altogether? (You may want to give up hope trying to find an end to the problem, but before you do, look through other texts for a formula for the sum of an infinite geometric progression.)

13. Farmer Claude Hopper wishes to start his son, Ralph, in the business of farming and gives him one grain of corn with the promise that he will furnish the land and provide for all expenses for the first five crops. The first year Ralph has a good season and his grain of corn produces one stalk which yields one ear. This one ear has 100 grains suitable for seed for the following year. If this process continues through the fifth harvest and then Ralph sells all his corn for $1 per bushel, how much money will he have? (Figure that it takes 75 ears of corn for each bushel.)

4.2. Combinations: An Application of Pascal's Triangle

When we come to talk about probability and odds, we will have to have a thorough view of counting, either by one-to-one matching with fingers, toes, pebbles, wives, etc., or by shortcut counting methods which will be developed in this section. Because the whole study of probability grew out of the maneuvering and chicanery of Chinese puzzles, dice, cards, and mathematical tricks, it seems appropriate to use games of chance to illustrate probabilistic methods of decision making. For example, what are the odds of selecting the ace and king of spades from the set of five spades {ace, king, queen, jack, ten}, as shown in figure 4.1? There are ten ways, by listing, of putting two cards from this set together (see figure 4.2).

Only one of these is the desired pair. Thus the odds are one to nine for success. For the moment, we accept this statement as pure conjecture. However, we should be able to develop formulas which would allow us to answer such questions without listing.

After an *affaire d'honneur* with logic we should not become guilty of falling into the quicksands of making illogical assumptions. In the preceding exercises we have not really challenged your choice of numbers for elements of each sequence as long as they fit the pattern. Take

Figure 4.1

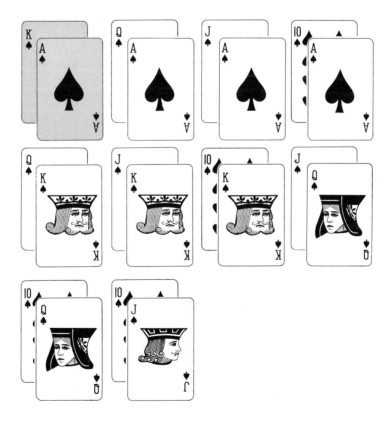

Figure 4.2

warning! Sequences do not always follow obvious patterns. Let's look at a particular sequence,

$$3, 6, 9, 12, \text{\underline{\ \ } \underline{\ \ } \underline{\ \ }}$$

and try to guess at the next three entries. Obviously they are 15, 18, 21, you say. Anyone can see that we are counting by 3's. But, those are not the numbers that *we* had in mind. Here is our answer:

$$3, 6, 9, 12, \cancel{87}, \cancel{387}, 21\underset{\smile}{7}8$$

That's unfair! Perhaps it is, but consider the following pattern.

$$3n + n(n - 1)(n - 2)(n - 3)(n - 4)$$

where n is a counting number 1, 2, 3, 4, 5, 6, 7. Thus if N_1 represents our first entry, N_2 our second, and on down the list, for $n = 1$,

$$N_1 = 3(n) + n(n - 1)(n - 2)(n - 3)(n - 4)$$
$$N_1 = 3(1) + 1(1 - 1)(1 - 2)(1 - 3)(1 - 4)$$
$$= 3 + 1(0)(-1)(-2)(-3)$$
$$= 3 + 0$$
$$= 3$$

and for $n = 2$,

$$N_2 = 3(n) + n(n - 1)(n - 2)(n - 3)(n - 4)$$
$$N_2 = 3(2) + 2(2 - 1)(2 - 2)(2 - 3)(2 - 4)$$
$$= 6 + (2)(1)(0)(-1)(-2)$$
$$= 6 + 0$$
$$= 6$$

if $n = 3$ then,

$$N_3 = 3(3) + 3(3 - 1)(3 - 2)(3 - 3)(3 - 4)$$
$$= 9 + 0$$
$$= 9$$

for $n = 4$,

$$N_4 = 3(4) + 4(4 - 1)(4 - 2)(4 - 3)(4 - 4)$$
$$= 12 + 0$$
$$= 12$$

but for $n = 5$,

$$N_5 = 3(n) + n(n-1)(n-2)(n-3)(n-4)$$
$$= 3(5) + 5(5-1)(5-2)(5-3)(5-4)$$
$$= 15 + 5(4)(3)(2)(1)$$
$$= 15 + 72 \quad 120$$
$$= 87 \quad 135$$

Following this pattern, our sequence becomes

$$3, 6, 9, 12, 87, \ldots, 3n + n(n-1)(n-2)(n-3)(n-4)$$

If the pattern for a different sequence is $3n + n(n-1)(n-2)$, what are the first 7 elements?

$$N_1 = 3(1) + 1(1-1)(1-2)$$
$$N_2 = \ldots$$

Maybe you are beginning to feel that we have been trying to start a fire by rubbing two sticks together, even though we have had a pocket full of matches all the while. Our aim, however, has been to accumulate a potpourri of ideas and manipulations with which we can now light our numerical fire.

We wish to build a symmetrical table of numbers so that each number in the system is somehow related to every other number. Such a table will give us a mechanical tool for computing the number of different subsets that can be derived from n elements, and later it will be used to tally probabilities and determine the coefficients in binominal expansions.

For physical objects to fit together, they must have a particular shape. We can make a large rectangle by piecing together many little rectangles or with right triangles similar to those formed by drawing in the diagonal of the rectangle. The same is true for our cache of numbers. Patterns of figures like those of magic squares were classified in families, and the study of these family likenesses led to the discovery of series.

The typical Greek intellectual of Plato's time despised the art of calculation, and on the whole occupied his time with studying different number patterns. They produced no immediately useful results, but led to the study of series, which ultimately provided the understanding of numbers for representing measurements.

If we write the following sequence of numbers, it shouldn't be too difficult to recognize that each successive number is found by adding 0 to the previous one. Mathematically, though, we may write

$$\text{Row 0:} \quad 1 \quad 1 \quad 1 \quad 1 \quad 1 \quad 1 \ldots \frac{n}{n} \ldots$$

where n represents the term or position of each number.

The next row may be written

$$\text{Row 1:} \quad 1 \quad 2 \quad 3 \quad 4 \quad 5 \quad 6 \ldots \frac{n}{1} \ldots$$

and we see at a glance the natural number sequence where each successive term is obtained by adding 1 to the previous one. We continue to let n count the position of each term in a row in each sequence for the whole table. Now we have started learning about important things early, and will continue to learn more.

$$\text{Row 2:} \quad 1 \quad 3 \quad 6 \quad 10 \quad 15 \quad 21 \ldots ? \ldots$$

The Pythagoreans called the elements of row 2 *triangular numbers,* from which they developed many other sequences — in fact, the rest of our table will be derived from them. By using the proper number of stars with their cardinal number, we can see why they are called triangular numbers.

By placing the terms of this sequence under the corresponding entry in row 1, we may be able to spot a rule to help us write the formula for any term n. Notice that we could use the elements of row 1 to count the elements of all the other rows.

	Term 1	Term 2	Term 3	Term 4	Term 5	Term 6	Term n
Row 0	1	1	1	1	1	1	$\cdots \frac{n}{n} \cdots$
Row 1	1	2	3	4	5	6	$\cdots \frac{n}{1} \cdots$
Row 2	1	3	6	10	15	21	$\cdots ? \cdots$
Row 3	1	4	10	20	35	56	$\cdots ? \cdots$

Figure 4.3

The question still remains, "How do we create a pattern that will let us find any single element for our table?" First, choose any term n in row 1 as a starting position. (Say, for example, term $n = 5$.) Now, with a thimbleful of arithmetic and plenty of thought and imagination, we can find the preceding term, $n - 1$ (in this case, since $n = 5$, then $n - 1 = 4$), for row 2.

Starting with

$$\frac{\text{term}}{\text{row}} \quad \frac{n}{1} = \frac{5}{1}$$

and

$$\frac{\text{term}}{\text{row}} \quad \frac{n - 1}{2} = \frac{5 - 1}{2} = \frac{4}{2}$$

then

$$\frac{n}{1} \cdot \frac{n - 1}{2} = \frac{5}{1} \cdot \frac{4}{2} = 10$$

If we wish to start with the term $n = 4$ in row 1, then for terms $n - 1$, in row 2,

$$\frac{\text{term}}{\text{row}} \quad \frac{n}{1} = \frac{4}{1} \quad \text{and} \quad \frac{\text{term}}{\text{row}} \frac{n-1}{2} = \frac{4-1}{2} = \frac{3}{2}$$

then

$$\frac{4}{1} \cdot \frac{3}{2} = 6$$

If our whim is to start in row 1 with term 6, then term 5 in row 2 is

$$\frac{\text{term}}{\text{row}} \quad \frac{n}{1} \cdot \frac{\text{term}}{\text{row}} \quad \frac{(n-1)}{2} = \frac{6}{1} \cdot \frac{5}{2} = 15$$

and we see that 10, 6, and 15 are the fourth, third, and fifth terms, respectively, in row 2. Thus our recipe for the elements of row 2 is

$$\text{Row 2:} \quad 1 \quad 3 \quad 6 \quad 10 \quad 15 \quad 21 \ldots \frac{n(n-1)}{1 \cdot 2} \ldots$$

Let's try this idea for finding the terms of the next row, row 3.

We have already made a bold assertion that if we find a pattern for row 2 it could be extended to find any number in our table. Thus it appears that, since row 1 terms are $\frac{n}{1}$ and row 2 terms are $\left[\frac{n}{1} \cdot \frac{n-1}{2} \right]$, then terms for row 3 might be, and are,

$$\frac{n}{1} \cdot \frac{n-1}{2} \cdot \frac{n-2}{3} \quad \quad (\text{where } n \text{ is a term in row 1})$$

For a specific example, let's find term 4 in row 3. Since any term in row 3 is represented by $n - 2$, for the fourth term,

$$\frac{\text{term}}{\text{row}} \quad \frac{n-2}{3} = \frac{4}{3}$$

then

$$\frac{\text{term}}{\text{row}} \quad \frac{n-1}{2} = \frac{5}{2}$$

and

$$\frac{\text{term}}{\text{row}} \quad \frac{n}{1} = \frac{6}{1}$$

thus
$$\frac{n}{1} \cdot \frac{n-1}{2} \cdot \frac{n-2}{3} = \frac{\overset{1}{\cancel{6}}}{1} \cdot \frac{5}{\underset{1}{\cancel{2}}} \cdot \frac{4}{\underset{1}{\cancel{3}}} = 20$$

Now we might guess correctly that for the third term in row 3

$$\frac{n-2}{3} = \frac{3}{3}; \quad \frac{n-1}{2} = \frac{4}{2}; \text{ and } \frac{n}{1} = \frac{5}{1}$$

and
$$\frac{n}{1} \cdot \frac{n-1}{2} \cdot \frac{n-2}{3} = \frac{5}{1} \cdot \frac{4}{2} \cdot \frac{3}{3} = 10$$

In general, then, we write for row 3

Row 3:   1   4   10   20 $\dfrac{7}{1} \cdot \dfrac{6}{2} \cdot \dfrac{5}{3}$ 56 ... $\dfrac{n(n-1)(n-2)}{1 \cdot 2 \cdot 3}$ ...

Following through with this pattern for any element of row 4,

$$\frac{n}{1} \cdot \frac{n-1}{2} \cdot \frac{n-2}{3} \cdot \frac{n-3}{4} = \frac{n(n-1)(n-2)(n-3)}{1 \cdot 2 \cdot 3 \cdot 4}$$

and for row 5 the elements are

$$1 \quad 6 \quad 21 \quad \frac{8}{1} \cdot \frac{7}{2} \cdot \frac{6}{3} \cdot \frac{5}{4} \cdot \frac{4}{5} \quad 126 \ldots$$

$$\frac{n(n-1)(n-2)(n-3)(n-4)}{1 \cdot 2 \cdot 3 \cdot 4 \cdot 5}$$

As we continue with this pattern, our table gets out of hand, for writing out the fifteenth term of row 10 becomes unbelievably long and cumbersome. Even if we write the pattern, we wouldn't care to do all the multiplication to evaluate it. If you should wish to know its value, hire a computer or electronic calculating machine. Just poke in the numbers, push a button or pull a lever, and it automatically selects the right answer — and does it all day long! We are not at present interested in the numerical value of the number, but in finding a simple way of *expressing* it and then locating it in the table.

Step a little closer, friend, and watch some of the digits disappear. If we retrace our steps, we discover that in each case that we have tried, the numbers in the denominator begin with 1 and continue the sequence of counting numbers up to some *r* for the *r*th row. With examples, then, let us make this compact and convenient definition:

$$4 \cdot 3 \cdot 2 \cdot 1 \qquad \text{is called } \textit{four factorial, } \text{written 4!}$$

$$7 \cdot 6 \cdot 5 \cdot 4 \cdot 3 \cdot 2 \cdot 1 \text{ is called } \textit{seven factorial, } \text{written 7!}$$

We shall agree to substitute the digit 4 for the word "four," the digit 7 for the word "seven" (in these cases), and replace the word "factorial" with the exclamation sign, ! It does not necessarily mean to shout loudly with much emphasis, but simply, as indicated,

$$5! = 5 \cdot 4 \cdot 3 \cdot 2 \cdot 1$$

and also $\qquad\qquad 5! = 1 \cdot 2 \cdot 3 \cdot 4 \cdot 5$

It may be wise to acquaint yourself with the following patterns to use as a guide.

$$1! = 1$$
$$2! = 2 \cdot 1 = 2$$
$$3! = 3 \cdot 2 \cdot 1 = 6$$
$$4! = 4 \cdot 3 \cdot 2 \cdot 1 = 24$$
$$5! = 5 \cdot 4 \cdot 3 \cdot 2 \cdot 1 = 120$$
$$6! = 6 \cdot 5 \cdot 4 \cdot 3 \cdot 2 \cdot 1 = 720$$
$$7! = 7 \cdot 6 \cdot 5 \cdot 4 \cdot 3 \cdot 2 \cdot 1 = 5,040$$
$$r! = r(r-1)(r-2)(r-3)\ldots(r-r+1)$$

There is one special case that we should not overlook — zero factorial, 0!

Since $\qquad\qquad 7! = 7 \cdot 6 \cdot 5 \cdot 4 \cdot 3 \cdot 2 \cdot 1$
$$= 7 \cdot (6 \cdot 5 \cdot 4 \cdot 3 \cdot 2 \cdot 1)$$
$$= 7 \cdot (6)!$$
$$= 7 \cdot (7-1)!$$

and $\qquad\qquad 2! = 2 \cdot (2-1)!$

and $\qquad\qquad n! = n(n-1)!$ where *n* is a positive integer,

for $n = 1$, $\qquad 1! = 1(1-1)!$
$$= 1 \cdot (0)!$$

But we know that $1! = 1$; then we may argue that if the formula is to hold $0!$ must also equal 1. With all our denominators meeting the factorial definition, with the largest number being the rth row itself, we can now write for the fourth term of row 5 $\dfrac{n(n-1)(n-2)(n-3)(n-4)}{5 \cdot 4 \cdot 3 \cdot 2 \cdot 1}$

$$= \frac{8(8-1)(8-2)(8-3)(8-4)}{5!} = \frac{8 \cdot 7 \cdot 6 \cdot 5 \cdot 4}{5!}$$

We may have put the cart before the horse, so to speak, in building our system of numbers. Like the ancients, we seem only to have amused ourselves with magic numbers and charades by beginning anywhere at all and proceeding in both directions at the same time, producing only a fashionable assortment of figures.

Pythagoras (580-501 B.C.) and his secret societies also toyed with their mystic numbers and such arrays, and may have given mathematics much of its mystery that has prevailed ever since. Members of the cult communicated their mathematical discoveries under oath and, it has been said, Hippasus, one of the members, drowned in his bath after announcing in public the secret of the regular solid with twelve faces.

Omar Khayyam, the Persian poet-mathematician, knew of our triangular table of numbers as early as the 11th century and spoke of them as Khayyam's beautiful numbers. In 1300 A.D. the Chinese mathematician Chu Shi Kei spoke of them in his *Precious Mirror of the Four Elements*. At that time, to speak of the numbers was only a display of wit, but, during the first half of the 17th century, when aristocrats were squandering their wealth at gaming tables, Blaise Pascal (1623-1662) ingeniously applied these numbers to solve problems of mathematical probability. The priestly superstitions of numbers and series were exchanged for investigations into practical problems. Pascal, by viewing the table in the position shown in figure 4.5, gained an extremely useful counting tool. (Notice that we have named the rows n and the diagonal columns r. By comparing figures 4.4 and 4.5 we can satisfy ourselves that each number in its relative position is the same — only the tabulation has changed.)

For example, suppose we wish to determine how many subsets of five elements can be formed from a given set of twelve elements. We could list them all, but probably would have neither the time nor the patience to do so. Instead, let's use figure 4.5. Follow down the rows to row 12 ($n = 12$ elements in the set) and then locate its intersection with

	Term 1	Term 2	Term 3	Term 4	Term 5	Term 6	Term 7	Term 8	Term 9	Term 10	Term 11	Term 12	Term 13	Term 14	Term 15	Term 16	Term 17	⋯	Term n
Row 0	1	1	1	1	1	1	1	1	1	1	1	1	1	1	1	1	1		
Row 1	1	2	3	4	5	6	7	8	9	10	11	12	13	14	15	16			
Row 2	1	3	6	10	15	21	28	36	45	55	66	78	91	105	120				
Row 3	1	4	10	20	35	56	84	120	165	220	286	364	455	560					
Row 4	1	5	15	35	70	126	210	330	495	715	1001	1365	1820						
Row 5	1	6	21	56	126	252	462	792	1287	2002	3003								
Row 6	1	7	28	84	210	462	924	1716	3003	5005									
Row 7	1	8	36	120	330	792	1716	3432	6435										
Row 8	1	9	45	165	495	1287	3003	6435											
Row 9	1	10	55	220	715	2002	5005												
Row 10	1	11	66	286	1001	3003													
Row 11	1	12	78	364	1365														
Row 12	1	13	91	455	1820														
Row 13	1	14	105	560															
⋯																			
Row r																			

Term 6

$$\frac{12 \cdot 11 \cdot 10 \cdot 9 \cdot 8 \cdot 7 \cdot 6}{1 \cdot 2 \cdot 3 \cdot 4 \cdot 5 \cdot 6 \cdot 7} = 792$$

Row 7

Figure 4.4

n	r=0	r=1	r=2	r=3	r=4	r=5	r=6	r=7	r=8	r=9	r=10	r=11	r=12	r=13	r=14	r=15	r=16
n=0	1																
n=1	1	1															
n=2	1	2	1														
n=3	1	3	3	1													
n=4	1	4	6	4	1												
n=5	1	5	10	10	5	1											
n=6	1	6	15	20	15	6	1										
n=7	1	7	21	35	35	21	7	1									
n=8	1	8	28	56	70	56	28	8	1								
n=9	1	9	36	84	126	126	84	36	9	1							
n=10	1	10	45	120	210	252	210	120	45	10	1						
n=11	1	11	55	165	330	462	462	330	165	55	11	1					
n=12	1	12	66	220	495	792	924	792	495	220	66	12	1				
n=13	1	13	78	286	715	1287	1716	1716	1287	715	286	78	13	1			
n=14	1	14	91	364	1001	2002	3003	3432	3003	2002	1001	364	91	14	1		
n=15	1	15	105	455	1365	3003	5005	6435	6435	5005	3003	1365	455	105	15	1	
n=16													1820	560	120	16	1
⋮																	
n																	

The far-right column is headed **Term n**.

number of elements in a set → n

number of elements in a subset → r

$$\frac{n(n-1)(n-2)\cdots(n-r+1)}{r!}$$

$n=12$
$r=5$

$$= \frac{12 \cdot 11 \cdots (12-5+1)}{5!}$$

$$= 792 \text{ subsets, each containing 5 elements}$$

Figure 4.5

the diagonal column 5 ($r = 5$ elements in each subset). The number at the intersection of the row and column is 792, and indicates how many different subsets, each containing five elements, can be formed from a set of twelve elements.

Recall, now, that each entry in the table was formed by the formula $\dfrac{n(n-1)\ldots(n-r+1)}{n!}$. Thus, by using our numbers $n = 12$ and $r = 5$, we should be able to accomplish the same result.

$$\frac{12(12-1)\ldots(12-5+1)}{5!} = \frac{12 \cdot 11 \cdot \ldots \cdot 8}{5!}$$

$$= \frac{12 \cdot 11 \cdot 10 \cdot 9 \cdot 8}{1 \cdot 2 \cdot 3 \cdot 4 \cdot 5} = 792$$

A few observations from the example and others to follow should make our work somewhat easier.

(a) In the formula, the cardinality of the numerator and denominator is the same — that is, the numerals are in one-to-one correspondence with each other.

(b) The denominator meets the factorial definition with the largest numeral, r, indicating the number of elements in each subset.

(c) The largest numeral in the numerator, n, denotes the total number of elements to be used; the smallest numeral is indicated by $n - r + 1$. (For more about $n - r + 1$, see the remark following exercise 16 at the end of this section.)

(d) For sets that contain more elements than are listed in figure 4.5, the formula can be used.

Using the table in figure 4.5 as a check, let's evaluate some entries, and then use the notational device to indicate entries not listed, keeping in mind that a computer can do a faster and more accurate job of evaluating those out in the "back 40." As a final reminder, in figure 4.5, n represents the *number of elements* in a set, r is the *how many* of these n elements we wish to put in a subset, and the *solution* is the *number of subsets* that will contain an r number of elements.

Example 1 Determine the number of subsets that contain 6 elements chosen from a total of 7 elements.

Solution Let $n = 7$ and $r = 6$. Then,

$$\frac{7 \cdot 6 \ldots (7 - 6 + 1)}{6!} = \frac{7 \cdot 6 \ldots \cdot 2}{6!} = \frac{7 \cdot \overset{1}{\cancel{6}} \cdot \overset{1}{\cancel{5}} \cdot \overset{1}{\cancel{4}} \cdot \overset{1}{\cancel{3}} \cdot \overset{1}{\cancel{2}}}{\underset{1}{\cancel{6}} \cdot \underset{1}{\cancel{5}} \cdot \underset{1}{\cancel{4}} \cdot \underset{1}{\cancel{3}} \cdot \underset{1}{\cancel{2}} \cdot 1} = 7$$

Example 2 Determine the number of subsets containing 2 elements chosen from a set of 6.

Solution Let $n = 6$ and $r = 2$. Then,

$$\frac{6 \ldots (6 - 2 + 1)}{2!} = \frac{6 \cdot 5 \ldots}{2!} \text{ but } 6 - 2 + 1 = 5, \text{ which is the smallest and last component,}$$

thus,
$$= \frac{\overset{3}{\cancel{6}} \cdot 5}{\underset{1}{\cancel{2}} \cdot 1}$$

$$= 15$$

Example 3 If $n = 9$ and $r = 3$, find the number indicated for Pascal's triangle.

Solution

$$\frac{9 \cdot 8 \ldots (9 - 3 + 1)}{3!} = \frac{9 \cdot 8 \cdot 7}{3!} = \frac{\overset{3}{\cancel{9}} \cdot \overset{4}{\cancel{8}} \cdot 7}{\underset{1}{\cancel{3}} \cdot \underset{1}{\cancel{2}} \cdot 1} = 84$$

Again we ask the question that was presented at the beginning of the section: What are the odds of selecting the ace and king of spades from a set of five spades? We are really asking for the number of two-element subsets that we can form from the universal set of five elements. We have already listed the subsets and counted them one by one, finding that there was one successful subset and nine unsuccessful attempts, or a total of ten ways. If we can apply the formula that we have just developed we need not itemize to find out "how many." If n equals the total number of cards and r is the number of cards that we are to choose at a time, then the total number of ways of choosing two cards out of five is

$$\frac{5 \ldots (5 - 2 + 1)}{2!} = \frac{5 \cdot 4}{2 \cdot 1} = 10$$

of which only one is our success, as we already found.

More generally, suppose we have a set of n objects and we wish to choose a subset that contains r of them, necessarily, $0 \le r \le n$. Such a subset is called a *combination*. Combinations are numbers which tell us the number of subsets we can take from a given set when we are allowed to choose "just so many" at a time. (Recall that in a set or subset of elements, order doesn't count, i.e., the set $\{a,b,c\}$ is identical to the set $\{b,c,a\}$.) A convenient notational device is ${}_nC_r$ or $\binom{n}{r}$ and to evaluate each, we write

$$_nC_r = \binom{n}{r} = \frac{n(n-1)(n-2)\ldots(n-r+1)}{r!}$$

(See Problem Set 4.2, exercise 1(j).)

Now to answer the question presented at the beginning of this section. How many ways can you take 2 cards from a deck of 52 cards?

$$_nC_r = {}_{52}C_2 = \binom{52}{2} = \frac{52 \ldots (52 - 2 + 1)}{2!} = \frac{52 \cdot 51}{2 \cdot 1} = 1326$$

Example 4   Solve each of the following and verify your answers with the table as shown in figure 4.5.

$$_4C_4, \quad {}_4C_3, \quad {}_4C_2, \quad {}_4C_1, \quad {}_4C_0$$

$$_4C_4 = \frac{4 \cdot 3 \ldots (4 - 4 + 1)}{4!} = \frac{4 \cdot 3 \cdot 2 \cdot 1}{4 \cdot 3 \cdot 2 \cdot 1} = 1$$

$$_4C_3 = \frac{4 \cdot 3 \ldots (4 - 3 + 1)}{3!} = \frac{4 \cdot 3 \cdot 2}{3 \cdot 2 \cdot 1} = 4$$

$$_4C_2 = \frac{4 \ldots (4 - 2 + 1)}{2!} = \frac{4 \cdot 3}{2 \cdot 1} = 6$$

$$_4C_1 = \frac{4}{1} = 4$$

Notice that $4 - 1 + 1 = 4$; therefore the first number is the last number, 4, and must be the only entry in the numerator, and in every case where $n \geqslant 1$, $_nC_1 = n$.

$_4C_0$ asks for the number of subsets which contain no objects that we may derive from a set of four objects. This, of course, refers to the empty set. Therefore we shall define $_nC_0$ to equal 1 for all $n \leqslant 0$, and $_4C_0 = 1$.

Example 5   Suppose we are to flip n number of coins. How many ways can we get r number of heads? (Assume, of course, that it is impossible for the coin to land on its edge.) List all outcomes.

(a) On a toss of a single coin, $n = 1$ coin (maximum heads $= 1$) and we can get subsets of r heads where r can only be equal to 1 or 0. If $r = 1$ head, then

$$_nC_r = {_1C_1} = 1 \text{ way of getting 1 head}$$

Or, r can be equal to 0 (i.e., no heads — a tail). Then

$$_nC_r = {_1C_0} = 1 \text{ way of getting no heads}$$

We are letting a coin represent any situation in which there is a single decision to make from two possibilities: heads or tails; yes or no; true or false; on or off. On a toss of one coin, we can get 1 head (H) or 0 heads (T) and we write $(H + T)^1 = 1\,H + 1\,T$ (Recall from Chapter 1 that "or" refers to addition.)

(b) If $n = 2$ coins, then $r = 2$ heads, 1 head, and 0 heads, respectively, thus,

$_2C_2 = 1$ way of getting heads on both coins on the same toss

$_2C_1 = 2$ ways of getting one head, and

$_2C_0 = 1$ way of getting no heads (both coins tails).

Thus we indicate $(H + T)^2 = 1\,HH + 2\,HT + 1\,TT$.

REMARK:

   (H, T) is counted as being different from (T, H)

Coin 1   Coin 2   Coin 1   Coin 2

(c) If $n = 3$ coins, $r = 3$ heads, 2 heads, 1 head, and 0 heads in turn.

$$_3C_3 = 1; \ _3C_2 = 3; \ _3C_1 = 3; \ _3C_0 = 1$$

or $$(H + T)^3 = 1 \ HHH + 3 \ HHT + 3 \ HTT + 1 \ TTT$$

That is, there exists:

> 1 way of getting all three coins to show heads simultaneously,
>
> 3 ways of getting two heads and one tail,
>
> 3 ways of getting one head and two tails, and
>
> 1 way of getting no heads (all tails).

(d) In example 4, setting the problem to words, "If we continue to toss four coins, what are the outcomes?" we may write it thus:

$$(H + T)^4 = 1 \ HHHH + 4 \ HHHT + 6 \ HHTT + 4 \ HTTT + 1 \ TTTT$$

As you can see, should we use several more coins it would require too much time and space to list the outcomes; therefore, as usual in this mathematical language of symbols, we eliminate the chaff and write the following for the four-coin problem in the preceding example.

$$(H + T)^4 = 1 \ H^4 + 4 \ H^3T^1 + 6 \ H^2T^2 + 4 \ H^1T^3 + 1 \ T^4$$

which merely states that, on a toss of four coins,

1 H^4	there is only 1 way for four heads and no tails,
4 H^3T^1	there are 4 ways for obtaining three heads and one tail,
6 H^2T^2	there are 6 ways to get two heads and two tails,
4 H^1T^3	there are 4 ways for one head and three tails, and
1 T^4	there is only 1 way for no heads and four tails to show.

Thus there is a total of 16 different subsets possible from a universal set of four elements, which are, in this case, coins.

PROBLEM SET 4.2

1. Find the numerical value of each of the following.

   (a) $9!$

   (b) $4! + 5!$

   (c) $(4 + 5)!$

   (d) $\dfrac{10!}{9!}$

   (e) $\dfrac{12!}{6!6!}$

   (f) $(n + 1)!$ where $n = 5$

   (g) $n! + 1$ where $n = 5$

   (h) $(n - r)!$ where $n = 0$ and $r = 7$

   (i) $\dfrac{n!}{(n - r)!}$ where $n = 12$ and $r = 3$

   (j) $\dfrac{n!}{r! (n - r)!}$
   where $n = 12$ and $r = 3$; also
   where $n = 9$ and $r = 0$.
   (Compare these values with those from
   Pascal's triangle.)

2. Which of the following are true?

   (a) $8! = 8 \cdot 7!$

   (b) $2! - 1! = 1!$

   (c) $4! + 4! = 8!$

   (d) $\dfrac{10!}{9!} = 9$

   (e) $n! = n \cdot (n - 1)!$

   (f) $n! = (n^2 - n) \cdot (n - 2)!$

3. Evaluate

   (a) $_7C_4$

   (b) $_{13}C_{13}$

   (c) $_{79}C_0$

   (d) $\dbinom{9}{3}$

   (e) $\dbinom{3}{2}$

   (f) $_4C_6$

   (g) $\dbinom{250}{249}$

   (h) $\dbinom{27}{22}$

4. Write each of the following in terms of factorials, as in part (a).

   (a) $8 \cdot 7 \cdot 6 \cdot 5 = \dfrac{8 \cdot 7 \cdot 6 \cdot 5}{1} \cdot \dfrac{4 \cdot 3 \cdot 2 \cdot 1}{4 \cdot 3 \cdot 2 \cdot 1} = \dfrac{8!}{4!}$

(b) $12 \cdot 11 \cdot 10$ (c) $\dfrac{13 \cdot 12!}{12!}$

(d) $\dfrac{8 \cdot 7 \ldots (8 - 3 + 1)}{3 \cdot 2 \cdot 1}$ (e) $\dfrac{n(n - 1)(n - 2) \ldots (n - r + 1)}{r!}$

(Compare with problem 1 (j).)

5. Show $_6C_2 = {}_6C_4$.

6. From Pascal's triangle, the coefficients in the expansion of

$$(a + b)^3 = 1a^3 + 3\, a^2b + 3\, ab^2 + 1b^3$$

Use this pattern and expand each of the following.

(a) $(a + b)^4$

(b) $(1.1)^3$ (*Hint:* $(1.1)^3 = (1 + .1)^3$)

(c) $(.99)^3$

7. Make a list of the different outcomes as a result of flipping five coins (or one coin five times). Compare the number of each result with line 5 of Pascal's triangle.

8. A certain psychologist has four patients in the waiting room: Mr. Id, Mr. Libido, Mr. Ego, and Mr. Superego. If he has two couches, how many ways can he "treat" two patients at once?

9. How many subsets of three letters are there in the letters of the alphabet?

10. There are ten salesmen for the Cable Company, of which three are to be transferred to a new office. In how many ways can the three to be transfered be selected?

11. The Cable Company makes ding-a-lings. How many ways can one of their machines produce 40 ding-a-lings with half of them defective? How many ways if no two consecutive pieces are both good or both defective?

12. Gene has a penny, a nickel, a dime, a quarter, and a half dollar in his pocket. He reaches in and randomly takes out three coins. How many ways can he do this? (Assume that he cannot tell one from another by feeling.)

13. If an examination consists of nine questions of which the student is to answer any seven and omit two:

(a) How many ways can a student make his selection?

(b) If he must answer the first four, how many choices?

    (c) How many ways of answering at least three of the first five questions?

    (d) If he is to answer any two and omit seven, how many ways?

14. Five students go to a football game, but two of them won't sit next to each other. How many ways can the students be seated all on the same bench?

15. The musical scale has essentially twelve notes.

    (a) How many different "tunes" can be played that use each note once?

    (b) How many tunes can be played that use any number of notes without repeating any?

16. How many natural numbers are there from 37 to 93 inclusive?

REMARK: A convenient formula for counting consecutively placed elements is n − r + 1 *where* n *is the total number of elements and* r *is the number of them to be placed in some order. Consider the problem as selecting from* n *objects to place in* r *boxes until each box contains one object. We have:*

Chose from   n   *objects, one to place in the first box*   ✱

There are now n − 1 *objects, place one in the second box*   ✱

Leaving   n − 2 *objects. Choose one for the third box*   ✱

Now we have n − 3 *objects left. Place one in the fourth box* ✱

               •
               •
               •

Until finally   n − (r − 1) *objects remain for a selection for the* r*th box* □

Note that   n − (r − 1) = n − r + 1.

We could therefore think of our problem as putting 93 *numbers into* 37 *boxes. We can place number* 1 *in the first box, number* 2 *in the second box, etc., until we reach the* 37*th box. How many numbers do we have to select from for the* 37*th box?*

17. Professor Ichabod Grinch has made a homework assignment of reading textbook pages 288 to 354, inclusive. How many pages are to be read?

18. Kelly, Tony, and Mike are counting the tomato plants in their garden. Kelly starts the count and counts from 1 to 151. Mike then takes up the count and goes from plant number 152 to 307. Then Tony finishes the counting from 308 to 442, inclusive. How many plants did each boy count? How many plants are there in all?

19. There are 13 denominations (ranks) in each of 4 suits in a standard deck of playing cards. One "hand" in a game of poker is a straight flush (5 consecutively ranked cards of the same suit). If the ace plays at either end, how many straight flushes can be dealt from the deck?

20. If a poker hand consists of 5 cards drawn from a standard deck of 52 cards, how many poker hands are there?

21. A flush, in poker, has 5 cards all the same suit.

    (a) How many spade flushes are possible?

    (b) How many flushes are possible?

    (c) The royal flush is the best hand in the game. It is the five highest cards all the same suit. How many are possible? See figure 4.2.

    (d) How many straights are there that are not flushes?

REMARK: Occasionally we are to place identical (indistinguishable) objects into different containers and need a short-cut counting method. For example, Dad may wish to distribute four new dimes to his two children, Kelly and Tony. How many ways can this be done?

   Pictorially we represent the children by putting up dividers and placing the coins within the two spaces. There are 5 ways of distributing the dimes.

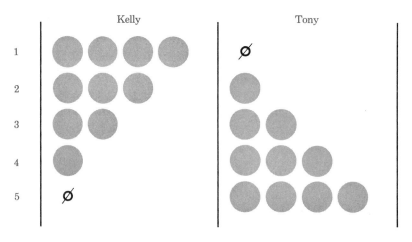

Since each child, in turn, can get no coins at all, we consider them as the empty set whenever their time is due. Thus we can think, if we try, of distributing four coins and one empty set, i.e., five "things" in all. Of these five things, only four can actually be partitioned, and we have combinations of 5 things taken 4 at a time, or $_5C_4 = 5$.

Were the coins to be divided among three people and one person got all four coins, there would be two empty sets to distribute (i.e., two of the people would get nothing at the same time). Then we have 6 things taken 4 at a time, or $_6C_4 = 15$ ways of dividing four identical coins among three people. Try listing all 15 ways. In general, then, if we have n *objects which cannot be distinguished one from another and they are to be divided into* r *cells, it can be done in*

$$_{n+r-1}C_n \text{ ways.}$$

22. The Fuddy Duddy toy store sells whee-whods in 5 different colors at 10¢ per dozen. How many color combinations are available for 10¢? (*Hint:* Think of placing the objects in groups according to colors.)

23. A mailman has five identical letters to be put into three mailboxes. The letters are advertisements from the same company and all are addressed to Boxholder. How many ways can he "drop" the letters?

24. John is having a poker party for the boys and is going to use red, white, and blue chips. At the start of the evening if he gives each player a stack of 10 chips and enough fellows come to use every possible color combination, exactly once (that is, one player may get 6 red and 4 white; another 3 red, 5 white, and 2 blue; etc.), how many are at the party? (*Hint:* Think of the chips as being partitioned into three different spaces called red, white, and blue; consider the chips as being indistinguishable.)

4.3. Tree Diagrams

In the first chapter we agreed that, given the set of statements $\{p,q\}$, we could combine them as to the truth or falsity of each in 4, or 2^2, ways: the set in which both were true $\{p,q\}$, the universal set; the unit truth sets $\{p\}$ and $\{q\}$; and the set in which neither p nor q was true, the empty set ϕ.

We also agreed that the three-element set had 8, or 2^3, subsets of the same nature: the universal and empty sets, $\{p,q,r\}$ and ϕ; the two-element subsets $\{p,q\}$, $\{p,r\}$, and $\{q,r\}$; and the singletons $\{p\}$, $\{q\}$, and $\{r\}$. Obviously, the universal set containing the one element $\{p\}$ has only two subsets, or 2^1: $\{p\}$ itself, and ϕ. To generalize, then, if we decide to put every element of a given set U into a set S we have the universal set. If we decide to put no elements of U into set S, then we have the empty set. For the most part, S will contain some, but not all, of U. Therefore, with n elements in U, we have two decisions to make about each element — whether it goes into set S or it doesn't. It follows, then, that there are 2^n subsets that can be formed from a set containing n elements. This is not a proof, but a logical discussion following a few patterns of 2^n that point us in the right direction. The proof follows the principle of mathematical induction, which is beyond the scope of this text. (Which means we just can't find a *simple* explanation that will suffice.) A geometrical approach may help clarify the concept.

Consider the old adage, "There are always two sides to every argument." The following picture is suggested that reaches toward infinity. If we let a represent one side of an argument and b the other, then each side to the argument makes two new alternate sides, a and b. If we stop at

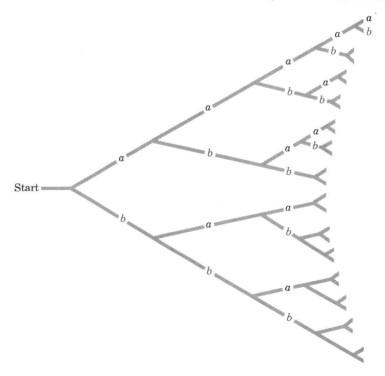

Figure 4.6

any time and count all the branches of the tree — or all the sides of all arguments — it will be a multiple of two or, in particular, 2^n.

2^n	n	2^{-n}
1	0	1.0
2	1	0.5
4	2	0.25
8	3	0.125
16	4	0.062 5
32	5	0.031 25
64	6	0.015 625
128	7	0.007 812 5
256	8	0.003 906 25
512	9	0.001 953 125
1 024	10	0.000 976 562 5
2 048	11	0.000 488 281 25
4 096	12	0.000 244 140 625
8 192	13	0.000 122 070 312 5
16 384	14	0.000 061 035 156 25
32 768	15	0.000 030 517 578 125
65 536	16	0.000 015 258 789 062 5
131 072	17	0.000 007 629 394 531 25
262 144	18	0.000 003 814 697 265 625
524 288	19	0.000 001 907 348 632 812 5
1 048 576	20	0.000 000 953 674 316 406 25
2 097 152	21	0.000 000 476 837 158 203 125
4 194 304	22	0.000 000 238 418 579 101 562 5
8 388 608	23	0.000 000 119 209 289 550 781 25
16 777 216	24	0.000 000 059 604 644 775 390 625
33 554 432	25	0.000 000 029 802 322 387 695 312 5
67 108 864	26	0.000 000 014 901 161 193 847 656 25
134 217 728	27	0.000 000 007 450 580 596 923 828 125
268 435 456	28	0.000 000 003 725 290 298 461 914 062 5
536 870 912	29	0.000 000 001 862 645 149 230 957 031 25
1 073 741 824	30	0.000 000 000 931 322 574 615 478 515 625
2 147 483 648	31	0.000 000 000 465 661 287 307 739 257 812 5
4 294 967 296	32	0.000 000 000 232 830 643 653 869 628 906 25
8 589 934 592	33	0.000 000 000 116 415 321 826 934 814 453 125
17 179 869 184	34	0.000 000 000 058 207 660 913 467 407 226 562 5
34 359 738 368	35	0.000 000 000 029 103 830 456 733 703 613 281 25
68 719 476 736	36	0.000 000 000 014 551 915 228 366 851 806 640 625
137 438 953 472	37	0.000 000 000 007 275 957 614 183 425 903 320 312 5
274 877 906 944	38	0.000 000 000 003 637 978 807 091 712 951 660 156 25
549 755 813 888	39	0.000 000 000 001 818 989 403 545 856 475 830 078 125
1 099 511 627 776	40	0.000 000 000 000 909 494 701 772 928 237 915 039 062 5
2 199 023 255 552	41	0.000 000 000 000 454 747 350 886 464 118 957 519 531 25
4 398 046 511 104	42	0.000 000 000 000 227 373 675 443 232 059 478 759 765 625
8 796 093 022 208	43	0.000 000 000 000 113 686 837 721 616 029 739 379 882 812 5
17 592 186 044 416	44	0.000 000 000 000 056 843 418 860 808 014 869 689 941 406 25
35 184 372 088 832	45	0.000 000 000 000 028 421 709 430 404 007 434 844 970 703 125
70 368 744 177 664	46	0.000 000 000 000 014 210 854 715 202 003 717 422 485 351 562 5
140 737 488 355 328	47	0.000 000 000 000 007 105 427 357 601 001 858 711 242 675 781 25
281 474 976 710 656	48	0.000 000 000 000 003 552 713 678 800 500 929 355 621 337 890 625
562 949 953 421 312	49	0.000 000 000 000 001 776 356 839 400 250 464 677 810 668 945 312 5
1 125 899 906 842 624	50	0.000 000 000 000 000 888 178 419 700 125 232 338 905 334 472 656 25

Interesting Fact: We cannot give an exact formula for finding the number of digits in the expanded form of 2^n, but from the tabulations in the figure above, it appears that an approximate formula would be $(\frac{1}{3})\,n$. For example, if $n = 15$, $2^{15} = 32{,}768$ and there are five, $(\frac{1}{3})\,15$, digits in 2^{15} expanded. There are ten, $(\frac{1}{3})\,30$, digits in 2^{30}, which is equal to 1,073,741,824. There are five digits in 2^{14} expanded, however, and $(\frac{1}{3})\,14 = 4\frac{2}{3}$, which is approximately 5. Whenever $(\frac{1}{3})\,n$ is a fraction, round off to the next positive integer. 2^{-n} is just another form of $(\frac{1}{2})^n$. That is, if $n = 4$, then $2^{-n} = (\frac{1}{2})^4 = \frac{1}{16} = .0625$.

Figure 4.7

A noteworthy and handy phenomenon that may be unearthed by exploration with pencil and paper is that 2^n is the sum of all the numbers of any line n in Pascal's triangle. For a start, the sum of the numbers in line 4, figure 4.4, is

$$2^4 = 1 + 4 + 6 + 4 + 1 = 16$$

and for line 5,

$$2^5 = 1 + 5 + 10 + 10 + 5 + 1 = 32$$

We shall make use of this little gem in the next section on probability, but for now we are using it only as a method of counting "how many" subsets can be made from a universal set.

If we were to flip a single "fair" coin, for example, how many different outcomes are possible as shown in figure 4.6? With one coin, $n = 1$, there should be, if our 2^n is correct, 2^1 or 2 results — a head or a tail. If we toss two coins simultaneously (or one coin twice, the results would be the same), we can expect to have 2^2 or 4 outcomes.

To go on, for listing the logical possibilities for 3, 4, 5, . . . coins, a convenient method is by designing a *tree diagram*. To list the various occurrences for a toss of three coins, we start from left to right and the number of branches at each point corresponds to the number of ways that the next event can take place.

Example 1

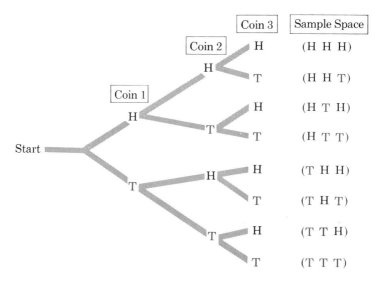

Listing the results from the base (start) of the tree to the end of each branch gives us a complete set of outcomes, which we shall call a *sample space*. An *event* is a subset of the set of all possible outcomes. Furthermore, the empty subset, ϕ, is called an impossible event; to throw 10^9 ones in succession with a die seems infinitely impossible.

Example 2   Mrs. B. is planning picnic lunches and wants to make each one different. If she plans to use ham, wieners, and steak for the meats, potato salad and bean salad for salads, apple pie and cake for dessert, and iced tea for the drink, how many different lunches can she pack?

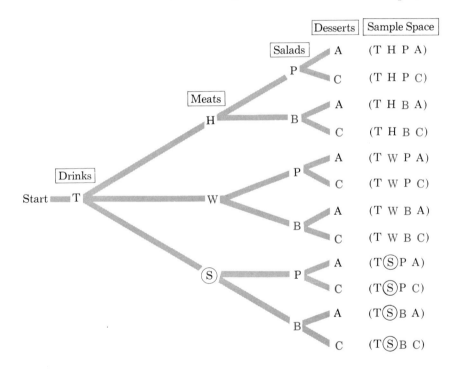

Notice that the number of ways that each lunch can be planned is as follows:

Type of Food	Number of Varieties
Beverage	1
Meat	3
Salad	2
Dessert	2

The total sample space, then, has $1 \cdot 3 \cdot 2 \cdot 2 = 12$ outcomes and it can be thought of as the *product set*.

Example 3   How many "different" consequences can be obtained from one toss of a pair of dice (two tosses of a single die)? If we care to list them, we can count 36 outcomes if the event (4,3) is considered to be different from (3,4), even though the sums are the same. Therefore, it should be apparent that if the first die has six choices for a number and the second die has six choices, then together there are $6 \cdot 6 = 36$ different consequences. See figure 4.8.

In general, we say that if some event can occur in m different ways, and if, following this event, a second event can take place in n different ways, then together the total number of different events that can be performed is $m \cdot n$. This principle can be extended if other events are to follow. We then have $m \cdot n \cdot r \dots$.

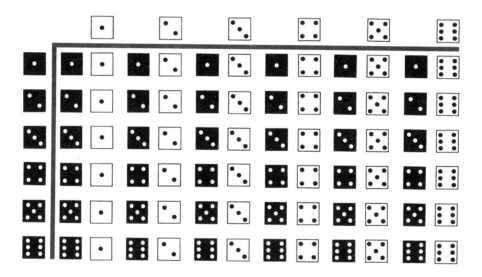

Figure 4.8

Example 4   How many 3-digit numbers greater than 649 can be formed from the digits 2, 4, 6, and 8? Use the tree diagram.

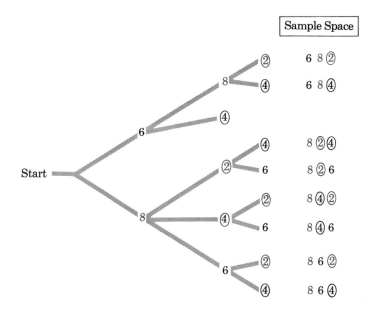

Example 5   Betty and Ralph are to play a tiddledywinks tournament. The winner must win 3 games out of 5 or 2 in a row. How many ways can the tournament take place? List the sample space.

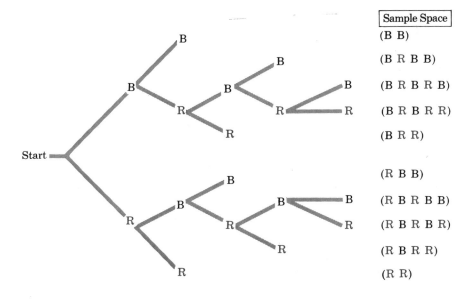

Example 6 Jim B. has five sons: Bert, Arthur, Jack, John, and Buck. He also has three fields of corn that need to be weeded. Counting himself, how many ways can Jim B. put two workers in one field, three in another field, and one worker in the last field?

Solution If Bert and Arthur, for example, are to work in the same field, this is the same pair as Arthur and Bert. That is, it does not matter which of the pair of workers is mentioned first, the result is the same. Therefore it should be obvious that we are to use combinations of workers. Since there are a total of 6 to choose from, $n = 6$, and for one corn field we need any 2 of the boys, thus $r = 2$, and

$$_6C_2 = \frac{6 \ldots (6 - 2 + 1)}{2!} = \frac{6 \cdot 5}{1 \cdot 2} = 15$$

ways of selecting two boys for one field.
But this leaves four workers from which three are to be selected for the next field.

$$_4C_3 = \frac{4 \cdot 3 \cdot 2}{1 \cdot 2 \cdot 3} = 4$$

ways of putting three boys in another field.
We now have one worker left to put in the last field, which can be done in

$$_1C_1 = 1$$

way. There are 15 ways of completing the first task, 4 ways for the next, and 1 way of doing the last. Then, there are

$$_6C_2 \cdot {}_4C_3 \cdot {}_1C_1 = 15 \cdot 4 \cdot 1 = 60$$

ways of dividing the six workers into three groups of workers of two, three, and one, respectively. Suppose, though, that Jim B. selected the three-man work squad first, then the one-man team, and finally the group of two. We would have

$$_6C_3 \cdot {}_3C_1 \cdot {}_2C_2 = 20 \cdot 3 \cdot 1 = 60$$

ways. Using combinations in this fashion, order is not important because it does not alter the final result.

Example 7   In example 6, how many ways can the work teams be selected if Jim B. decides to work in the one field by himself?

Solution   If Jim is to work by himself, there is *no* decision to be made concerning him and the field that he is to work in — it can be done in only one way. The question remaining, then, is how can we place the five boys, three in one place and two in another. We can choose three from the five in

$$_5C_3 = \frac{5 \cdot 4 \cdot 3}{1 \cdot 2 \cdot 3} = 10$$

ways, leaving the other two boys to work in the remaining field in only one way. Thus, we have

$$1 \cdot {_5C_3} \cdot {_2C_2} = 1 \cdot 10 \cdot 1 = 10$$

ways. Or if we care to choose the pair of boys first, it can be done in

$$_5C_2 = \frac{5 \cdot 4}{1 \cdot 2} = 10$$

ways and the remaining three boys must work in the other field. Then the total number of ways to distribute the boys is the same as before.

$$1 \cdot {_5C_2} \cdot {_3C_3} = 1 \cdot 10 \cdot 1 = 10$$

PROBLEM SET 4.3

1. Show that $2^n = {}_nC_n + {}_nC_{n-1} + {}_nC_{n-2} + \ldots + {}_nC_0$ where $n = 1, 2, 3,$ 6, 8. How many different *terms* are there in each of the sums?

2. If John flips a coin 20 times,

    (a) how many different events are possible?

    (b) how many of these events will result in 20 heads? 19 heads? 10 heads? 2 heads? 1 head? No heads?

    (c) after the 20th toss, what are the possible events on the 21st toss?

3. Patty, Janet, Niki, Jo, Deanna, Lila, Bridgette, and Sophia are eight pretty young lassies. You may have a date with any one of them if you can identify her by name. You are allowed to ask three "yes/no" questions. Show how this can be done.

4. There are approximately 455,000 entries in a current Funk and Wagnall's dictionary. Develop a method for identifying any one entry by asking a minimum number of "yes" or "no" questions. What is this minimum number?

5. Draw a tree diagram showing the possible outcomes from tossing four coins.

6. Mr. C. Nile has two quarters and Mr. O. P. Tomistic has one. They agree to match coins until one of them is broke or they have played four games, whichever happens first. Construct a tree diagram showing all possible plays of the game.

7. A traveling salesman, Arthur B., is to call upon the following six towns and, using the available highways as shown by the following diagram, he is to stop and spend the night when he cannot continue without taking the same highway twice. By using a tree diagram find the number of ways that he can travel on his sales route before stopping for the night if he is to begin his journey at Podunk. What is the most number of towns that Arthur can visit in one day? At what city is he most likely to spend the night?

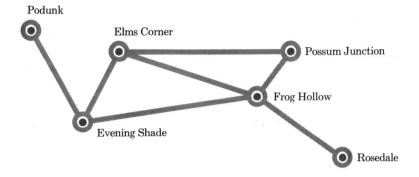

Podunk
Elms Corner
Possum Junction
Frog Hollow
Evening Shade
Rosedale

8. The ten finalists for the Miss America Contest are parading in front of the judges. At that moment the *Daily News* is ready to go to press and the typesetter has been instructed to make lists for all possible results for queen, first runner-up, and second runner-up. How many lists must the printer prepare?

9. During registration, Mathew Matics, a college student, discovers that he may enroll in a math class for the hours of 8:00, 10:00, 11:00, or 2:00; English at 9:00, 10:00, 1:00 or 2:00; and science at 8:00, 11:00, 2:00, or 3:00. How many different ways can he schedule three courses?

10. A sack contains two red, two green, one blue, and one white lollipop. How many different color combinations of two lollipops may be selected?

11. If the U. S. Senate has 54 Democrats and 46 Republicans, how many committees consisting of 5 Democrats and 4 Republicans can be formed?

12. A student senate group consists of 5 members from each class. How many councils of 4 seniors, 3 juniors, 2 sophomores, and 1 freshman can be formed from this group?

13. The seven basic colors of the rainbow, from top to bottom, are red, orange, yellow, green, blue, indigo, and violet, represented by the letters R, O, Y, G, B, I, V, respectively.

    (a) How many "different rainbows" can be made by rearranging these colors?

    (b) How many "three-colored rainbows" could be created?

14. A Gizmo has 14 movable parts which can be assembled in any order. An efficiency expert decides to time each possible order of assembly. If it

takes an average of 40 minutes to make a Gizmo, how long will it take to time all possible orders of assembly?

15. A college history class has 18 unhappy students who are dissatisfied with "D-grading" conditions.

   (a) How many ways can they choose a protest committee consisting of four students?

   (b) A committee of three is to be selected by votes. The person receiving the most votes will be the first spokesman for the committee, the person receiving the second highest number of votes will be the second speaker if the first fails to return, and the third highest vote getter is to report to the class in case the number two man vanishes. In how many ways can the committee be formed?

16. In problem 15, the committee confiscates the professor's grade book. But, much to the dismay of the students, the professor recalls his grade distribution to be one A, two B's, four C's, eight D's, and three F's. In how many ways can he assign grades at random, since he doesn't recall which student was to get which grade?

17. Three men, three women, and five children are to have a group picture taken.

   (a) How many ways are there for the people to be arranged in a row?

   (b) If the picture was so blurred that no one could be identified individually, except that each person could be classified as man, woman, or child, how many interpretations could be contrived for the picture?

18. A recent TV advertisement stated that there were more than 5000 color choices for a new Rolls-Canardly automobile. In checking the validity of the ad, it was found that there were nine different exterior colors which could be selected as a solid color or a two-tone. (*Note:* Black over white is a different colored auto from white over black.) Also, a purchaser could choose from ten interior solid colors or two-toned interiors using seven of the ten colors. How many color choices are there for consumers of this auto?

19. Floyd is playing scrabble and has seven letters: two A's, one D, two I's and two N's. One arrangement of the letters is INDIANA.

   (a) How many ways can the letters be arranged? (*Hint:* Interchanging the two A's forms another arrangement.)

(b) How many ways can the letters be placed on the board to spell INDIANA? (See hint given in part (a).)

(c) How many *distinguishable* arrangements are there of the seven letters?

(d) In how many arrangements in part (c) will the two A's be side by side?

(e) In how many arrangements will the two A's not be side by side?

20. A department store employs 15 clerks. How many ways can the clerks be divided so that 4 work in the home and garden department, 3 in men's wear, 2 in notions, 3 in women's wear, and 3 in sporting goods?

21. How many arrangements are there of the letters in the word DIVIDED? How many of these arrangements are different?

22. The coach at P.U. has 60 players on his football squad. How many different teams can he use when two teams made up of the same players are considered different teams if the men are assigned different positions?

23. If 64 players enter an elimination tennis tournament for a singles championship, how many matches must be played to determine the winner?

24. Fifteen members of the local church have formed a softball squad. How many different nine-man teams can they field:

(a) if two teams are considered the same whenever the same men play, regardless of position?

(b) if two teams are considered different whenever the same men play but are assigned different positions?

(c) If one particular team is going on the field and the players are prompted to switch positions, how many ways can they rearrange the team?

(d) Compare the product of (a) and (c) with the solution of part (b).

(e) How many teams can be formed using the assumption of part (a) except that three of the men can be used only as pitchers and three only at short stop?

25. The Cable Company produces gilgadgets. An inspector haphazardly draws a sample of four gilgadgets from a lot of ten which contains six good ones and four defective ones. If each piece is distinguishable, how many samples can be formed:

(a) with no restrictions?

(b) with 4 good pieces?

(c) with 3 good pieces and 1 defective?

(d) with 2 good pieces and 2 defectives?

(e) with 1 good piece and 3 defectives?

(f) with all 4 defective?

(g) What is the sum of (b) through (f)?

26. Twelve of the Cable Company employees file their income tax forms but five of them contain errors. If the IRS computer randomly selects samples of four, how many of the samples will contain:

(a) all correct forms?

(b) all incorrect forms?

(c) exactly 2 incorrect forms?

(d) at most 2 incorrect forms?

(e) at least 2 incorrect forms?

(f) how many of the samples will not contain exactly 2 incorrect forms?

(g) Among the 12 forms is that of Mr. I. M. Istaken which is, of course, incorrect. In how many of the samples of 4 will his tax form appear?

27. In a recent you-may-have-won-a-car promotional merchandising sweepstakes contest, you win a prize by revealing the "dealer's" hand and then disclosing any three numbers picked at random from 16 hidden possibilities. How many "hands" are possible in one game for John Q. Consumer? There is exactly one of the total possible choices that will add up to more than the dealer's hand. What percent of the time would you expect to win a prize? How much extra would you pay for the product to play this game?

4.4. Probability

Win! One Million Dollars; or One Thousand Dollars Each Week for the Rest of Your Life; or A Trip for Two Around the World. Nothing to write! Something to buy! Nothing to match, scratch, collect, or . . . .

So go the promises of the admen and promoters of products, appealing to the all-too-human urge to have a fling, make a bet, get something for nothing — to take a chance.

Or perhaps we do not succumb to their spell and are not enticed to pay for a microscopic chance to win one of these "grand prizes." We may choose to indulge our impulsive natures by grabbing a piece of the action on a weekend at some casino, or an afternoon at the race track, or even a night out playing cards with the "boys." It is not difficult to fall into a mystical trance, itching to make a fast buck and satisfy our vanity because we have beaten the odds. Yet it always seems to take just one more turn of the wheel, just one more turn of a card or roll of the dice before Lady Luck will smile.

A U. S. Commission on Law Enforcement estimates that the gambling-bug has bitten some 90 million Americans and more than 80% of them are losers — parting with 50 billion dollars annually. Only 800 million is reported to the Internal Revenue Service. In comparison, the total American auto industry earnings are only 9 billion dollars annually.

Those who are more reserved, and shudder at the thought of wagering "hard-earned money" on luck or speculation, may flirt with Dame Fortune by walking down the street or traveling the highways. Even this is a game of chance, but with much higher stakes. Every day there are those who are reduced to statistical numbers. Whether you choose to gamble with one or the other, the chances that you win or lose are taken up in the study of probability.

If we toss a coin into the air, it is bound to land somewhere, but it is not known beforehand whether the coin will come up heads or tails. If we repeat the same experiment over and over, then, *in the long run,* it will be inductively observed that the percentage or fractional part of the events showing heads is 50% or $\frac{1}{2}$ the time. By experiment we might collect the following data by tossing a single coin.

Number of tosses n		1	2	5	10	100	200	500	1000	10,000
Number of heads s		0	1	2	6	47	110	245	489	5,097
Relative frequency	$\frac{s}{n}$	0	$\frac{1}{2}$	$\frac{2}{5}$	$\frac{3}{5}$	$\frac{47}{100}$	$\frac{11}{20}$	$\frac{49}{100}$	$\frac{489}{1000}$	$\frac{5,097}{10,000}$
	%	0	50	40	60	47	55	49	48.9	50.97

Figure 4.9

It appears that the number of heads that show relative to the number of tosses approaches ½. Accordingly, then, it seems only logical to assign the value ½ as the probability that this particular coin will show heads on any one toss.

Likewise, if we cast a single die, we cannot predict which one of the possible numbers {1,2,3,4,5,6} will face up, but if we assume that the die is fair — that each of the numbers will show the same amount of times in the long run, or that there is no reason why the 5 should show rather than the 2 — we regard each outcome as being *equally likely* and the probability that any *one* of the numbers will show face up is ⅙.

In both of these experiments it is obvious that only one of the outcomes can take place in any one event. That is, if we toss a coin and it comes up heads, then it is physically impossible for the tails to show at the same time. In a roll of a die, we can get only one of the possible outcomes on each trial — getting a 3 prevents us from getting a 6 or any other number on the same trial. When one of a set of events must occur, but only one in each trial, the events are said to be *mutually exclusive*.

We now state a definition for probability:

If a random experiment has *n* equally likely outcomes and an event consists of *s* logically possible "successes," then the probability of an event *A* occurring is $P(A) = \dfrac{s}{n}$.

Example 1   What is the probability that we can select the ace and king of spades from the set of spades {ace, king, queen, jack, ten}?

Solution   From figures 4.1 and 4.2, it is shown that the number of ways of selecting pairs of cards from the given set is: {AK, AQ, AJ, A10, KQ, KJ, K10, QJ, Q10, J10} = $_5C_2$ = 10 ways. Now we are asking for the subset consisting of the pair ace and king, which can be done in only one way, {AK}. Thus

$$P(\text{AK}) = \frac{s}{n} = \frac{1}{_5C_2} = \frac{1}{10}$$

If two (or more) mutually exclusive events, *A* and *B*, take place, then the probability that *A* or *B* happens, $P(A \cup B)$, is the sum of the probabilities of *A* and *B*. In this case we add to our definition

$$P(A \cup B) = P(A) + P(B)$$

Example 2   What is the probability of rolling a 2 or a 4 on a single roll of one die?

Solution   Since the events, that of rolling a 2 and of rolling a 4, are mutually exclusive,

$$P(2 \cup 4) = P(2) + P(4)$$
$$= \frac{1}{6} + \frac{1}{6} = \frac{2}{6} = \frac{1}{3}$$

Example 3   Find the probability of rolling an even number or a number greater than 4 on a single roll of one die.

Solution   These events are not mutually exclusive, since rolling a 6 would also produce an even number, therefore we must subtract the probability of obtaining a number that is both even and greater than 4 from the sum of the probabilities:

$$P \text{ (even or greater than 4)} = P \text{ (even)} + P \text{ (greater than 4)}$$
$$- P \text{ (even and greater than 4)}$$
$$= \frac{3}{6} + \frac{2}{6} - \frac{1}{6} = \frac{4}{6} = \frac{2}{3}$$

We cannot take for granted that all outcomes are equally likely; this can only be settled by past experience, intuition, or taken on blind faith. When we toss a coin, for example, we do not doubt that tails has the same chance to come up as heads, but if we continue to toss the coin, say for 30 times, and 27 tosses show heads, we might become suspicious that the coin was "loaded" or weighted in favor of heads, and if continued tosses favored heads we might conclude that the two events were not equally likely. In our discussion, however, we assume that we have only "fair" coins and dice.

If we roll a pair of dice, the possible results (events) are the eleven numbers that form the set $\{2,3,4, \ldots ,12\}$. These numbers are not equally likely, for, if we again refer to figure 4.8, we see that the 2 and 12 each can occur in only one way; while the 3 and 11 each can happen in two ways; 4 and 10 each of three ways; the 5 and 9 four ways each; the 6 and 8 each in five ways; and 7, in the maximum number of ways, six. We do assume that each of the 36 outcomes in which the dice can be paired (listed in figure 4.8) is equally likely. It is impossible to get a 1 or any number greater than 12 on a single roll of a pair of dice; thus the probability of any of these events is

$$P(1 \cup (n > 12)) = \frac{0}{36} = 0$$

The probability of each possible event for the experiment of rolling a pair of dice is:

$$P(1) = P(13) = 0 \qquad\qquad P(5) = P(9) = \frac{4}{36}$$
$$P(2) = P(12) = \frac{1}{36} \qquad\quad P(6) = P(8) = \frac{5}{36}$$
$$P(3) = P(11) = \frac{2}{36} \qquad\quad P(7) = P(7) = \frac{6}{36}$$
$$P(4) = P(10) = \frac{3}{36}$$

Taking into account all possible events, we can determine the probability of each. By simple addition of fractions, the sum of the probabilities is:

$$2\left(\frac{1}{36}\right) + 2\left(\frac{2}{36}\right) + 2\left(\frac{3}{36}\right) + 2\left(\frac{4}{36}\right) + 2\left(\frac{5}{36}\right) + 1\left(\frac{6}{36}\right)$$
$$= \frac{36}{36} = 1$$

Some observations are now in order. First, the probability of any event can never exceed 1, but may be equal to 1 if the event is sure to happen. Such an event would be the probability that we get a number less than 100 in the dice experiment. Every combination of numbers is a winner and the chances are $\frac{36}{36} = 1$. Second, the likelihood that an event takes place when it is contrary to reason is 0. We may conclude, then, the probability that an event occurs is greater than or equal to 0, and less than or equal to 1. We write:

$$0 \leqslant P(E) \leqslant 1$$

for any event E.

Since the sum of the probabilities for all possible events of an experiment is equal to 1, if we subtract the probability that one of the events happen from 1 we will have the probability that all other events of the experiment will happen. For example, if the probability that a 2 shows on a toss of a single die is $\frac{1}{6}$, then $1 - \frac{1}{6}$ is the probability that we will get a 1, 3, 4, 5, or 6 — in short, the probability of *not* a 2, or $P(2_c)$.

$$P(1,3,4,5, \text{ or } 6) = \frac{1}{6} + \frac{1}{6} + \frac{1}{6} + \frac{1}{6} + \frac{1}{6} = \frac{5}{6} = P(2_c)$$

$$P(2_c) = 1 - P(2) = 1 - \frac{1}{6} = \frac{5}{6}$$

By using this sort of subtraction rule, it is often possible to short-circuit the amount of work involved in solving problems, especially those that call for a chance of getting an *at least* or *at most* combination. Such a case is the renowned controversy between Pascal and Fermat in the 17th century, prompted by the French gambler Chevalier de Meré. De Meré had made a fortune by betting on small favorable odds that he could get a six at least once in 4 tosses of a fair die. As gamblers will, after making a fortune, de Meré played a variation of the game, betting that a double-six (12) would come up at least once in 24 tosses of two dice. He reasoned that for each outcome on one die, there would be 6 outcomes, or 6 times as many, using two dice. Therefore, he would need to toss the dice six times for each toss of the original game, that is $6 \cdot 4 = 24$ tosses of the pair of dice — but he went broke. De Meré wrote to Fermat, and Fermat in turn consulted with Pascal, and they uncovered the paradox of the problem.

In the original game, the probability of getting a 6 on each toss of a die is $\frac{1}{6}$; the probability of not getting a 6 is $1 - \frac{1}{6}$ or $\frac{5}{6}$. We shall see later, in Section 4.6, that the method used to obtain the probability of not getting a 6 in four tosses is:

$$\left(\frac{5}{6}\right)^4 = \frac{5}{6} \cdot \frac{5}{6} \cdot \frac{5}{6} \cdot \frac{5}{6} = \frac{625}{1296}$$

Therefore,

$$P \text{ (at least one 6)} = 1 - \frac{625}{1296} = \frac{671}{1296} = 52\% \text{ of the time.}$$

Upon changing the game, Fermat and Pascal showed that, since the probability of getting a 12 on one roll of a pair of dice is $\frac{1}{36}$, the probability of not getting a 12 on each roll is $1 - \frac{1}{36}$ or $\frac{35}{36}$. Then, in 24 tosses, the probability of not getting a 12 is $\left(\frac{35}{36}\right)^{24}$, and the probability of getting at least one 12 is $1 - \left(\frac{35}{36}\right)^{24} = 1 - .51 = .49$ or 49% of the time, approximately. Thus, it was obvious that if Chevalier de Meré lost his fortune, it was with approximately the same small margin on which he had won.

Suppose we were asked, "What is the probability of tossing five coins simultaneously and not getting all heads?" Some of us would take a shot in the dark, and, if that was wrong, shed a few tears and give up. Others have that strange property of thinking and doing, and, like Fermat and Pascal, realize that any event is a success except the case where each of the five coins jointly comes up heads. Therefore, it would be easier to calculate the probability of *getting* heads on each of the five coins and, using the subtraction rule, determine the probability of not heads. Since probability is asked for, let's jot down the definition of probability, just to keep us straight in our score keeping.

$$P \text{ (all heads)}_c = 1 - P \text{ (all heads)} = 1 - \frac{s}{n}$$

We could find the value of n by listing all the events in our universal set, but we have already learned how to sidestep this complicated process by regarding the toss of a coin as a twofold sample involving the alternatives of success or failure — heads or tails. With five coins, then, there are 2^5 possible events, of which only 1 is in our number of successes, s. Our formula now reads:

$$P \text{ (all heads)}_c = 1 - P \text{ (all heads)} = 1 - \frac{s}{n} = 1 - \frac{1}{2^5} = 1 - \frac{1}{32} = \frac{31}{32}$$

Thus, the probability of not getting all heads on the same toss is $^{31}/_{32}$.

In a previous situation, we found Kelly about ready to receive three coins chosen at random from his grandfather's pocket, in which were stashed a penny, nickel, dime, quarter, and half-dollar. We now ponder over the probability of Kelly's getting the half-dollar. The answer to the number of ways Kelly could receive three coins is, by the way, $_5C_3$, or a total of ten ways. The half-dollar could be given with the penny and nickel with the penny and dime with the . . . but some of us are blessed with the impatience of youth, and we soon tire of counting by the one, two, three, . . . method. Let's find the answer by using the formulas derived in the preceding sections. Since there are $_5C_3$ ways of choosing three coins from the set of five which includes the half-dollar, then there should be $_4C_3$ ways of choosing three coins from the set of four which does not include the half-dollar, or of choosing three out of a set of four. Thus, by adding another coin to the set of four, presumably the half-dollar, there exist $_5C_3 - _4C_3$ new ways of doling out three coins, each containing the half-dollar. We now have

$$P \text{ (getting the half-dollar)} = \frac{_5C_3 - _4C_3}{_5C_3} = \frac{10 - 4}{10} = \frac{6}{10} = \frac{3}{5}$$

In an experiment, if we let s represent "successes" and f "failures," the probability of success or failure is

$$P(s) + P(f) = 1$$

or

$$P(s) = 1 - P(f), \text{ and } P(f) = 1 - P(s).$$

We shall now attack and lick a few more problems to stiffen our morale.

Example 4 What is the probability of rolling seven or an eleven on a single roll of a pair of dice?

Solution Consulting the sample space in figure 4.8, we see that

$$P(7 \cup 11) = P(7) + P(11)$$
$$= \tfrac{6}{36} + \tfrac{2}{36} = \tfrac{8}{36}$$
$$= \tfrac{2}{9}$$

Example 5 We toss three coins. Find the probability that all three coins show heads.

Solution Refer to the sample space in example 1, Section 4.3. We have

$$P(3 \text{ heads}) = \tfrac{1}{8}$$

Example 6 What is the probability of obtaining at least one head on a toss of three coins?

Solution We shall use the expression

$$P(\text{at least one head}) = 1 - P(\text{no heads})$$

From the sample that we used in example 5 above, we see that $P(\text{no heads}) = \tfrac{1}{8}$. Thus,

$$P(\text{at least one head}) = 1 - \tfrac{1}{8}$$
$$= \tfrac{7}{8}$$

Example 7 You are dealt three cards from a deck of 52 cards. What is the probability that they are all spades?

Solution There are ${}_{52}C_3$ ways of being dealt three cards and ${}_{13}C_3$ ways of being dealt three spades. Therefore

$$P(3 \text{ spades}) = \frac{{}_{13}C_3}{{}_{52}C_3} = \frac{286}{22,100} = \frac{11}{850}$$

PROBLEM SET 4.4

1. What is the probability of throwing a 5 on a roll of one die? Roll a die "many" times and record the number of times that the 5 shows face up in 10, 20, 30, 40, . . . throws.

2. What is the probability of throwing a 5 on each of two dice? A 5 on one die and a 2 on the other?

3. On a cast of two dice, find the probability that the sum of the numbers that face up is (a) even, (b) odd, (c) greater than 10, (d) less than 3, (e) greater than 5, (f) at least 5.

4. A die is weighted so that the probabilities of the numbers 1, 2, 3, 4, 5, 6 come up respectively $1/6$, $1/12$, $1/12$, $1/6$, $1/6$, $1/3$. What is the probability of rolling:

   (a) a four or a six
   (b) an even number
   (c) an odd number
   (d) neither a four nor a six

5. On a single draw from a pack of cards, what is the probability of selecting:

   (a) the ace of spades
   (b) a seven
   (c) a black jack
   (d) a red card
   (e) a king or queen
   (f) the ace of spades or a face card
   (g) a red 7 or a black 9

6. In a game of cards, Sister Sue received the following poker hand: ace, king, queen, and jack of spades, and the 7 of diamonds. If Sue discards

the 7 of diamonds and receives another card from the dealer, what is the probability that this card is:

    (a) the 10 of spades, making a royal flush?

    (b) any 10 other than the 10 of spades, making a straight?

    (c) a spade other than the 10, making a flush?

    (d) a spade or a 10?

7. What is the probability of being dealt a heart flush? a royal flush? the royal flush in clubs?

8. Emily, Edith, Mary, and Minnie decided to play poker instead of their weekly game of bridge. Being beginners at poker, and not knowing much about the game, the girls disagreed as to which was the best hand. Edith and Mary held that a flush was the best; Emily and Minnie stated that a straight flush was better. Figure the probability of each hand and make a prediction as to their rank.

9. Find the probability that Craig can flip five coins and get:

    (a) exactly three heads.   (b) exactly four heads.

    (c) exactly five heads.   (d) at least three heads.

    (e) at most three heads.

10. Terrible Tom had two weighted coins, one coin with probability greater than ½ that heads would show and the other with probability greater than ½ that tails would show. He wanted to wager some ice cream on the flip of a coin with Timid Tim, who had only fair coins, of course. Timid Tim, knowing of Terrible Tom's reputation, consented to the sporting event, if they would each choose and toss a coin at the same time and if a match occurred, HH or TT, he would win, but if a nonmatch, TH or HT, resulted, Terrible Tom would win. Is this a fair game for both boys? Defend your answer.

11. When John does his laundry, he places all his socks in the same dryer load. If he has one pair of blue, two pairs of green, three pairs of black, and one pair of white socks in the dryer, what is the probability that he will reach in and at random get one blue sock? What is the probability that it will be blue or green? What is the probability that it is black or white? What is the probability that John can randomly draw two socks and come up with a pair of black socks?

12. Hardnocks High is selecting the cast for the school play from the Theatrical Club, which consists of 10 girls and 9 boys. If the play calls

for parts for 5 boys and 4 girls, how many ways can the cast be selected? What is the probability that John will get the male lead if players are chosen by lot? What is the probability that Patty will get the female lead by the same process? What is the probability that John or Patty will get a lead part? That John and Patty both get the lead parts?

13. Suppose the seven-year-itch is an inherited trait. If both Mr. and Mrs. Cantwin have genes I (dominant) and i (recessive) and each parent can pass either gene to their children, make a tree diagram showing the chance combinations of genes. If the itch characteristic has outward signs only if the dominant gene is absent, what is the probability that a child born to such parents as the Cantwins will be afflicted by the itch? What is the probability that their child will not pass the gene on to succeeding generations?

4.5. Odds and Expectation

Reno Red had been saving and planning a long time to make his bid for striking it rich. He had read about games of chance, odds, expectation, the "big timer" who had already struck it rich, and he even studied the errors of the other 99% — the ones who went broke. Now, Reno Red, by his own admission, was an expert about a lot of things, and especially about the roulette wheel. He knew that roulette was played with a small rolling ball inside a rotating wheel, each taking opposite directions, and when they both came to rest the ball would be on only one of the equally spaced numbers embossed in either red or black on the wheel. He knew that there are eighteen red and eighteen black numbers in alternate positions. Reno Red also knew that for each chip that was placed on a winning number on the betting cloth he would get 35 chips in return. In other words, Reno Red thought that the *odds* were 1:35 (read "one to thirty-five") that he would win, or 35:1 ("thirty-five to one") that he would lose. This meant to Red that, if he played 36 games, in the long run he should win one game and lose 35. But, since he would get 35 chips each time that he won, he would win $1 \cdot 35 = 35$ chips in each set of 36 games; and if he lost the other 35 games in the set, one chip at a time, he would lose $35 \cdot 1 = 35$ chips. He couldn't lose! Red's strategy was to win early in the set of 36 games and then quit while he was ahead. Reno Red, with all his faults, was fair, and he supposed that all casinos gave their guests a fair game.

What Reno Red didn't see was the two other numbers on the wheel — numbers that were neither black nor red. These two insignificant numbers, 0 and 00, were Red's downfall.

The obvious factors that Red had failed to take into account were the croupier operating the roulette wheel, the beautiful murals, plush wall-to-wall carpeting, and great cut-glass chandeliers. Of course, someone had to pay for this setting — no one else but those two dastardly culprits, Zero and Double Zero.

Here's the way Reno Red *should* have been figuring. Instead of 36, there are 38 positions in which the ball could stop (numbers 1 through 36 plus 0 and 00). If Red chose any one position to win, there would be 37 losing positions, thus the *odds for winning* were 1:37 and his *odds for losing* were 37:1. But, a player still gets paid for winning at the declared odds of 35:1.

Before witnessing Reno Red's complete undoing, let's compare the ideas of "probability" with those of "odds." In the previous section, we defined the probability of winning as being

$$\frac{\text{the number of successes}}{\text{total number of events}} = \frac{s}{n}, \text{ and the probability of losing as}$$

$$\frac{\text{the number of failures}}{\text{total number of events}} = \frac{f}{n} \text{ where } \frac{s}{n} + \frac{f}{n} = \frac{s+f}{n} = 1, \text{ or } s+f=n.$$

In our roulette example, the probability of winning when playing one number is $\frac{1}{38}$ and the probability of losing is $\frac{37}{38}$. Intuitively, we might guess that, since our real odds for winning in roulette are 1:37, and for losing 37:1, then, in general, the odds *for winning* are $s:f$, and the odds *for losing,* or the odds *against winning,* are $f:s$, where s represents the number of successes and f the number of failures.

Meanwhile, back at the wheel, Reno Red, still doling out his chips, is doing some fast calculating, trying to figure what has gone wrong with his "system." He had originally figured that his *expectation* would be 0 — that is, *in the long run,* he would neither win nor lose. But he "knew" that his time was ripe — he would win early, before all his losses occurred, and then go home with his bundle. This is the way he had figured: If his probability of winning was $\frac{1}{36}$ and he received 35 chips on a winning number, then he would take in $\frac{1}{36}$ of 35 chips, on the average, each time he played, or $(\frac{1}{36})$ $(35) = \frac{35}{36}$ of a chip each game. Obviously, no croupier is going to cut his chips in $\frac{35}{36}$ of their original value; he is too busy playing. He doesn't need to make the cut. Either Red wins the whole thing, or loses it. All that Red need consider is that, if the winnings were equally distributed among all the games, he would have an average income per game. But this is income. What about the games in which Red would lose? Same situation, only the croupier has the advantage — Red's loss. That is, the house takes in one chip each time it wins, which is $\frac{35}{36}$ of the time. Recall that if Red wins with probability $\frac{1}{36}$, then he loses with probability $\frac{35}{36}$, which is the house's gain. Therefore, Red loses one chip, denoted by -1, $\frac{35}{36}$ of the time, or $(-1)\frac{35}{36} = -\frac{35}{36}$ of a chip each game. Red had expected to get $\frac{35}{36} + (-\frac{35}{36}) = 0$ chips on the average for each game, or his expectation is 0. All this was, of course, before Red knew about those two rascals, Zero and Double Zero. Now his reckoning would look like this: Since there are 38 positions for the ball, the probability of winning on any one is $\frac{1}{38}$, with a prize of 35 chips. The average he would take in on each game, then, is $\frac{1}{38} \cdot 35 = \frac{35}{38}$ of a chip. The average amount lost each game is the probability of losing, $1 - \frac{1}{38} = \frac{37}{38}$ times the amount lost (-1), or a negative win of

$$\frac{37}{38} \cdot (-1) = -\frac{37}{38}$$

and the end result in Red's favor is

$$\frac{35}{38} - \frac{37}{38} = -\frac{2}{38} = -\frac{1}{19} \text{ or approximately } -.0525.$$

Reno Red finally realized that he was facing the unbeatable disadvantage of losing, in the long run, almost $5\frac{1}{4}$ cents out of every dollar that he waged. Alas, he realized this too late.

To this day, however, if you should ask Red what *expectation* meant to him, he would answer correctly:

> The probability that an event will happen times the amount to be received if that event occurs; or, if more than one possible outcome may occur, it is the sum of the products,

$$E = (P_1)(A_1) + (P_2)(A_2) + (P_3)(A_3) + \ldots$$

where P_1, P_2, P_3 ... are the probabilities of each event occurring, and A_1, A_2, A_3 ... are the amounts to be received on each event. Notice that in some instances the amount of the reward could be negative $(-A)$, or a loss.

Example 1   Find Reno Red's odds for winning and his expectation, if he plays three chips on the black numbers. (The ball stopping on any black position pays Reno Red the same number of chips that he bets.) On the surface, considering only amounts won or lost, what would appear to be the odds in this case?

Solution $P(s) = {}^{18}\!/_{38}$ (there are 18 black positions)

$$P(f) = 1 - {}^{18}\!/_{38} = {}^{20}\!/_{38}$$

amount won $= 3$

amount lost $= 3 = -3$ win

It would seem that from the money angle the odds would be even, that is, $1:1$. However, our definition of odds leads us to the correct conclusion:

odds for win $= s{:}f = 18{:}20 = 9{:}10$

expectation $= P(s) \cdot$ amount won $+ P(f) \cdot$ amount lost

$$= {}^{18}\!/_{38} \cdot 3 + {}^{20}\!/_{38}\,(-3)$$

$$= {}^{54}\!/_{38} - {}^{60}\!/_{38}$$

$$= -{}^{6}\!/_{36}$$

$$= -\tfrac{1}{6}$$

Reno Red should expect to lose $\frac{1}{6}$ chip each game.

Example 2   What are the odds of obtaining three heads on a toss of three coins?

Solution   We have seen from the result of example 5, Section 4.4, $P(\text{3 heads}) = \frac{1}{8}$ and that $P(\text{3 heads})_c = 1 - \frac{1}{8} = \frac{7}{8}$. Thus, the odds for obtaining three heads are $1:7$. We also see that the odds against three heads are $7:1$.

Example 3   You are to toss two coins. If both land heads, you win $2. If one coin shows heads and the other tails, you lose $1. If both are tails, you neither win nor lose. What is your expectation?

Solution   In example 1, Section 4.3, we have designed the tree diagram showing the outcomes from tossing three coins. From this same diagram we can list the sample space for tossing two coins: HH, HT, TH, TT. From this we can write:

$$P(2 \text{ Heads}) = \tfrac{1}{4}$$

$$P(1 \text{ Head}) = \tfrac{2}{4}$$

$$P(0 \text{ Heads}) = \tfrac{1}{4} = P(2 \text{ Tails})$$

Thus, if we let E represent expectation, then

$$E = P(2\text{H}) \cdot (2) + P(1\text{H}) \cdot (-1) + P \cdot (2\text{T}) \cdot (0)$$
$$= \tfrac{1}{4}\,(2) + \tfrac{2}{4}\,(-1) + \tfrac{1}{4}\,(0)$$
$$= \tfrac{2}{4} - \tfrac{2}{4} + 0$$
$$= 0$$

The game, therefore, is even. In the long run, we should neither win nor lose — but if your capital is limited, don't quote us.

PROBLEM SET 4.5

1. You buy a $2 ticket on Hedy the Hayburner to win at the race track. Assume that she wins the race and you claim your winnings. The man at the window gives you $4. What were the odds for your horse?

2. What are the odds against drawing two spades from an ordinary bridge deck of 52 cards? Odds for?

3. Find the probability of an event taking place if the odds that it will occur are (a) 7 to 5, (b) 7 to 11, and if the odds that it will not occur are (c) 2 to 1.

4. There are five sets of twins at a party, four boys and six girls. If two people are chosen at random, what are the odds that they are a pair of twins? What are the odds that one is a boy and one a girl?

5. In Reno Red's roulette game, what are the odds that the ball will stop on an odd number? What are the odds against the ball stopping on a number from 13 to 21, inclusive? What is the probability of getting an odd number? What is the probability of getting a number between 13 to 21, inclusive?

6. Reno Red would like to play all the numbers 25 to 36, inclusive, with a $1 chip. If he should win on any one of these numbers, he would receive $2; what is his expectation? If he places a bet of $1 on black and wins, he will receive $1; what is his expectation? If a $1 winning chip is placed on an even number, he will receive $1; what is his expectation?

7. What is your expectation if you receive $1 when a pair of dice roll a number less than 7 and you lose $1 if the number is 7 or more?

8. In a game played with a pair of dice, you win if on one roll you get an 11. What is your expectation if it pays 15:1?

9. What is the expected number of heads if we toss a fair coin one time? Two times? Three? Fifty?

10. The Cable Company manufactures ding-a-lings, of which 2% are defective. In a lot of 700 shipped from the factory, how many are expected to be defective?

11. A company offers $1,000 to a lucky consumer who buys its product. The Director of the Fair Trade Commission states that the chances for a consumer to win are one in a million. What is the consumer's mathematical expectation? What amount would the consumer expect the company to add to the original purchase price (before contest) of the product to make the game "fair"?

4.6. Conditional Probability

Helpful Harry, the Missionary, was captured by a savage tribe in the wilds of Borneo and was sentenced by the chief to either marry his daughter or jump into the snake pit. Now, Harry was inclined to decline the offer of marriage, but was concerned no end about his own welfare. He convinced the chief to give him a sporting chance for freedom. They agreed that Harry should select one of two identical reed baskets in which were placed live snakes. In one basket were to be two snakes, both nonpoisonous. In the second basket were to be three snakes, one poisonous and two of a harmless variety. As stated, he was to select one of the baskets, reach in, and retrieve a pet. The question troubling Harry was, "What is the probability of *not* getting that one vicious viper?"

Harry faced a two-stage operation: (1) selecting a basket, and (2) selecting a snake from that basket. If the baskets were identical, or equally likely to be selected, the probability of selecting the fatal basket would be one chance out of two, or $\frac{1}{2}$. After selecting that particular basket, there would be one chance in three, or probability of $\frac{1}{3}$, of getting the poisonous pet. Harry knew that the probability of getting this particular pet was $\frac{1}{2} \cdot \frac{1}{3} = \frac{1}{6}$ and, therefore, the probability of *not* getting it was $1 - \frac{1}{6} = \frac{5}{6}$. Life looked brighter for Harry. Figure 4.10 gives a picture of the situation.

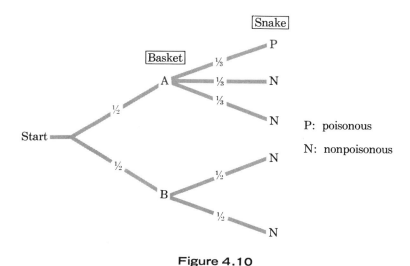

Figure 4.10

The probability that P, the poisonous pet, is selected depends on the fact that basket A is chosen; or the *conditional probability* that P occurs depends on the assumption that basket A is chosen and we denote $P(P \mid A)$. In general,

$P(P \mid A)$ asks for the probability that P will take place given the information that A has happened, will happen, or is happening.

We also have the information that the probability of choosing basket A is $\frac{1}{2}$, or $P(A) = \frac{1}{2}$.

We were to first choose a basket and, second, select the poisonous snake, in that order, and since we have decided that the probability of this operation is ⅙, then

$$P(A \cap P) = ⅙ = P(A) \cdot P(P \mid A)$$

which gives a rule for assigning probabilities to conditional outcomes:

If we are given two events, *A* and *B*, the probability of their occurring, one after the other, is the product of the probability of *A* and the conditional probability of *B*, given that *A* has already occurred.

$$P(A \cap B) = P(A) \cdot P(B \mid A)$$

In any event, conditional probabilities are computed in the same way as ordinary probabilities — the number of equally likely outcomes in which an event occurs is divided by the total number of possible outcomes. The condition reduces the number of possible outcomes, making the probability of an event more likely.

A few fanciers of mathematics may look upon the previous example with some coolness. Let us examine another, more subtle, situation.

Example 1 Suppose Kelly has a bag of candy containing five red, seven white, and eight black jelly beans. Niki gets to choose two at random. (a) What is the probability that she will get a red jelly bean and then a white one? (b) What is the probability that the second jelly bean grabbed is white, if the first one was put back in the bag before selecting the second one? (c) Under the conditions of part (b), what is the probability that Niki will get a red and then a white jelly bean?

Solution (a) The probability of getting a red jelly bean first is

$$P(R) = \frac{s}{t} = \frac{5}{20} = \frac{1}{4}$$

The probability of getting a white one, given that the first was red, is

$$P(W \mid R) = \frac{s}{t} = \frac{7}{19}$$

The probability of getting a red followed by a white jelly bean is

$$P(\text{R} \cap \text{W}) = P(\text{R}) \cdot P(\text{W} \mid \text{R}) = \frac{1}{4} \cdot \frac{7}{19} = \frac{7}{76}$$

(b) The probability of getting a red jelly bean first is the same as in part (a):

$$P(\text{R}) = \frac{s}{t} = \frac{5}{20} = \frac{1}{4}$$

But, since this was put back before selecting the second, neither selection depends on the other. The operations are independent, and

$$P(\text{W}) = P(\text{W} \mid \text{R}) = \frac{7}{20}$$

(c) Since the two events are independent, the solution is the product of the two probabilities.

$$P(\text{R}) \cdot P(\text{W}) = \frac{1}{4} \cdot \frac{7}{20} = \frac{7}{80}$$

Just pass the jelly beans, please!

Example 2   Find the probability of obtaining three heads on a toss of three coins.

Solution   From our definition of conditional probability we have

$$P(3\text{H}) = P(\text{H}) \cdot P(\text{H}) \cdot P(\text{H})$$
$$= \tfrac{1}{2} \cdot \tfrac{1}{2} \cdot \tfrac{1}{2}$$
$$= \tfrac{1}{8}$$

Or, if we again refer to our tree diagram in example 1, Section 4.3, we see that three heads show once out of the eight possibilities in the sample space.

Example 3   You are dealt three cards from a deck of fifty-two cards. What is the probability that all three are spades?

Solution   The probability that the first card is a spade is $\tfrac{13}{52}$. If this was a success, then the second card has probability $\tfrac{12}{51}$ of being a spade, and the third has probability $\tfrac{11}{50}$. Thus,

$$P(3 \text{ spades}) = \tfrac{13}{52} \cdot \tfrac{12}{51} \cdot \tfrac{11}{50}$$
$$= \tfrac{11}{850}$$

Compare these results with the solutions to examples 5 and 7 in Section 4.4.

PROBLEM SET 4.6

1. Kelly could scarcely reach over the edge of his big sister's box of candy which was sitting on the top shelf. The top layer contained chocolates with different flavored fillings: nine peppermint, six caramel, and five maple. If light-fingered Kelly pilfers two chocolates, what is the probability that:

   (a) both will be maple flavored?

   (b) both will be the same flavor?

   (c) the second will be caramel if the first is peppermint?

   (d) the second is not peppermint if the first one is peppermint?

2. Mr. and Mrs. Normal have two children. They can be: two boys, a boy and a girl with the boy the older, a girl and boy with the girl the older, or two girls. Assume that each case is equally likely, and find the probability that both children are boys if it is known that one of them is a boy. What is the probability of both being boys if it is known that the youngest is a boy?

3. In a family of five children, what is the probability that they are all boys? Assume that $P \text{ (boy)} = P \text{ (girl)} = \frac{1}{2}$ for each child. If we know that four of them are boys, what is the probability that all are boys?

4. Lucky Larry rolls a pair of dice. What is the probability that he rolls a 7? If you know that neither die shows a 2, what is the probability that he rolls a 7?

5. At Failem University $\frac{1}{4}$ of the students failed chemistry, $\frac{1}{5}$ failed physics, and $\frac{1}{10}$ failed both chemistry and physics. If a student is picked at random, what is the probability that:

   (a) he failed chemistry, given that he failed physics?

   (b) he failed physics, given that he failed chemistry?

   (c) he failed physics or chemistry?

   (d) he failed physics and chemistry, given that he failed physics?

   (e) he failed physics and chemistry, given that he failed chemistry?

6. In Yeehaw Junction it is suspected that 50% of the people are Democrats, 35% are Baptists, and 10% have college degrees. If this information is correct, and one person is selected at random from the town, what is the probability that:

    (a) he is a Baptist if he is a Democrat?

    (b) he is not a Democrat if he is a Baptist?

    (c) he is neither a Democrat nor a Baptist?

    (d) he has a degree if he is both a Democrat and a Baptist?

7. If the probability that a Miami Beach resident has a Cadillac is $\frac{1}{6}$, the probability that a Miami Beach resident is still making payments on an auto is $\frac{1}{3}$, and the probability that a Miami Beach resident has a Cadillac and is making payments is $\frac{1}{12}$, what is the probability that:

    (a) he has a Cadillac, if it is known that he is making payments on a car?

    (b) he is making payments on a car, given that he has a Cadillac?

    (c) he has a Cadillac or is making payments on a car?

    (d) he does not have a Cadillac, given the added information that he is not making payments on a car?

Chapter 5
STATISTICS

Measures of Central Tendency

Standard Deviation

The Normal Curve

Confidence in a Sample

A Motor Vehicle Bureau survey has revealed that in 1940 each car on the road contained an average of 3.2 persons. In 1950, occupancy had declined to 2.1 persons per car. By 1960, the average was down to 1.4 persons. If we project the statistics to 1980, every third car going by will have nobody in it.

5.1. Measures of Central Tendency

Both sandlot teams had been unyielding. The bigger East Side Gang had been winners all summer, but the West Siders were bound and determined not to lose again. Kelly was at bat. The score was 4 to 3, last half of the last inning — two out, one boy on base, and the count was three balls and two strikes. . . . The pitch came in shoulder high, splitting the plate. Kelly swung, and the crack of the bat was like the "shot heard 'round the world." There was no doubt that it was a home run and that the West Siders had won.

There was another "shot"— perhaps it didn't sound much at all like a shot, but more like a "C-R-R-R-A-A-S-H!" You guessed it — Mr. Nichodemus' window was done for. Now, Mr. Nichodemus lived adjacent to the vacant lot and was a very demanding individual, especially with the neighborhood kids; he owned the lot on which the boys were playing.

Someone had to pay for the window, everyone agreed, or there would be no more ball games. The question was, "Who?" Kelly had hit the ball, but if he had to pay the whole bill he would be cleaned out. Besides, wasn't everyone partly to blame? After talking it over, all the boys decided to chip in their equal share of dimes and quarters to pay for a new windowpane. That way it wouldn't cost any one of them very much. That is, several boys shared the cost so that no one individual had to bear the entire cost of the damage. This is similar to the way insurance companies operate. The whole business of insurance, with its mortality tables, lists of cash benefits, and heaps of arithmetical data, is an example of statistical theory applied, in general, to human affairs; and the companies' balance sheets and inventories bear eloquent testimony to their success. In 1965, $9.6 billion was paid out to Americans in some sort of health benefits. This amounts to more than $26 million for each day of the year, supported by 81% of the American population, according to statistics. And there was a big profit!

Now, if Mr. Nichodemus had had a homeowners' policy on which he paid a few dollars per year, and a greater disaster than a baseball — a tornado, hurricane, or fire, for example — had completely demolished his home, then his insurance company could have paid him several thousand dollars for its value because many other homeowners, who had escaped the curse, also had paid a few dollars for similar protection.

Suppose that Betcha Insurance, Inc., has insured 10,000 homes for a total of $200,000,000. By past experience, over many years, the company has determined that its annual expected loss due to hurricanes is $240,000. Then the cost of the insurance (including the company's expenses and operating costs) per $1000 property value to the homeowner is

$$\frac{240,000}{200,000,000}(\$1000) = \$1.20 \text{ per year}$$

Insurance is not a new gimmick. In medieval Europe, when world trade was centered around the Mediterranean, the Phoenician, Greek, and Roman ship owners contributed to a "kitty" to pay for ships and cargoes lost at sea.

Three hundred years ago, ship owners, merchants, and money lenders met to talk business in coffee houses near London docks. Lloyds of London, a company which has built an international reputation by insuring the colossal and slightly preposterous, was developed in Edward Lloyds' popular meeting place by a club of old acquaintances who got together to cover risks. They will now insure dancers against becoming fat and circus fat ladies against becoming thin. We hear that they are insuring the appearance of the Loch Ness monster in Scotland.

Insurance won't keep you from becoming fat or thin or keep hurricanes from destroying your home or prevent death. It only eases the pain of heavy monetary losses when such disasters happen. Insurance means sharing a risk, where the definition of the risk is based upon averages. It is an excellent example of statistical theory applied to human affairs.

However, insurance was not the first venture into the science of statistics. The Egyptians levied taxes according to population and wealth 5000 years ago in order to build the pyramids.

During the 17th century, two seemingly independent preoccupations contributed to the modern theory of statistics — one from work, the other from play. From both emerged the recognition that certain events beyond our control are more rhythmic on a long-term basis than on a close-up one. For instance, the annual rainfall over several periods of five years each is, more often than not, less erratic than the figures for two consecutive years. In approved lingo, we speak of this belief as the *law of averages*. This persistence of quantitative numbers gains credibility from our experience of games of chance, as seen in Chapter 4, Probability. The fundamental difference between games of chance and useful statistical applications of probability is that, for all possible outcomes of a game, risk can be counted — difficult perhaps, but possible — whereas in real life all possibilities are seldom known in advance.

It is not at all difficult to grasp some notion of the chores of a statistician. His work is fourfold: he collects data, he organizes it, he analyzes it, and then he makes conclusions or inferences based upon the data that he has collected.

The first questions that present themselves, then, are just how much information must be collected, and how to go about collecting it. The answers are extremely important whenever we wish to make valid generalizations after a careful analysis of the data. It is a rare occasion, indeed, for all, or 100%, of the items desired to be accessible as a source of data. This 100% — the universal set of information that we seek — consists of all conceivable possibilities for an observation and is called the *population*. A population is defined when the common characteristics have been specified, such as the number of people who live in a certain area, the population of a certain hybrid corn planted in a given year, the population of a particular breed of dairy cattle, or the population of defective automobiles distributed to consumers in a given length of time. It is literally impossible to examine all the elements of a population, due to their distribution through time and space. The expense and length of time involved would not be justified. The geneticist, for example, in coding the DNA molecule would find $10^{2,400,000,000}$ ways in which the genes could unite; it would be out of the question to list them all. Yet, with his techniques he can make reasonable predictions about an offspring. Often, a quality test for strength and durability is destructive to the item in question. Therefore, testing all items would not be practical. We have heard of a company, now defunct, that manufactured flash bulbs. The president of the company clamored for perfection and ordered the testing division to put every bulb to the test as it came off the production line!

In most situations, then, we must be content with the investigation of a subset of the population. In statistics such a subset of numerical or quantitative data, collected for the purpose of analyzing inductive questions, is called a *sample*. From these samples we generalize about the total population. We must be careful in collecting a sample, or samples, to avoid poor results or results that are invalid. One of the most embarrassing errors in statistical inference was created prior to the presidential election of 1948. According to the Gallup Poll, and others, Harry Truman didn't have a whisper of a chance of winning the election. Headlines appeared claiming Dewey the winner. Evidently the sample and the method used for collecting it were not correct, for President Truman won 303 electoral votes versus 189 for Dewey, upsetting all predictions based on "valid" statistical data.

To make a sample representative, we must collect it in such a way that every element (or every sample of the same size) in the population has an equal chance of being selected. Such samples are called *random samples,* and we cannot know in advance which elements or measures will be obtained. There are several techniques used to "insure" randomness, such as tables of random numbers, systematic sampling, stratified sampling, and cluster sampling. All these involve the element of chance; thus, we may well use the notion of tossing a coin, rolling a die, choosing a card, pulling numbers from a hat, or even drawing marbles from a grab bag.

Although we may now have a concept of a random sample, we may find situations in which randomness is difficult to obtain. For example, how can a random sample of trees be chosen in a forest, or a ramdom sample of fish in a lake? How can a random sample of public opinion be obtained in a large city? In our problems, however, we shall make the assumption that we can successfully obtain a random sample of a population and that our sample will be large enough for us to base inductive inferences on it.

Consider the following sampling plan. For a statistical project, Fred Fink decides to find the average height of the students in Sandcut High, a school with a population of 3600 students. To complicate matters, the students are divided into two sessions — morning and afternoon. It is out of the question for Fred to measure all students, and the individual health records are not available to him, so he takes the next best step — a sample. Now, Fred isn't the most ambitious student, nor is he too intelligent. He decides to use the twenty-one players on the basketball team as elements for his sample, because they represent both morning and afternoon school sessions, and also because it will be easy for him to measure the players as they show up for practice. The measurements that Fred makes are shown in the table of *raw data,* figure 5.1. He also classifies each player as a guard, g; forward, f; or center, c. The players are numbered as they are measured. (Measurements are exact to the nearest inch.)

Player	Height	Position on Team		Player	Height	Position on Team
1	6 ft. 1 in.	g		12	6 ft. 1 in.	f
2	5 8	g		13	5 11	f
3	6 3	g		14	5 9	g
4	5 11	g		15	6 3	c
5	6 2	f		16	5 10	f
6	5 10	g		17	6 2	f
7	6 5	c		18	6 10	c
8	5 11	g		19	5 10	f
9	5 11	g		20	5 11	g
10	6 0	f		21	6 1	g
11	6 2	f				

Figure 5.1 Raw data

So far, Fred Fink has completed only the first of the four statistical operations. He has collected data. The way in which the measures are presented, as they were taken, makes it difficult to tell much about the sample. The next step, then, is to organize the *scores* (the measurements), so that we can make sense out of this list of numbers.

One way to organize the data is to use a *frequency table,* as shown in figure 5.2. We list all the possible measures in some order — in this case, with the smallest first and ascending routinely, with the largest last, and then tally the recurrence of each score.

Scores, x	Tally	Frequency, f
5 ft. 8 in.	I	1
5 9	I	1
5 10	III	3
5 11	IIII	5
6 0	I	1
6 1	III	3
6 2	III	3
6 3	II	2
6 5	I	1
6 10	I	1

Figure 5.2 Frequency table

The data begins to take on some meaning. We can easily see that the tallest player is 6 ft. 10 in., the shortest is 5 ft. 8 in., and the greatest difference between any two players is 1 ft. 2 in.

$$6 \text{ ft. } 10 \text{ in. } - 5 \text{ ft. } 8 \text{ in. } = 1 \text{ ft. } 2 \text{ in.}$$

This difference between the maximum and the minimum scores is called the *range* of scores.

Sometimes it is an advantage to organize our data in a "picture" form called a *frequency polygon*. Often, many conclusions become obvious just by looking at the picture. We can see in figures 5.2 and 5.3 that many of the scores tend to be centered around the fourth score, 5 ft. 11 in., and there are more of this particular measure than any other one. This measure, the most often occurring, is called the *mode* of the data under consideration. In most sets of data there seems to be a tendency for the scores to group themselves about some interior value, possibly toward the center. This phenomenon suggests that some central value may be characteristic of the scores and may be used to represent or describe the data in the sense that it is near the "middle" of the distribution.

Also, we can see that there are as many players taller than 6 ft. as there are less than 6 ft. The height 6 ft. 0 in. is the *median*. The median is the numerical middle score of the set and is simple to calculate. First, place the scores in order and choose the midmost measure which is neither greater than half the scores nor less than half of them.

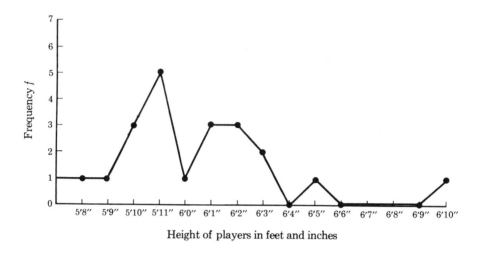

Figure 5.3 Frequency polygon

Most students are aware of the third measure of central tendency, the *mean,* or arithmetical average, for this is the most used score in comparing class test results. If Fred Fink should place all the players end to end, they would measure 126 ft. 11 in. which, in itself, is not very meaningful — unless someone is interested in the fact that this length is about two and a half times the width of the basketball court. But, if Fred divides this length by the number players measured, 21, he would get the mean, average height, of the players, although, according to figure 5.1, no player is listed as being 6.04 ft. tall.

$$126 \text{ ft. } 11 \text{ in. } \div 21 = 6.04 \text{ ft. (approximately)}$$

The basic method for computing the mean, represented by the symbol $\overline{X}$, is to add the values of all the scores (each score can be represented by the variables, x_1 for the first score; x_2 for the second; x_3 for the third . . . x_n for the nth) and then divide by n, the number of scores. We can write the directions for finding the mean in cookbook fashion:

$$\text{mean} = \overline{X} = \frac{x_1 + x_2 + x_3 + \ldots x_n}{n}$$

We can write a more sophisticated recipe if we agree to let the Greek symbol Σ, sigma, indicate the process of addition. That is, Σx means the sum of all the x's.

$$\overline{X} = \frac{\Sigma x}{n}$$

Then we have a more concise way to say a lot in a little bit of space. It is understood that we are to add all the scores with which we are concerned in the distribution.

Since constructing the frequency polygon, Fred Fink, with our help, has been taking the third step of a statistician, making analyses. Before concluding this step, however, Fred wants to make one grand gesture — construct a *histogram*. A histogram is a series of rectangles, each having as its base a convenient width, an interval chosen to represent the difference between scores and measured along the horizontal axis. The frequency, f, of the scores is shown by a height on the vertical axis, as in figure 5.4. The sum of the areas of all the rectangles in a histogram is equal to unity, the lump sum of the sample taken. By connecting the midpoints of the frequencies (altitudes) with straight-line segments, we can duplicate the frequency polygon as shown by the dotted line in figure 5.4.

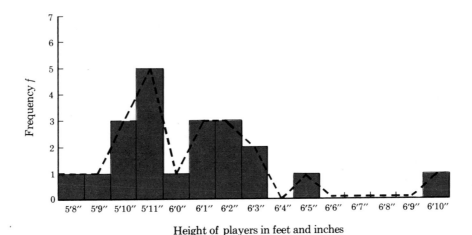

Height of players in feet and inches

Figure 5.4 Histogram

Fred now feels that he has completed the task of collecting data, organizing it, and making some analyses. That is, he has found that his sample has:

1. Range: 1 ft. 2 in.

2. Mode: 5 ft. 11 in.

3. Median: 6 ft. 0 in.

4. Mean: 6.04 ft.

The problem now at hand is to draw a conclusion about the student body of Sandcut High based upon measurements taken from a small sample, the school basketball team. This was the business that he had started out to do. Supported by the analysis of his sample, Fink is about to forecast that the mean height for the 3600 members of the student body is 6.04 ft. But now that he has become more aware of tallness of students, Fred takes mental note of the height of friends, other members of his classes, and of students on campus in general; he is becoming more and more skeptical of his project.

Do you believe that Fred may have made some kind of error? What is your opinion of Fred's sample? Is it possible that he could have made a better choice of elements for his sample? Did he have a random sample of students? Fred Fink, we suspect, has done a reputable job working with his data, but he has made no better choice in collecting his sample than the *Literary Digest* did in making its straw-vote efforts in predicting the outcome of the presidential election in 1936. In that year the publishers of the magazine predicted that Alfred Landon, the Republican candidate from Kansas, would win with 57% of the popular vote. They had polled the public, some 2,375,000 mail votes, selected from lists of automobile and telephone owners. These people, following the depression years of the early 1930's, were above average in income. The higher-income people tended to support the Republican party. Thus, the sample was biased in favor of Landon, who received only 37% of the actual vote and, of course, lost to Franklin Roosevelt. In comparison to the number of elements in the sample, today's scientific poll may often base national results on one to two thousand interviews.

Statistically speaking, the 1970 draft lottery — the drawing of birthdates enclosed in capsules randomly picked from a bowl — was inadvertently rigged, according to some mathematicians. If the names were placed in the bowl in chronological order beginning with January 1, they would have tended to stay together, and those put in first would be drawn last. The actual drawing seemed to bear out this fact, for December had the highest ranking for draftees, followed by November, August, and October, with March having the lowest ranking, meaning that young men born in March would be less likely to be drafted. The deviation between December and March was too great for each date to have had an equal chance to be drawn.

As you can see, we make use of games in the theory of statistics and decision making, keeping in mind only those items which are significant. We stress that games are models to make a situation seem more objective. Biologists often use balls strung on a wire shaped like a spiral staircase to represent the DNA molecule, in order that they may study just how living things pass their characteristics to later generations with mathematical regularity. Therefore we do not feel bashful in asking you to participate in a game with us, if we can show that the game has some merit in representing a real situation. Too, it may prove to be more interesting to play games — after all, we know that many accolades and grand salaries are priorities of players of games. There are those who earn $100,000 to $250,000 a year for moving a little pigskin up and down a pretty green pasture laid out with white lines. An objection to game theory, as compared to studying the real subject of inquiry, is that a game may measure only one variable, which may not be the only significant variable influencing the real subject. For example, you may think that the force of attraction between two bodies is described by the theory of gravity and is rehearsed by falling apples and autumn leaves; but you have forgotten that you cannot credit that same force with the attraction between a boy and a girl alone on a park bench. Our purpose, then, in playing our games, is to improvise methods for collecting data and to suggest applications of game ideas to problems encountered.

As early as the 15th century, the merchants with capital would lay wages on the sex of an unborn child. They agreed to pay 30 clams (or whatever their unit of exchange was) if the child was a girl, on condition that they were to receive 48 clams on the birth of a son. Such wagers were strictly a gamble, but it should be apparent that a speculator with a large amount of capital could safely undertake wagers beyond his resources, for if the distribution was calculated on the assumption that boy and girl births are exactly equal (it may be closer to 51:49 in favor of boys), then he stood to reap a net gain of 60%. By the way, the early merchants would also gamble with anyone on the time of a person's death. Great fortunes were built upon this basis.

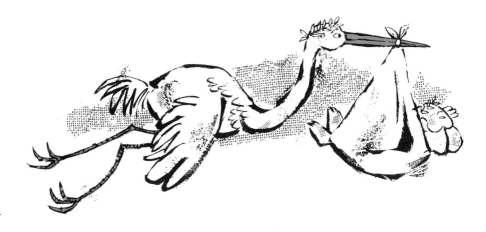

Besides being about equal in numbers, experience shows that the frequency with which one sex occurs is not appreciably affected by the circumstance of the sex of a previous birth. That is, boys and girls come into the world rather like drawing blue and green marbles from a grab bag in which equal amounts of each color are mixed thoroughly before drawing, with each marble replaced before a subsequent draw. If the analogy is valid, we may calculate the statistics, say, on how often exactly two boys occur in a family of five children. Since we wish to determine the possible sex of each youngster in a five-child family we must draw five marbles; for a three-child family we draw three marbles; for nine children, nine marbles — always with replacement — but we must use some discretion in choosing the size of the family, for the larger numbers of marbles may become as difficult to manipulate as a large number of children.

We have played the game, drawing blue and green marbles from a hat, in an attempt to give a simple example of game theory similar to the proportionate frequency of boy and girl births.

The first family (score) was G, G, G, G, G — five green marbles, five girls. Unusual, perhaps, for the first draw to yield five girls; if we recall our work in probability, the chance of this happening is $(\frac{1}{2})^5$, or one chance in 32, but this is actually the game as we played it. This may possibly be some clue as to the number of scores that we may use in our sample, 32, for there are 32 different types of five-child families, different in the sense of the number and order of boys and girls in the mixture. The data in figure 5.5 represents our sample — 32 scores, each consisting of five children. We would interpret the order of the G's and B's as being the relative ages of the children from the oldest to the youngest, or vice-versa.

x_1 = G G G G G	x_{12} = B B G G B	x_{23} = B B B B G
x_2 = G G G B B	x_{13} = G G B B G	x_{24} = G G G G B
x_3 = G G G G B	x_{14} = G G B G G	x_{25} = G G B G B
x_4 = B B G B G	x_{15} = B B G G G	x_{26} = G G B B B
x_5 = G B G G G	x_{16} = B B B B B	x_{27} = G G B B G
x_6 = B B B G B	x_{17} = G B B B G	x_{28} = G B G G B
x_7 = B B B B B	x_{18} = G G G B B	x_{29} = B G G B G
x_8 = B G G B B	x_{19} = B G G B G	x_{30} = B B B B G
x_9 = G B B G B	x_{20} = B B B G B	x_{31} = G B B G G
x_{10} = G G B B B	x_{21} = B B G G	x_{32} = B B G G B
x_{11} = G B B G B	x_{22} = G G G G B	

Figure 5.5   Raw data scores

We have now collected our sample and, like Fred Fink, have a meaningless hodgepodge of data — although we hope to have been wiser than he and not have chosen a biased sample. If our information is to become significant, then, we should organize it in some fashion. We can begin by making a frequency table. Since we are only interested in numbers of boys (there may be some argument here) in a five-child family (recall that we were investigating the occurrence of two boys out of five), we can make our table as shown in figure 5.6.

What have we gained from organizing the data in this manner? First, the range of scores, the difference between the largest and smallest number of boys per family, is

$$5 - 0 = 5$$

Scores (number of boys) x	Tally	Frequency f
0	I	1
1	IIII	4
2	THH THH II	12
3	THH IIII	9
4	IIII	4
5	II	2

Figure 5.6 Frequency table

For a quick estimate of the central tendencies, we could find the mid-range by dividing the range by 2 and adding the smaller score. That is,

$$5 \div 2 + 0 = 2\frac{1}{2}$$

and we might guess that the average family of five children contains $2\frac{1}{2}$ boys, which may or may not seem ridiculous. The mid-range, though, is not dependable except as a quick estimate. We need a more reliable score, and, from our frequency table, figure 5.6, the mode is obviously 2 — the greatest number of families include two boys among their five children.

The median, the midmost score, is not quite so apparent as in the earlier example of the height of students. In that example, if you recall, there was a single score which was less than the same number of scores that it exceeded. Let's construct a histogram of our data. If we count along the horizontal axis the number of boys per family, 0 to 5, and count on the vertical axis how often each occurred, we come up with figure 5.7. The median, by the way, splits the histogram into two equal areas; that is, 50% of the area is above the median and 50% below. Frequently the median is referred to as the *50th percentile*. The median for the lower half of scores in a histogram, then, is the 25th percentile, with 25% of the area below it; and the median for the upper half of the histogram is the 75th percentile and has 75% of the scores or area below it, and 25% above. If you have taken a test, for example, and the report shows that you are in the 84th percentile, feel mighty good, for that means that only 16 out of every 100 people who have taken that same test did better than you.

The median for our families must be (according to both figures 5.6 and 5.7) somewhere in the third group of scores, for the median is 2. There are 32 scores; 16 scores above the median and 16 below indicates that the median is somewhere *between* the 16th and 17th, both of which are 2. That being the case, our median is $(2 + 2) \div 2 = 2$. Our game playing seems to indicate that we might expect to find two boys out of a family of five children, in the event that we "investigate" many cases.

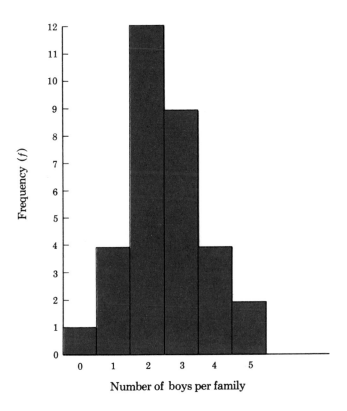

Figure 5.7 Histogram

To find the arithmetic mean of boys per family of five (that is to say, the measure we seem to imply when we say the "average") we need to do some computation. We could go through each family, one by one, and count the boys, then divide by the number of families, 32, and end up with the mean, $\overline{X}$. There is an easier way, unless you really get a kick out of counting. From our frequency table, we know the number of boys in each type of family (each type differs only in the number of boys) and also the number of families of each type. Simple calculations show that there is a total of

$$(0)1 + (1)4 = 0 + 4 = 4 \text{ boys}$$

in all families which contain either no boys or one boy. Carrying this idea through for all the families, as in figure 5.8, we find that by multiplying each score, x_i, by its frequency, f_i, adding all these products, and then dividing by the number of scores, n, we have calculated the mean. Using our summation symbol again, we can write

$$\overline{X} = \frac{\Sigma x \cdot f}{n} = \frac{81}{32} = 2.53 \text{ boys per family.}$$

Scores x	Frequency f	Scores $\times$ Frequency $x \cdot f$
0	1	0
1	4	4
2	12	24
3	9	27
4	4	16
5	2	10
Totals	32	81

Figure 5.8

In general, we call this the *weighted mean*, giving due weight to the relative importance of each score. Each college student should be familiar with the weighted mean; his grade-point average is such a measure, found by multiplying the numerical values of letter grades by their respective credit hours, adding these products, and dividing the sum by the total credit hours.

Just what have we accomplished, if anything? We have several scores that seem to be some kind of an "average." These are referred to as *measures of central tendency.*

1. Mid-range $= 2.5$

2. Mode $= 2$

3. Median $= 2$

4. Weighted mean $= 2.53$

We hope to have taken a well-judged experimental sampling from the bag and then to assess the validity or fallacy of its representing the entire contents of the bag, the entire population. The population in this case is all families that contain five children. We would like to say with some authority that, on the average, there are a certain number of boys in each of these families. But which of these "averages" do we use? Generally speaking, the mean is by far the most widely used in problems of inference, but there is a certain amount of flexibility in selection. In a country, for example, where there may be a premium on boy babies, the mean would certainly be quoted (since it is the largest number). After all, a land that produces more boys would have an advantage in manpower, production, and GNP, they may argue. On the other hand, if girls were in demand, then either the mode or the median might be chosen, since the smaller the percentage of boys, the greater the percentage of girls. The persons doing the analysis can claim that "on the average . . . ," and use any one of the measures of central tendency that does the trick for them. One should be careful, though, when comparing data to use the measure typical of each sample.

But we never did make any conclusions or inferences about our experiment, did we? Of course, our sample of 32 was rather small when compared to all five-child families. Yet, on the strength of our sample, we say that we expect to find more families with either two or three boys, with a slight edge in favor of the two-boy family occurring three times out of eight; that one out of every four families has only one boy or one girl; and we predict that there are few families with no boys or all boys.

We find that the mode is simple to calculate, but may not always be present. It is not affected by extreme high or low values in a sample. The median, too, is not affected by extremes and is easy to spot once the data have been organized in some fashion. The third measure, the mean, lends itself to mathematical and theoretical treatment, is more stable by showing less variation among large numbers of sets of data from the same population, and is often referred to as the center of gravity of a set of data.

Senator Phil E. Buster has an affluent business, organized prior to entering politics. He claims that the annual salary for all the employees of the company, Bogus Bonds, Inc., is $9,945 per year, on the average.

Now we happen to know that the company has six employees, including Buster, and that the salaries paid are: $6,255, $3,940, $4,375, $5,725, $4,375, and $35,000. There seems to be more bogus than just the name of the company, for absolutely nobody except Buster makes as much as the quoted mean, $9,945, and only one person makes less than the mode, $4,375. Therefore, the median would possibly have been the best of the three central tendencies to use.

The median is somewhere between the two middle scores, $4,375 and $5,725, since there is an even number of scores.

$$\frac{4,375 + 5,725}{2} = \$5,050$$

If the senator's salary had dropped considerably, this score would not be affected. Suppose that his take, the other salaries remaining constant, was $7,000. The mode is still $4,375 and the median remains between the same two middle scores, $4,375 and $5,725. If one of the employees who had received $4,375 should get a raise to, say, $5,000, then there is no mode at all.

The mid-range for the original salaries is

$$\frac{35,000 - 3,940}{2} + 3,940 = \$19,470$$

which is also completely out of proportion to use as a central score, for it is more than twice any salary except Senator Buster's.

A 19th century British statesman once said something to the effect that there are liars, damned liars, politicians, and statisticians, in about that order.

PROBLEM SET 5.1

1. Bills are to be presented to the legislature related to the following topics: safety standards for public goods and services; sex education in public schools; gun control; population control; censorship of news media and entertainment; exemption of all college students from taxes; and a two-day school week. Senator Phil E. Buster plans to poll his district about these topics by selecting subscribers to certain periodicals. From the following list of magazines which might possibly give the most accurate views of the individuals affected by each bill? Why? *Playboy, Medical Journal, Batman, Consumers Digest, Mathematics Teacher, Sports Illustrated, TV Guide, True Story, Ladies' Home Journal, Life, Watchtower.*

2. If the probability of a boy is ½ in the boy-girl example, what is the expected number of boys?

3. In Fred Fink's student height project, what are the mean, median, and modal height of the forwards? The guards? The centers? Make a histogram of the heights of the guards. How many guards are there below the 100th percentile? 99th percentile? 50th percentile? 75th percentile?

4. Discuss the following statements:

   (a) The average July temperature for Florida is 82° and for Indiana 76°. Therefore, it is always 6° warmer in Florida during the month of July than it is in Indiana.

   (b) Farmer Squeezum has two cows. From one he takes 5 gallons of milk per day which contains 3% butterfat; from the other, 3 gallons with 5% butterfat. He has, then, 8 gallons of milk with an average of 4% butterfat.

   (c) The highway commission was making a study of roads under consideration for improvement. Priorities were to go according to the amount of traffic that used the roads. For a one-month period, the commission set up counting stations for the different roads according to the following time table.

ROAD	TIME OBSERVED	VEHICLES COUNTED
First Street	5 a.m.-9 a.m.	26,800
Northway South	9 a.m.-1 p.m.	13,300
Wrongway West	1 p.m.-5 p.m.	12,700
Last Street	5 p.m.-9 p.m.	30,200

Therefore Last Street should be repaired first and Wrongway West should be repaired last.

5. Suppose that the results of a test show that most of the scores are concentrated around 85%. Which measure of central tendency will be affected most: mean, median, mode, or mid-range?

6. Would you classify the "common man" as an average (mean) or modal man?

7. In a class of 35 students, 19 of them make a score of 100 on a quiz. What is the median?

8. Professor U. R. A. Dilly instructed his class to study diligently for the final exam so that more students might score above the median. Comment on the professor's statement.

9. In the following sets of scores, which measure would probably be the most meaningful?

(a) 21, 25, 73, 41, 40, 14, 17

(b) 87, 85, 90, 86, 79, 89, 91, 84

(c) 2, 5, 5, 7, 10, 13, 15, 18, 22, 23

10. Three samples with 10, 15, and 20 scores in each were taken from a population. The means of each sample were, respectively, 92, 87, and 88. What is the mean of the three samples?

11. Last semester Jim studied calculus, physics, history, and physical education; he received C, C, A, and A, respectively, and the semester hour credits were 5, 4, 3, and 1, in that order. If an A has a point value of 4, B a point value of 3, C a point value of 2, and D, 1, what is his grade-point average? Mary took the same courses and received an A, B, C, and D in each, respectively. Which student has the highest average?

12. Given:

$$x_1 = 2 \qquad x_5 = 2$$
$$x_2 = 4 \qquad x_6 = 5$$
$$x_3 = 1 \qquad x_7 = 3$$
$$x_4 = 3 \qquad x_8 = 2$$

Find: (a) Σx from x_1 to x_8 inclusive; written $\sum\limits_{i=1}^{8} x_i$

(b) $(\Sigma x)^2$ from x_1 to x_8 inclusive; written $\left(\sum\limits_{i=1}^{8} x_i \right)^2$

(c) Σx^2 from x_1 to x_8 inclusive; written $\displaystyle\sum_{i=1}^{8} x_i{}^2$

(d) $\Sigma(x - 3)$ from x_1 to x_8 written $\displaystyle\sum_{i=1}^{8}(x_i - 3)$

(e) $\Sigma(x - 3)^2$ from x_1 to x_8 written $\displaystyle\sum_{i=1}^{8}(x_i - 3)^2$

13. Find the mean, median, mode, range, and mid-range for each of the following sets of numbers.

    (a) 2, 4, 6, 8, 10

    (b) 1, 3, 5, 5, 7, 0

    (c) 10, 1, 7, 5, 2, 1, 3, 1

    (d) 4, 10, 2, 4, 9, 10, 8, 50, 3

    (e) 2, 0, −4, 2, −6, 0, −4, 6, 4, 2

14. Professor U. R. A. Dilly has given his final examination in mathematics. There were a total of 50 points, and his 21 students made the following scores: 27, 32, 26, 32, 45, 29, 34, 37, 35, 29, 25, 40, 37, 29, 39, 36, 32, 27, 34, 32, 15. Using the data, make a frequency table, frequency polygon, and histogram. Find the mean, median, mode, range, and mid-range. Comment on the use of each central tendency value as a representative score for the sample. On the basis of this information, what conclusions can you make?

5.2. Standard Deviation

Now we might consider ourselves quite clever — endowed with savoir-faire in the ways of finding whichever may be the most characteristic score of a set. In this section we shall, for the most part, confine our discussion to the use of the mean.

From experience we have learned to formulate notions of the normal size of things. These judgments seem to be a natural occupation. We hear, and make, expressions like: "My, that's a large orange!" "That certainly was a hard rain!" "What a hot day it is for April!" "But, she's so tiny!" "What a long ear of corn!" All of these expressions imply that a norm has been established and that some measurements vary from that norm.

We have also learned, by observation, to fashion relative variations with respect to a norm. That is, a nose one inch longer than what we may consider as being normal is more monstrous than a man's height that is one inch more than the average height of men. A variation is large or small depending upon the norm with which it is associated.

Let's muse over the following two samples of a population.

$$A = 5, 5, 6, 8, 9, 9, 10, 10, 10$$

$$B = 1, 2, 3, 4, 8, 10, 10, 11, 12, 19$$

Since the samples are already ordered from lowest to highest score, we can spot the mode for sample A, 10; the median is 9; and, with a minimum of computation, we can find the mean, $\dfrac{\Sigma x}{n} = \dfrac{72}{9} = 8$. Then, turning to sample B, we have 10 as the mode, the median $\dfrac{8 + 10}{2} = 9$, and the mean $\dfrac{\Sigma x}{n} = \dfrac{80}{10} = 8$.

We have two samples whose scores appear to be quite different in number and size, yet they have identical means, medians, and modes. Obviously, then, if we knew only these central scores about two samples, we would assume that they were about the same. This is not the case. Sample A seems to be more closely clustered; B has a much larger score — almost twice that of the largest score of A — and also a much smaller score. We would not be tempted to compare these two samples if they were measures of some performance of two groups of individuals. That is, the achievement of one group is not comparable to that of the other. We need, then, some idea of how the scores of a sample are dispersed or bunched about its mean. Since the sample range is easy to compute and understand, we might be tempted to use this spread of scores as a measure of variation. In the two examples above, A has a sample range of $10 - 5 = 5$; sample B has a range of $19 - 1 = 18$. But, since these ranges are based solely on the extreme values, they are not useful measures, giving us no information about the scores in between. In figure 5.9, we plot each of the scores from sample A as points above the real number line, exhibiting a pattern of the scores scattered about the mean. The characteristic of the closeness (or remoteness) of the scores may suggest that we make use of the average of these distances as a single representative variation. The difference between the value of

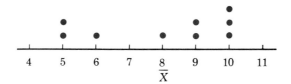

Figure 5.9

a score and the mean of the set of scores will be the amount of variation for that raw score. For instance, the first score is 5, the mean is 8, and the amount of dispersion or *deviation* is $5 - 8 = -3$. That is, the amount that a score varies from the mean is:

$$\text{raw score} - \text{mean or } x - \overline{X}.$$

We can now compute the deviation of each raw score in sample A:

$$x_1 - \overline{X} = 5 - 8 = -3 \qquad x_6 - \overline{X} = 9 \ - 8 = 1$$

$$x_2 - \overline{X} = 5 - 8 = -3 \qquad x_7 - \overline{X} = 10 - 8 = 2$$

$$x_3 - \overline{X} = 6 - 8 = -2 \qquad x_8 - \overline{X} = 10 - 8 = 2$$

$$x_4 - \overline{X} = 8 - 8 = 0 \qquad x_9 - \overline{X} = 10 - 8 = 2$$

$$x_5 - \overline{X} = 9 - 8 = 1$$

Since the score we seek is one which describes the average deviation of all the scores above and below the mean, as a first possibility we might choose to add these variations and divide by the number of them. Unfortunately, this will not work, since some of the variations are positive and some are negative; the sum will always be zero, and in our example

$$-3 + (-3) + (-2) + 0 + 1 + 1 + 2 + 2 + 2 = -8 + 8 = 0.$$

In Chapter 2 we learned that the product of two negative numbers produces a positive number, so we can now make use of that information by squaring each of our deviations.

$$(-3)^2 = 9 \qquad 0^2 = 0 \qquad 2^2 = 4$$

$$(-3)^2 = 9 \qquad 1^2 = 1 \qquad 2^2 = 4$$

$$(-2)^2 = 4 \qquad 1^2 = 1 \qquad 2^2 = 4$$

To find the average of these squares we add

$$\sum_{i=1}^{9} (x_i - \overline{X})^2 = (x_1 - \overline{X})^2 + (x_2 - \overline{X})^2 + \ldots + (x_9 - \overline{X})^2$$

$$= 9 + 9 + 4 + 0 + 1 + 1 + 4 + 4 + 4$$

$$= 36$$

Dividing by 9, the number of scores, we have

$$\frac{36}{9} = 4$$

In spite of our valiant efforts, you may be disappointed to learn that we still haven't found the number which we are seeking. Our number now is in terms of the squares of our original measurements. Thus, if we take the square root of our last quotient,

$$\sqrt{4} = 2$$

we have finally reached our goal. We have arrived at a number which represents the average amount that all scores in the distribution vary, or are dispersed, about the mean. This number is called the *standard deviation*. It is represented by the lower-case Greek letter sigma, σ.

Should we now care to put our work into a compact formula, we can write

$$\sigma = \sqrt{\frac{(x_1 - \overline{X})^2 + (x_2 - \overline{X})^2 + \ldots + (x_n - \overline{X})^2}{n}}$$

or

$$\sigma = \sqrt{\frac{\sum_{i=1}^{n} (x_i - \overline{X})^2}{n}}$$

which means, in sample *A*, that most of the scores tend to deviate by no more than about 2 points above and 2 points below the mean.

But seemingly, after all our fine work, there is a fly in the ointment. If we should have very many scores to contend with, the procedure outlined by this formula would make our work notoriously tedious. Fortunately, there is a way out. We present another cookbook formula, which lends itself more readily to machine computation. In words it says to:

1. square each score.

2. find the sum of these squares.

3. divide this sum by the number of scores.

4. subtract the square of the mean.

5. find the square root of this number.

We write

$$\sigma = \sqrt{\frac{\Sigma\, x^2}{n} - \overline{X}^2}$$

Let's use this formula on the same data, sample A, and compare the results of the two standard deviation formulas. We have already determined $\overline{X} = 8$, leaving us only to square each score and find the sum of the squares.

x_n	x_n^2
5	25
5	25
6	36
8	64
9	81
9	81
10	100
10	100
10	100
	$x_n^2 = 612$

Figure 5.10

Then, the standard deviation for the sample is

$$\sigma = \sqrt{\frac{\Sigma x^2}{n} - \overline{X^2}}$$

$$= \sqrt{\frac{612}{9} - 8^2}$$

$$= \sqrt{68 - 64}$$

$$= \sqrt{4}$$

$$= 2$$

Both formulas, essentially, will yield the same results — depending, of course, on how precise we are about decimal fractions.

Shall we try this formula with sample B at the beginning of the section? As before, let's start by making a table of values:

x_n	x_n^2
1	1
2	4
3	9
4	16
8	64
10	100
10	100
11	121
12	144
19	361
$\Sigma x_n = 80$	$\Sigma x_n^2 = 920$

Figure 5.11

We can now calculate our mean.

$$\overline{X} = \frac{\Sigma\, x_n}{n} = \frac{80}{10} = 8$$

then

$$\sigma = \sqrt{\frac{920}{10} - 8^2}$$

$$= \sqrt{92 - 64}$$

$$= \sqrt{28}$$

$$= 5.3 \ (\text{approximately})$$

We conclude that in sample B most of the scores lie within 5.3 points above or below the mean. If we compare the standard deviations of samples A and B, we might conclude that a relatively small standard deviation indicates that the scores tend to be clustered close to the mean (low variability), while a relatively high standard deviation may suggest that the scores are more widely scattered (high variability).

PROBLEM SET 5.2

1. Find the mean and the standard deviation by using the first formula given in this section; then check the standard deviation by using the second formula. Is $\Sigma(x_n - \overline{X}) = 0$?

x_n	x_n^2	$x_n - \overline{X}$	$(x_n - \overline{X})^2$
0			
1			
2			
3			
4			
5			
6			
$\Sigma x_n =$	$\Sigma x_n^2 =$		$\Sigma(x_n - \overline{X})^2 =$

2. Find σ (the standard deviation) for each of the following:
   (a) 31, 25, 73, 41, 40, 14, 7
   (b) 88, 85, 90, 86, 79, 89, 91, 84
   (c) 2, 5, 5, 7, 10, 13, 15, 18, 22, 23

3. Find the standard deviation of all the basketball players from the first example in Section 5.1.

4. Find the standard deviation of the boy-girl birth example in Section 5.1.

5. From problem 3, Problem Set 5.1, find the standard deviation of the guards of the basketball team.

6. Consider the following scores. Which would appear to have a relatively high σ?
   (a) 2, 4, 6, 8, 10
   (b) 1, 3, 5, 5, 7, 0
   (c) 10, 1, 7, 5, 2, 1, 3, 1
   (d) 4, 10, 2, 4, 9, 10, 8, 50, 3
   (e) 2, 0, -4, 2, -6, 0, -4, 6, 4, 2

7. Write ten scores that exhibit a low variability and ten scores that exhibit a high variability.

8. Professors Dilly and Grinch have given the same test in their respective classes. Both classes scored the same mean, but Grinch's class has a σ which is twice that of Dilly's class. What can we say about the deviation of scores? Which class may be the easier to instruct, determined by the σ? (Assume that all other conditions in the two classes are relatively equal.)

9. Over a 24-hour period there were seven accidents at the intersection of Wrongway and First Streets. There were also seven accidents during the same period at the intersection of Last Street and Rightway Boulevard, but the standard deviation of intervals of time between accidents at First and Wrongway is much larger. What does this possibly imply? Which intersection would you judge to be safer? Why?

10. Find the standard deviation of the test scores for Professor Dilly's class in problem 14, Section 5.1.

11. Determine the standard deviation for sample B by the first method presented. Compare your results with the "machine formula."

5.3. The Normal Curve

Investigation shows that many real-life distributions have scores greater than the mean occurring with about the same frequency as scores less than the mean; there also tend to be relatively few scores of great deviation. Departures from the scores that we conventionally accept as being "normal" are rather infrequent. An IQ of 105, for example, is accepted as being quite normal or "average," whereas IQ's of 140 and 60 are above and below average, respectively, and appear with about the same frequency. Most fishermen would seldom raise more than an eyebrow at the rumor that a friend had caught a two-pound bass, but would counter with a tale about the fifteen pounder that almost didn't get away. Seven-foot-tall basketball players and three-foot-tall circus midgets may cause us to stare in disbelief, while men close to five feet ten inches occur in great numbers.

One of the most important basic tools that mathematicians use to investigate populations of this nature is called the *normal distribution curve*. This so-called curve charts what is average or normal in a very large number of cases, and is symmetric about a line at which place the mean, median, and mode coincide.

The normal (or probability) curve was first investigated by the French mathematician Abraham de Moivre (1667-1745), and later developed by Carl Friedrich Gauss (1777-1855). Gauss wrote an intricate equation that expressed the curve in terms of factors that present themselves in experimental situations. The formula is useful in measuring the probable error and determining the reliability or validity of an experiment.

Consider, now, the task of constructing a histogram for a problem similar to that of example 5, Section 4.2, $(H + T)^5$. This indicates, you recall, that we are to toss five coins and list all possible outcomes. But, before we begin, let's make a notational change. Instead of using heads and tails $(H + T)$ in the coin tossing example, we will substitute boy or girl $(B + G)$ from the birth-incidence problem. Using Pascal's triangle, figure 4.5, we have $(B+G)^5 = 1\ B^5 + 5\ B^4G + 10\ B^3G^2 + 10\ B^2G^3 + 5\ B\ G^4 + 1\ G^5$, which implies that out of 2^5, or $1 + 5 + 10 + 10 + 5 + 1$, or 32 possible outcomes (i.e., families):

1 will contain 5 boys and 0 girls

5 will contain 4 boys and 1 girl

10 will contain 3 boys and 2 girls

10 will contain 2 boys and 3 girls

5 will contain 1 boy and 4 girls

1 will contain 0 boys and 5 girls

Organizing a frequency table, we have

Scores (number of boys) x	Frequency f	$x \cdot f$
0	1	0
1	5	5
2	10	20
3	10	30
4	5	20
5	1	5
	$\Sigma f = 32$	$\Sigma x \cdot f = 80$

Figure 5.12

As before, if we let the horizontal axis of our histogram represent the number of boys per family, 0 to 5, and the vertical axis exhibit the frequency of boy-girl family types, we can construct a histogram of the data as in figure 5.13. Then, connecting the midpoints of the altitudes of each successive rectangular section with a smooth continuous curve, we will have the normal bell shaped curve as shown by the solid line in figure 5.14.

Since the median is the midmost score and divides the histogram into two equal parts, the median of our normal distribution must necessarily be between the two rectangular areas that represent the two-boy and three-boy families, or

$$\text{median} = \frac{2+3}{2} = \frac{5}{2} = 2.5 \text{ boys per family.}$$

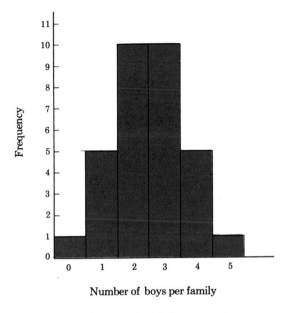

Figure 5.13 Normal distribution histogram

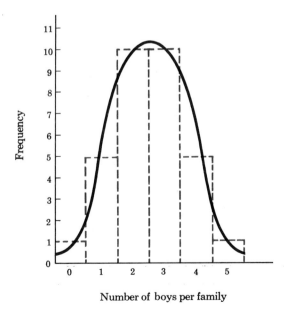

Figure 5.14 Normal curve distribution

Using data taken from the frequency table, the mean is

$$\text{mean} = \overline{X} = \frac{\Sigma\, x \cdot f}{n} = \frac{80}{32} = 2.5 \text{ boys per family.}$$

Suppose, now, we draw a smooth curve through the midpoints of the altitudes for the histogram in figure 5.7. Notice the similarity of this curve, which represents our families, determined by randomly picking marbles from a hat, and the normal curve, figure 5.14, theoretical families calculated by simple mathematical procedures.

Not all samples (nor populations, for that matter) are normally distributed relative to any characteristic. There is no reason to assume that they are, although many educators dole out all their grades by "curving the grades," presumably by the normal curve. They may be putting the cart before the horse, for such action would require the criteria for grading to be determined after the course was completed. To be accepted as normally distributed, the elements must be randomly chosen with variations among them due to chance, and a large enough sample taken for an accurate image of the population.

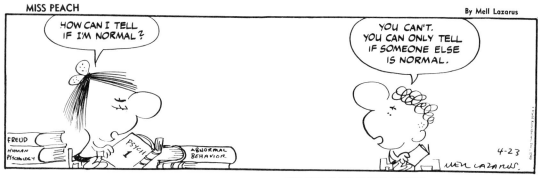

MISS PEACH BY MELL LAZARUS. COURTESY PUBLISHERS-HALL SYNDICATE.

Statisticians can show that if data are normally distributed, approximately ⅔ of the scores will be within a distance of one standard deviation above the mean to one standard deviation below the mean; that the area from two standard deviations above to two below the mean will contain about 95% of the scores; and that practically all (99.99%) of the scores will be within 4 σ above and below $\overline{X}$, as illustrated in figure 5.15. (The values for each area are approximate.)

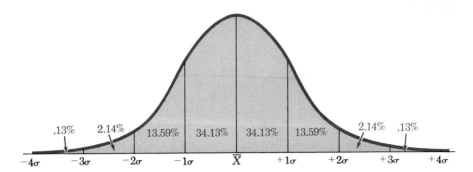

Figure 5.15 Area under the normal curve divided by σ's

No matter how far we extend the tails of the curve, they never quite touch the horizontal axis but, for all practical purposes, the area beyond ±4 σ is negligible. The curve is completely determined by the mean and σ in such a way that, with the use of prepared tables, we can find the area between any two points on the horizontal axis, or the probability that a certain sample score can be expected, if we know or can derive the mean and standard deviation for a set of data. The sum of the values for the sections of any distribution curve should total 100%, or the full amount of *one area* which must be necessary if we are to use the curve to interpret probability frequencies. That is, for a normally distributed sample, if we want to find the probability that a randomly selected score will be between two given scores, we have only to find the area under the curve between those two scores.

For normally distributed data, the following table gives the fractional parts, in decimals, represented by the enclosed area *from the mean*

z	Area	z	Area	z	Area	z	Area	z	Area
0.0	.000	0.7	.258	1.4	.419	2.1	.482	2.8	.497
0.1	.040	0.8	.288	1.5	.433	2.2	.486	2.9	.498
0.2	.079	0.9	.316	1.6	.445	2.3	.489	3.0	.499
0.3	.118	1.0	.341	1.7	.455	2.4	.492	4.0	.499
0.4	.155	1.1	.364	1.8	.464	2.5	.494		
0.5	.192	1.2	.385	1.9	.471	2.6	.495		
0.6	.226	1.3	.403	2.0	.477	2.7	.496		

Figure 5.16 Standard normal distribution

to specified deviations. For convenience, we let z represent the deviations about the mean, and we shall refer to them as z *scores,* or *standard scores.*

   The portion of scores or measurements in the area from the mean to .5 σ above the mean is .192 (approximately). The area enclosed by the horizontal axis, the curve, the mean, and a z score of -1.5 σ is .433 of the total area beneath the curve.

Example 1   For a set of normally distributed scores whose mean is 33 and standard deviation is 6, find the percent of scores above a score of 39.

Solution   First, let's sketch a normal curve, label with what information we have, and then compare it with the normal curve of figure 5.15. We see that the normal curve and normal curve tables are presented in terms of z scores which tell us the number of standard deviations there are in the distance between a particular score and $\overline{X}$ of a distribution.

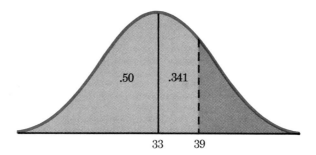

.50   .341

33   39

   Any raw data score can be changed to a z score by the following formula.

$$z = \frac{x - \overline{X}}{\sigma}$$

Thus, the z score for our problem is

$$z = \frac{x - \overline{X}}{\sigma} = \frac{39 - 33}{6} = 1.0$$

From the table of z scores, we find that the area between $\overline{X}$ and $z = 1.0$

is .341, or about 34.1%. But 50% of the curve is below $\overline{X}$; therefore, the percent of scores above 39 is

$$100 - (.50 + .341) = .159 = 15.9\%$$

We could have used only the upper half of the curve, in this case

$$.50 - .341 = .159 = 15.9\%$$

Example 2 For the same $\overline{X}$ and σ as example 1, find the number of scores between 27 and 35 if there are a total of 150 scores.

Solution Here, we must find two z scores and the area between them.

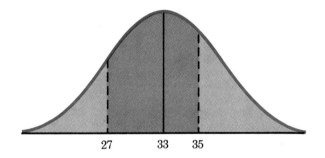

27   33   35

$$z_1 = \frac{27 - 33}{6} = \frac{-6}{6} = -1 \qquad z_2 = \frac{35 - 33}{6} = \frac{1}{3} = .333$$

Although we have $z_1 = -1$, only positive values are given in the table; there are no negative areas. The negative scores only indicate that the area is to the left of $\overline{X}$. Thus the area between z_1 and $\overline{X}$ is .341, and the area between z_2 and $\overline{X}$ is between .118 and .155, say .125. You may wish to consult a statistics text for a table of more precise values. Thus $.341 + .125 = .466 = 46.6\%$. But we have asked for the number ber of scores out of the 150, and

$$.466\,(150) = 66.9; \text{ approximately 67 scores}$$

are between the two given scores of 27 and 35.

PROBLEM SET 5.3

1. Toss ten coins at a time thirty times and tabulate the number of heads. Construct a histogram of your results and connect the midpoints of the altitudes to form a smooth curve.

2. Determine the theoretical distribution of heads for the experiment in problem 1, and compare the two results. Combine the results of all the students in the class and divide the frequencies by the number of students. Compare this result with the theoretical distribution.

3. Professor Cable gave a test to 100 students. If the grades A, B, C, D, and F were normally distributed between $+3$ and -3 standard deviations about the mean, how many of each grade was earned? (*Hint:* Since 5 grades are to be distributed among 6 σ, each base length will be $6 \div 5 = 1.2$ σ in length.)

4. Express each of the following raw scores as z score (standard score); the mean is 9 and the standard deviation is 2.5.

   (a) 14   (b) 9

   (c)   3   (d) 7

   (e) 11   (f) 8

5. In exercise 4 above, explain the significance of the negative z scores; the positive z scores; any z score equal to 0.

   REMARK: Standard scores (z scores) are common yardsticks used to compare scores or measurements taken from different groups of data. The standard deviation lets us compare the overall spread in one group with that of another. Standard scores, obtained from the standard deviation, let us compare the performances of individuals in one group with the performances of individuals in another, in terms of relative achievement with others in their own groups.

6. Kelly and Tony are both studying algebra, but are in different groups. Finish the following table and determine which boy did better on a test in comparison with others in his own group.

	x	$\overline{X}$	σ	z
Kelly	85	75	10	
Tony	80	70	6	

7. Niki received a score of 93 on an English test. The class mean was 90 and the standard deviation was 3. She got 79 on a mathematics test for which the class mean was 74, the standard deviation was 2. On which test did she have the better score when compared with her class?

8. Find the percent of a normal distribution that lies above a score of 24 if the mean is 33 and the standard deviation is 6. How many scores are above 24 if there are 125 scores in the distribution?

9. Determine the upper and lower scores for the middle 63% of a normal distribution whose $\overline{X} = 75$ and $\sigma = 10$.

10. Find the number of scores of a normal distribution below a raw score of 19 if $\overline{X} = 22$ and $\sigma = 6$.

11. An entrance examination is given to 15,000 students by Poly Tech University. The mean for all students is 100 and the standard deviation is 20. What percent of the students is expected to pass if a score of greater than 110 is needed? How many students' scores will fall in the range of 100 to 110? If a score is picked at random, what is the probability that it is greater than 110? (Assume that the scores form a normal distribution.) What can be said about the normal curve relative to probability?

12. Hugo Heimerdinger's score is picked at random from the distribution in problem 11. What is the probability that it will be greater than 140? Less than 80?

13. A large group of children are randomly selected and their IQ's are normally distributed with $\overline{X} = 100$ and $\sigma = 16$. If the lowest 2% are regarded as feeble minded, find the upper IQ limit for this group.

14. In a random sample of 1,000 children, how many can we expect to have an IQ greater than 140? Use $\overline{X}$ and σ from exercise 9.

5.4. Confidence in a Sample

Often an apple of discord grows in the fruitful domain of Mathland, and in particular in the back 40 of statistics. Statisticians may be at sixes and sevens over the method for obtaining a sample; others may be

Doubting Thomases as to the validity of the results of an experiment. Proclamations gush pellmell into the marketplace: Makers of Crudydent claim their users have 50% fewer cavities — they do not publish information regarding how many fewer teeth! John Q. may do as well using Nip-O-Dent with $99\frac{44}{100}\%$ alcohol, the only martini-flavored toothpaste in the large economy "fifth" tube. Consumers report 25% more cavities, but couldn't care less. Tempting testimonials from small samples — the mouthpiece for legions.

Obvious questions arise: By using a small sample mean, can we really get reasonably close to the population mean from which the sample was taken? Since we are dealing with uncertainties, how sure can we be that the sample mean doesn't differ from the population mean by more than a desired amount? If the performances of two matched groups have different means, what is the significance of this difference? When we lay out time and expense to collect data for an experiment in statistics, we hope to arrive at some conclusion and then make inferences about the population from which the sample is taken.

We have already agreed that the basketball team did not constitute a random sample for Fred Fink and his assignment. Suppose Fred uses a table of random numbers, assigns a number to each student in the school, and then randomly selects 25 numbers. By measuring the students designated by these numbers, Fred may now feel that he has achieved a good random sample. Suppose that this is true and that the mean of the sample is 66.8 inches and the standard deviation is 1.8 inches. How sure can we be that the true mean of the student body is within a chosen range? We could arbitrarily choose a range around the mean, 66.8, of ± 15.8 inches, or an interval of heights from 51.0 to 82.6 inches and say with 99% confidence that the real mean was somewhere between these two limits, but it would have little value, for, certainly, most senior high students are taller than 4.25 feet and shorter than 6.9 feet. On the other hand, we can reduce the width of the interval, but, at the same time, we would also be a little less certain that the population mean lies within our limits. Our task, then, is to determine a meaningful range, called the *confidence interval,* which will include the mean height of the population, say, 99% of the time. Our level of certainty that the interval contains the mean is the *degree of confidence,* and is stated in percents or decimals.

If we were to find the means for each of several samples taken from a population, we would expect these means to seesaw from sample to sample. We need a recipe to indicate the possible size of these fluctuations around the population mean. Such a formula is

$$SE_{\bar{x}} = \frac{\sigma}{\sqrt{n}} \quad (n \text{ is the sample size})$$

and is called the *standard error of the mean*. Thus in our example the standard error is

$$SE_{\bar{x}} = \frac{\sigma}{\sqrt{n}} = \frac{1.8}{\sqrt{25}} = \frac{1.8}{5} = .36$$

While the means of large samples (greater than 30) are normally distributed, the means of small samples (30 or less) are not. From the formula, $SE_{\bar{x}}$, we see that the shape of the distributions for small sample means depends largely on the size of the sample. The larger the sample size, the more nearly the distribution will approach the normal curve. Therefore, to convert the small sample standard error scores to standard scores we cannot use our Standard Normal Distribution table. Statisticians use a table of values investigated by W. S. Gosset and published in 1908 called the *t distribution*. These *t* values are actually standard scores for the distribution of small sample means.

Since we are dealing with a small sample in the example, we can find our confidence interval by multiplying $SE_{\bar{x}}$ by the proper value of *t* obtained from the *t* distributions table. That is, if we seek a .95 confidence interval for the heights, then use the value in the .05 (i.e., $1.00 - .95$) column for $n = 25$, which is 2.06, then the product is

$$t \cdot SE_{\bar{x}} = confidence\ limits$$

$$2.06\ (.36) = .74$$

We subtract this product from the mean to obtain the lower limit of the confidence interval, and add the product to the mean to obtain the upper limit.

66.80	66.80
$-.74$	$+.74$
66.06 lower limit	67.54 upper limit

Conclusion: We are 95% confident, or there is a probability of .95, that the true mean height for the students of Fred Fink's school lies within the interval from a height of 66.06 inches to 67.54 inches.

95% confidence   99% confidence

n	$t_{.05}$	$t_{.01}$	n	$t_{.05}$	$t_{.01}$
2	12.71	63.66	17	2.12	2.92
3	4.30	9.92	18	2.11	2.90
4	3.18	5.84	19	2.10	2.88
5	2.78	4.60	20	2.09	2.86
6	2.57	4.03	21	2.09	2.84
7	2.45	3.71	22	2.08	2.83
8	2.36	3.50	23	2.07	2.82
9	2.31	3.36	24	2.07	2.81
10	2.26	3.25	25	2.06	2.80
11	2.23	3.17	26	2.06	2.79
12	2.20	3.11	27	2.06	2.78
13	2.18	3.06	28	2.05	2.77
14	2.16	3.01	29	2.05	2.76
15	2.14	3.00	30	2.04	2.76
16	2.13	2.95	∞	1.96	2.58

Figure 5.17 Distribution of t values

lower confidence limit   upper confidence limit

Confidence Interval

Figure 5.18 t distribution. Shaded area represents values for the entries in figure 5.17.

Example   Tony had 9 pigs that were self-fed a prepared ration of rolled corn and oats, minerals, a high protein concentrate, and plenty of fresh water for 30 days. The mean gain for the period was 45 pounds per pig with a standard deviation of .42. What is the 95% confidence interval of the population mean for 30-day gains using this ration?

Solution   First we calculate the standard error of the mean

$$SE_{\bar{x}} = \frac{\sigma}{\sqrt{n}} = \frac{.42}{\sqrt{9}} = \frac{.42}{3} = .14$$

Then, from the t distribution table, we locate the t score for $n = 9$ with confidence level .95, which is 2.31.

$$t \cdot SE_{\bar{x}} = 2.31 \ (.14) = .32$$

The lower and upper limits are $\bar{X} \pm .32$

45.00	45.00
$-.32$	$+.32$
44.68	45.32

Thus we are 95% confident that the interval from 44.68 to 45.32 pounds will include the population mean (other conditions being equal or comparable).

Often, two samples are compared, and we wish to know if there is a significant difference between their means. If the subjects of the samples are measured before and after the introduction of some experimental factor, or each score in one sample has a mate or corresponding score in the second sample, we say that a *correlation* exists between them. Many scientific experiments have been conducted among humans using identical twins in different environments; litter mates of mice have been used extensively in determining the effects of drugs, and in tests for cancer. Individuals may be matched in pairs on education, occupation, urban-rural location, or age, and then compared on an attitude measure or opinion poll.

Suppose we wish to measure students' ability to study in a quiet atmosphere as compared to studying in a noisy room, other factors being constant. Suppose, too, that the study efficiency for each student can be rated on a scale from zero to ten, ten the maximum of efficiency and zero the minimum.

We randomly select ten students, administer the meaningful before-after tests, and calculate the mean and the standard deviation of the differences, D, of the scores for each individual. The same results can be obtained by computing the mean and standard deviation for each test separately, and then determining the differences between the two means and the two standard deviations. This is usually more burdensome, but the more adventurous student may wish to solve the problem using this method.

If we assume that these D scores are normally distributed, we proceed as follows.

Student	Quiet Score	Noise Score	Difference	D^2
A	4.2	1.3	2.9	8.41
B	7.4	3.4	4.0	16.00
C	1.0	3.0	−2.0	4.00
D	7.2	1.1	6.1	37.21
E	3.6	0.7	2.9	8.41
F	7.2	0.7	6.5	42.25
G	1.7	3.5	−1.8	3.24
H	8.4	0.4	8.0	64.00
I	3.0	2.9	0.1	.01
J	7.4	3.5	3.9	15.21
$n = 10$			$\Sigma D = 30.6$	$\Sigma D^2 = 198.74$

Figure 5.19

The table now shows the differences between the scores as well as the differences squared. We can juggle these difference scores and the D^2's the same as we have previously manipulated other scores for any sample data. That is, we can compute the mean of the differences,

$$\overline{D} = \frac{\Sigma D}{n} = \frac{30.6}{10} = 3.06$$

and the standard deviation of these differences,

$$\sigma_D = \sqrt{\frac{\Sigma D^2}{n} - \overline{D}^2} = \sqrt{\frac{198.74}{10} - (3.06)^2} = \sqrt{19.87 - 9.36}$$

$$= \sqrt{10.51} = 3.24$$

The standard error of the mean differences, $SE_{\bar{D}}$ is

$$SE_{\bar{D}} = \frac{\sigma}{\sqrt{n}} = \frac{3.24}{\sqrt{10}} = \frac{3.24}{3.16} = 1.02$$

We are now ready to determine a t score mathematically from the data. This value in some way will describe an interval that varies about the mean; in short, a t score is a ratio of the mean to the standard error of this mean. That is, for our data,

$$t = \frac{\overline{X}}{SE_{\bar{x}}} = \frac{\overline{D}}{SE_{\bar{D}}} = \frac{3.06}{1.02} = 3.0$$

But, we can also find a t score from the t distribution, Figure 5.17. For $n = 10$ at the 95% confidence level

$$t = 2.26$$

Compare these two t scores to determine the significance of any change brought about by studying in a noisy room relative to efficiency of studying in quiet surroundings. If we ask, "Does the noise produce a significant decrease in the mean score for study efficiency?" we are asking if the calculated t is greater than the 95% t value given in the table, and 3.0 is greater than 2.26. Therefore, the obtained value exceeds 95% of the values we would normally expect to find in a random sampling and we conclude there *is* sufficient evidence to say studying where it is quiet is better. (*Note:* In all the above calculations we have *rounded off* to the nearest hundredths. Therefore the answers are only approximate.)

A few words of caution. We must try with maximum effort to achieve random sampling. With some reservation we assume the sample fits the normal distribution curve, and the level of significance desired should be specified before any tests are performed.

We have only attempted to acquaint you with a few of the symbols, formulas, and problems of statisticians. There are too many to list all of them here. The average citizen is bombarded with masses of numbers, numerous opinion polls, and other quantitative "facts" by news and advertising media, making it almost essential for us to have some sort of understanding of statistics to have a fair understanding of the world around us.

PROBLEM SET 5.4

1. Would you expect the correlation between the variables of each of the following pairs of ideas to be high, moderate, low, zero, or negative? Discuss each possibility.

    (a) Height and weight of elementary school children.

    (b) Salary and intelligence of lawyers over 40.

    (c) Keenness of vision and marksmanship with a bow and arrow.

    (d) Social adjustment and technical knowledge in space scientists.

    (e) IQ and strength of grip of high school boys.

2. Compute the 99% confidence interval for the heights of students in Fred Fink's problem.

3. Compute the 99% confidence interval for the pig-weight example in this section.

4. Compute the 99% confidence interval for the before-after test example in this section. Is there a significant decrease in the mean score for study at the 99% level?

5. A sample of 9 oranges is taken from a load with an average diameter of 4 inches and a standard deviation of .3 inches. Find the 95% and 99% confidence intervals for the mean diameters of the oranges for the load.

Chapter 6
MATHEMATICAL SYSTEMS

Structure of Mathematics

Relations and Operations

Groups

Fields

Peano's Postulates

6.1. Structure of Mathematics

An exciting two-person struggle of wits, mentioned in Ovid's *Art of Love* (giving advice to women on how to be popular with men), can be played by using a square blocked off into nine smaller cells by drawing two parallel vertical lines and two parallel horizontal lines that intersect inside the square, and two sets of pawns. The only rules to follow are that each player, in turn, places one of his pawns on a small cell. The winner is determined by the contestant who first lines up three of his pawns either horizontally, vertically, or diagonally.

Wordsworth wrote in his *Prelude, Book I*

At evening, when with pencil, and smooth slate
In square divisions parcelled out and all
With crosses and with cyphers scribbled o'er
We schemed and puzzled, head opposed to head
In strife too humble to be named in verse.

The structure of mathematics has been parallel to that of a game. In a game we set down certain terms, some defined and others undefined, and then state a series of rules that must be followed. Each branch of mathematics is structured in a similar way. We shall begin with some undefined terms and definitions and then state the rules that must be obeyed. These rules are often referred to as *axioms* by mathematicians. We may set up any set of rules (axiomatic system) that we wish, as long as these rules do not conflict with each other.

In other words, the set of axioms must be consistent. Once we have stated our set of defined terms, undefined terms, and axioms, our purpose is to use them under the rules of logic in establishing new consequences which we call *theorems*. Let's invent a game and make up some rules (axioms) so that everyone will be playing exactly the same game. We will accept the bewitching terms "aba" and "daba" as undefined. Our axioms are as follows.

1. There are at least two abas.

2. For every two abas there is one and only one daba containing them.

3. Every daba contains at least one aba.

4. For every daba there is an aba not on that daba.

This is certainly a strange set of rules, and in order to obtain any meaning from them we are prompted to replace the terms aba and daba with terms with which we are more familiar. One such interpretation might be to replace aba with the word "airplane" and daba with the word "runway." Our axiom system then becomes:

1'. There are at least two airplanes.

2'. For every two airplanes there is one and only one runway containing them.

3'. Every runway contains at least one airplane.

4'. For every runway there is an airplane not on that runway.

With this interpretation we can better understand the meaning of the axioms and are able to draw a diagram which satisfies all the axioms. Such a diagram is shown in figure 6.1.

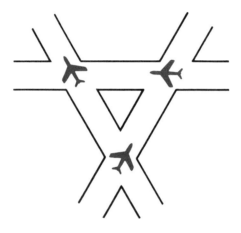

Figure 6.1

Now that we have a physical representation of the system, someone may say, "It appears to me that every airplane is on two runways." Let's state the observation as a theorem and then see if we can logically defend it using only the given axioms.

Theorem   *Every airplane is on at least two runways.*

Proof   Let *A* denote an airplane. By axiom 1′ there is another airplane, which we call *B*. Then, by axiom 2′, there must be a runway containing *A* and *B*. But axiom 4′ tells us there is another airplane, which we call *C*. Now, again using axiom 2′, we see that there must also be a runway containing *A* and *C*. Therefore airplane *A* is on two runways.

Going back to our original four statements, since airplane and runway are substitutions for aba and daba, our theorem could be stated, "Every aba is on at least two dabas." We see that, although "aba" and "daba" are undefined terms, our interpretation of them as the defined terms "airplane" and "runway" gives us statements with meaning.

We could just as easily have substituted other undefined terms for aba and daba. Such a substitution might be "point" for "aba" and "line" for "daba." Point and line are undefined terms. (Have you ever tried to tell someone, without using pencil and paper or hands, what a point or line is?) Our axioms now read:

1″. There are at least two points.

2″. For every two points there is one and only one line containing them.

3″. Every line contains at least one point.

4″. For every line there is a point not on that line.

Let us be careful here and not think of point and line as defined terms. They are not. We must give an *interpretation* to each of these terms in order to have meaning for the axioms. Just as we thought of aba as "airplane" and daba as "runway," we could illustrate a point with a dot, and a line with the mark that is made when a pencil is drawn along an edge of a ruler. This is the usual construction used in geometry. We now draw a diagram for our axioms (figure 6.2).

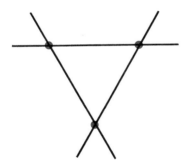

Figure 6.2

The theorem that was established should also hold, then, for these axioms; it would read, "Every point is on at least two lines." Other theorems can be proved and are left as intriguing exercises.

In our game of tick-tack-toe, instead of starting a new game as soon as it is obvious that no one can win, we might limit each player to three pawns. After each person has played his third pawn, and still no one has three in a row, we could continue each turn by moving a single pawn to any adjacent square along the orthogonal (not diagonally).

Just as changing a rule in a game creates a new game, altering one or more axioms results in a new branch of mathematics. We have a set of rules for Euclidean geometry. By changing one of them we develop a different (non-Euclidean) geometry. "Pure" mathematicians are interested in this area. They like to change one axiom in a system and see what interesting consequences result from the new set of axioms. They do not necessarily have any particular purposes in mind when they do this, but occasionally these new systems find important application. Einstein's work, for example, involved the use of non-Euclidean geometry.

PROBLEM SET 6.1

1. Using the set of axioms from this section which contain the terms "point" and "line," prove the following theorems.

   (a) *There are at least three points.* Does the set of axioms allow for more than three points?

   (b) *There are at least three lines.* Does the set of axioms allow for more than three lines?

2. Given the following axioms,

      1. There are exactly three clubs.

      2. Every two clubs have exactly one member in common.

      3. Every member belongs to exactly two clubs.

   (a) What is the total number of members?

   (b) Prove your answer to part (a).

3. From the following set of axioms, state some theorems that could be proved and prove one of them.

   (a) There are exactly four globs.

   (b) For every two globs there is exactly one glib containing them.

   (c) For each glib there are exactly two globs not on that glib.

6.2. Relations and Operations

We often wish to compare the elements of a set with each other. For example, the students in a class may be compared in age, sex, height, or weight. Such comparisons are called *relations*. A relation is a comparison of each element of a set with every other element of the set. We may denote this by $_xR_y$ (read "x is related to y") where x and y are elements of the set.

We may compare the elements of the set $S = \{1,2,3\}$ for relative size. The various comparisons are: $1 \not> 1$ (read "1 is not greater than 1"), $1 \not> 2$, $1 \not> 3$; $2 > 1$ (read "2 is greater than 1"), $2 \not> 2$, $2 \not> 3$, $3 > 1$, $3 > 2$, $3 \not> 3$. It will be necessary to list only the statements where it is true that $x > y$; we will assume all others are of the form $x \not> y$. Therefore our relation can be written as $2 > 1$, $3 > 1$, $3 > 2$.

Another comparison of the elements of the set S would be that of equality. The elements of the form $x = y$ are $1 = 1$, $2 = 2$, $3 = 3$. Thus, equality is also a relation.

Equality is an example of a special type of relation called an *equivalence relation*. An equivalence relation has the following three properties.

(1) Reflexive: For every x in the set, $_xR_x$. It would appear that everything is equal to itself; therefore, equality is reflexive. But, under some other relations we may not just be setting a thing equal to itself. Assume that the relation means to multiply numbers only from the set of natural numbers. Assume, also, that the relation must satisfy the property of getting only odd numbers for products. Then the reflexive property is not satisfied for $_2R_2$, since $2 \cdot 2 = 4$ and 4 is not odd. (Remember Section 2.6 on odd and even numbers.)

(2) Symmetric: If $_xR_y$ then $_yR_x$. If our relation was "put on x and then y," and defined on the set of clothing we wear, then the relation is not symmetric, for $_{socks}R_{shoes} \leftrightarrow$ *put on socks and then shoes*, and this would not end with quite the same results as $_{shoes}R_{socks} \leftrightarrow$ *put on shoes and then socks.*

(3) Transitive: If $_xR_y$ and $_yR_z$, then $_xR_z$. Here let us define the relation as "is as tall as." Then, if x, y, and z represent Kathy, Betty, and Sue, respectively, the transitive property would read, "If Kathy is as tall as Betty and Betty is as tall as Sue, then Kathy is as tall as Sue." This

would be a valid conclusion. Suppose, however, we chose as our relation "is ½ the value of," and use $x = 25¢$, $y = 50¢$, and $z = \$1$. The transitive property then reads, "If $25¢$ is ½ the value of $50¢$ and $50¢$ is ½ the value of $\$1$, then $25¢$ is ½ the value of $\$1$." This, of course, is not true.

"Four and two don't make six--three and three do! We LEARNED it, Billy!"

Equality is not the only example of an equivalence relation. If we consider the students in a class and use as a relation "is the same age as," we see we have an equivalence relation.

Another concept that will be important to us is that of a *binary operation*. Such an operation on a set associates with any two elements of the set a single element of the set. Consider the set of natural numbers $\{1,2,3,4,\ldots\}$ and the operation of addition. From our experience in arithmetic we know that if we add two natural numbers the result (sum) is a natural number. The operation is a binary operation and the set is said to be closed under the operation. Other possible binary operations are: choose the first of two numbers, choose the larger of two numbers, multiply two numbers.

PROBLEM SET 6.2

1. Let S be the set $\{1,2,3,7,9,14,16,18,28\}$ and consider the relation "is twice as large as."

    (a) Write the statements which belong to this relation in the form $_xR_y$.

    (b) Is this relation an equivalence relation?

2. Let T be the set {Cincinnati, Pittsburg, Cleveland, San Diego, Miami, Los Angeles, Philadelphia, Tampa, San Francisco} and let the relation be "is in the same state as."

    (a) List the statements which represent this relation in the form $_xR_y$.

    (b) Does the relation qualify as an equivalence relation?

3. Consider the following sets.

    $A = \{2,4,6,8,\ldots\}$ $C = \{1,3,9,27,\ldots\}$ $E = \{0\}$

    $B = \{1,3,5,7,\ldots\}$ $D = \{5,10,15,\ldots\}$ $F = \{0,1\}$

    In order for an operation to be a binary operation, the set must be closed under the operation.

    (a) For which of the above sets is addition a binary operation?

    (b) For which sets is multiplication a binary operation?

6.3. Groups

Nobody ever learns all about these things on a windy Thursday, but we hope to have gained enough momentum to look at another system of axioms. This set of axioms has far more consequences than our example in Section 6.1. We begin with a set of elements, a binary operation which we will denote by $*$, and an equivalence relation denoted by $=$. The set of elements, binary operation, and equivalence relation are undefined. We now state the rules (axioms) involving these quantities. (You may wish to refresh your memory of these terms, introduced in Chapter 2.)

1. (Associative)   *For any elements x, y, z, $x * (y * z)$*
                    $= (x * y) * z$

2. (Identity)   *There is an element i such that, for any element x, $x * i = x$*

3. (Inverse)   *For every element x there is an element $\bar{x}$ such that $x * \bar{x} = i$*

4. (Commutative) *For any elements x and y, $x * y = y * x$*

Any set which obeys axioms 1, 2, and 3 is called a *group*. If axiom 4 also holds, it is called a *commutative* or *Abelian group*. Niels Henrik Abel (1802-1829) was born in Kristiansand, Norway. At the age of 18, upon the death of his father, he assumed the role of breadwinner and head of the household for his mother and six brothers and sisters. Abel proved the impossibility of solving the general equation of the fifth degree which had been a thorn in the side of mathematicians for centuries. Abel's philosophy was, "You must always invert." That is, if he couldn't solve an equation directly, he would turn it upside down, inside out, or back-end to. Thus, his method was commutative.

From our definition of a binary operation, we know that a group must be closed under the operation. That is, $x * y$ must be a member of the set. We now look at some models of our system.

Example 1   The set of integers $\{\ldots,-3,-2,-1,0,1,2,3,\ldots\}$ forms an Abelian group under the operation of addition. The set is certainly closed under the operation, since the sum of two integers is an integer. Axiom 1 is satisfied, as shown by such examples as $2 + (3 + 5) = (2 + 3) + 5$. The identity element is 0. If we add 0 to any element, we obtain that element as a result (i.e., $-3 + 0 = -3$). Thus axiom 2 is satisfied. Each element has an inverse. The inverse of 5 is -5. The inverse of -8 is 8, etc. This satisfies axiom 3. Finally, we see that addition of the integers is commutative (i.e., $3 + 2 = 2 + 3$, etc.).

NOTE: We have only given a single example of axioms 1 and 3, and this in no way proves they hold for all cases.

Example 2   The set of integers $\{0,1,2\}$ forms an Abelian group under the operation of addition modulo 3. We first explain what is meant by the expression "addition modulo 3" (sometimes written "mod 3"). If we think of a three-hour clock, as in the illustration, we see that if we add two hours to 1 o'clock, the time is then 0. Likewise, if we add two hours to 2 o'clock, the time is then 1 o'clock. This suggests the addition table shown. This table is our definition of addition modulo 3.

+	0	1	2
0	0	1	2
1	1	2	0
2	2	0	1

We see from the table that the set is closed under the operation (i.e., all the entries in the table are members of the set {0,1,2}. The axioms are all satisfied. What is the identity element? Give the inverse of each element.

Once we have mastered the idea of unearthing inverses of elements, we have a quick check for the associative property. Essentially all operations with which we shall be confronted will be associative if the operation is commutative and each element has a *unique inverse* (one and only one inverse).

Example 3 The set {*a*,*b*,*c*,*d*} forms an Abelian group under the following definition. Let *a*, *b*, *c*, and *d* be rotations of a square, through clockwise angles of 90°, 180°, 270°, 360°, respectively.

Solution Take a square card or sheet of paper, label the corners as in (a), and play the game according to the directions in the example. Make your own table of results and compare it with our table.

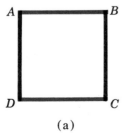
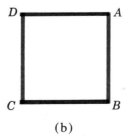

(a)   (b)

As an example, *a* would be a clockwise rotation of 90° sending vertex *A* into vertex *B*, vertex *B* into vertex *C*, etc. The result of this is shown in (b). We see also that *d* would generate a 360° rotation, resulting in the square returning to the same position that it started in. From this we can see that $a * c$ (90° rotation followed by a 270° rotation) would be the same as *d* (360° rotation). Therefore, we could say $a * c = d$. Also $a * b = c$, $b * c = a$, etc. The results are summarized in the table.

*	a	b	c	d
a	b	c	d	a
b	c	d	a	b
c	d	a	b	c
d	a	b	c	d

From the table entries, we can conclude that the set is closed under the operation. We can also see that the associative and commutative axioms hold. The identity element is *d*. Can you find the inverse of each element?

We have given three examples, each with a different set of elements and a different operation. Yet we have found a collection of properties common to all of them. It is almost unbelievable that we should be able to unify such apparently diverse situations. Such, however, is the task of modern mathematics.

PROBLEM SET 6.3

1. The set $\{0,1,2,3, \ldots\}$ does not form a group under addition. Why?

2. A set which satisfies the associative axiom under a binary operation is called a *semi-group*. The set in exercise 1 forms a semi-group. Give another example of a semi-group that is not a group.

3. Consider the set of even integers $\{\ldots, -4, -2,0,2,4, \ldots\}$ under the operation of addition. Does this set form a group? Give reasons.

4. Set up a multiplication table modulo 3 for the set of integers {0,1,2}. Does this set form a group? Give reasons.

5. Set up an addition table modulo 4 for the set of integers {0,1,2,3}. Determine if this set forms a group.

6. Consider the equilateral triangle (all sides equal) in figure (a). Our set will contain six elements, *a*, *b*, *c*, *d*, *e*, and *f*. Let *a* be a clockwise rotation of the triangle through an angle of 120°, *b* be a rotation through 240°, and *c* be a rotation through 360°. A rotation of 120° would change the position of the triangle in figure (a) to that of figure (b). Now let *d* be a rotation of 180° about altitude *AD* (this rotation would change figure (b) to figure (c)), *e* be a similar rotation about altitude *BE*, and *f* be a similar rotation about altitude *CF*.

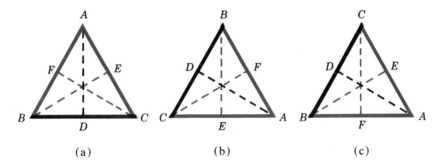

(a)   (b)   (c)

(a) Complete the following operation table for this set. (*a* ∗ *b* means perform rotation *a* followed by rotation *b*.)

∗	a	b	c	d	e	f
a	b	c	a	e	f	d
b	c				d	
c	a		c			
d	e					a
e	f	d				
f	d			b		

(b) Name the identity element if one exists.

(c) Does each element of the set have an inverse? If so, name them.

(d) Does the set form a group? An Abelian group?

6.4. Fields

The next system of axioms that we will consider is that of a *field*. For this system we need an undefined set of elements, two binary operations which we shall call addition and multiplication and which we will denote by $\oplus$ and $\odot$, respectively, and an equivalence relation which we shall denote by $=$. We should emphasize that addition and multiplication are merely names for the operations, and do not necessarily mean the operations of arithmetic with which we are familiar. The elements of the set must satisfy the following axioms.

> 1. The set forms an Abelian group under the operation of addition.
>
> 2. The set is associative under multiplication; i.e., $x \odot (y \odot z) = (x \odot y) \odot z$.
>
> 3. The set is commutative under multiplication; i.e., $x \odot y = y \odot x$.
>
> 4. The set has an identity under multiplication; i.e., there is an element e such that $x \odot e = x$.

What is the identity element under multiplication for the real numbers? (That is, $e = $ ___.)

> 5. Every element of the set, except the additive identity, has an inverse under multiplication; i.e., $x \odot x^{-1} = e$.

(x^{-1} is just a compact way of writing the multiplicative inverse (reciprocal) in real numbers. We know that the inverse for 2 is $\frac{1}{2}$; $\frac{1}{2}$ can be written as 2^{-1}.)

> 6. For any elements x, y, and z, multiplication is distributive over addition; i.e., $x \odot (y \oplus z) = (x \odot y) \oplus (x \odot z)$.

To help us understand the meaning of these axioms, let us take as an example a set which forms a field.

Example 1   Consider the set of rational numbers (integers and fractions), the binary operations of addition and multiplication that we are familiar with, and the usual equivalence relation of "equal to."

Solution   We can easily verify that this set satisfies the axioms for an Abelian group. The elements are commutative and associative under addition. The additive identity is 0. Each element can be put in the form $\frac{a}{b}$, where a and b are integers ($b = 0$), and, therefore, the additive inverse of $\frac{a}{b}$ is $-\frac{a}{b}$ (i.e., the inverse of $\frac{3}{5}$ is $-\frac{3}{5}$, the inverse of $-\frac{2}{7}$ is $\frac{2}{7}$, etc.). The set therefore forms an Abelian group under addition. We can also see that the set is associative and commutative under multiplication (i.e., $2 \cdot (3 \cdot 5) = (2 \cdot 3) \cdot 5$ and $3 \cdot 7 = 7 \cdot 3$). The multiplicative identity is 1, since $x \cdot 1 = x$ (i.e., $5 \cdot 1 = 5$). The multiplicative inverse of a rational number $\frac{a}{b}$ is $\frac{b}{a}$, since $\frac{a}{b} \cdot \frac{b}{a} = 1$ (i.e., $\frac{2}{3} \cdot \frac{3}{2} = 1$). The multiplicative inverse axiom also states that the additive identity (in this example the additive identity is 0) does not have a multiplicative inverse. Do you see why? If it did, the multiplicative inverse of $\frac{0}{1}$ would be $\frac{1}{0}$, but this has no meaning. $\frac{1}{0}$ implies that there is some number multiplied by 0 that would equal 1, but we see this is impossible. To help us see that axiom 6 is satisfied we look at an example. Does $3 \cdot (5 + 7) = 3 \cdot 5 + 3 \cdot 7$? Let us evaluate each side of the equality. $3 \cdot (5 + 7) = 3 \cdot (12) = 36$ and $3 \cdot 5 + 3 \cdot 7 = 15 + 21 = 36$. Trying several other examples should help convince us that the statement is true. Thus, all axioms are satisfied and the set forms a field.

Example 2   The set $\{0,1,2\}$ forms a field under addition and multiplication modulo 3. The addition and multiplication tables are summarized below.

+	0	1	2
0	0	1	2
1	1	2	0
2	2	0	1

•	0	1	2
0	0	0	0
1	0	1	2
2	0	2	1

We have already shown, in example 2 of Section 6.3, that the set forms an Abelian group under addition. The multiplication table shows us that the set is associative and commutative under that operation. The multiplicative identity is 1. Since 0 is the additive identity, we will not require that element to have a multiplicative inverse. The multiplicative inverses of 1 and 2 are 1 and 2, respectively. We also see that the distributive axiom holds. We therefore have a field.

PROBLEM SET 6.4

1. For the set $\{0,1,2,3,4\}$, set up tables for addition and multiplication modulo 5. Does the set form a field under these operations?

2. Set up multiplication and addition tables modulo 4 for the set $\{0,1,2,3\}$. Does this set form a field?

3. Does the set of integers form a field? Give reasons.

4. Construct the tables of addition and multiplication modulo 6 for the set $\{0,2,4\}$ and determine if it forms a field.

5. Axiom 6, as it is stated in this section, is often referred to as the lefthand distributive property. We can prove that multiplication is also distributive on the right. That is, if x, y, and z are elements of a field, then $(y \oplus z) \odot x = (y \odot x) \oplus (z \odot x)$. The steps of the proof are listed below. Give as a reason for each step one of the axioms from this section.

   (a) $(y \oplus z) \odot x = x \odot (y \oplus z)$ why?

   (b) $\qquad\qquad = (x \odot y) \oplus (x \odot z)$ why?

   (c) $\qquad\qquad = (y \odot x) \oplus (z \odot x)$ why?

6. Consider the following rational numbers: $5, \frac{2}{3}, \frac{7}{8}, -\frac{5}{9}, -8, 0$.

   (a) Give the additive inverse of each of these numbers.

   (b) Give the multiplicative inverse of each of these numbers.

6.5. Peano's Postulates

We close this chapter by briefly looking at an extremely powerful set of axioms. The reason for saying it is powerful is that from this set of axioms we may obtain an amazingly large number of theorems. Using the axioms, one theorem can be proved, then we have the axioms and that theorem to use to prove a different theorem. The chain and combination of tools to use become gigantic. Consider the following axioms in which natural number is an undefined term.

1. Every natural number x has a unique successor x_s which is also a natural number.

2. There is exactly one natural number which is not the successor of any other natural number. We will denote this natural number by the symbol a.

3. No two natural numbers have the same successor.

4. If S is a set of natural numbers such that (a) a is a member of S, and (b) for every natural number that is a member of S its successor is also a member of S, then S contains all the natural numbers.

These axioms were developed by Giuseppe Peano (1858-1932) and are often referred to as Peano's Postulates (the term "postulate" is often used in place of "axiom"). We now look at some models of this system.

Example 1 We have stated that natural number is an undefined term. In this section, however, we do recall a set of numbers $\{1,2,3,\ldots\}$ from arithmetic. Let us see if this set satisfies the axioms.

Solution   We will consider the successor of a number to be the next largest number in the set. Therefore the successor of 1 is 2 (we write $1_s = 2$). Also $2_s = 3$, $3_s = 4$, etc. We can see that each number in the set has a successor and that successor is unique (i.e., there is only one successor for each number). Axiom 1 is therefore satisfied. The natural number referred to as a in axiom 2 is the number 1 in our set. We can see that 1 is not the successor of any other number. Axiom 3 is satisfied, since each different number in the set has a different successor. To see that axiom 4 is satisfied, we consider a subset of our set. Part (a) of the axiom requires 1 to be in the subset. Part (b) requires the successor of 1 to be in the subset. Therefore 2 is in the subset. Again, part (b) requires 2_s, or 3, to be in the subset. This could be continued indefinitely, hence our subset will contain all the natural numbers.

The casual observer might conclude that the set of natural numbers that we have used in arithmetic is the only set which these axioms describe. Such is not the case, however, as illustrated in our next two examples.

Example 2   Consider the set $\{1,3,5,7, \ldots\}$. The successor of 1 is 3, $3_s = 5$, $5_s = 7$, etc. Can you find the pattern which will enable us to find the successor of 7?

Solution   If you found the pattern you should obtain 9 as the successor of 7. The pattern is to add 2 to each number to find its successor. Now read through each of the four axioms and convince yourself that each of them is satisfied by this set.

Now, suppose we wanted to find the 100th term of this sequence of numbers. Of course, one way to find it would be to repeatedly add 2 to each successive number until the 100th term is reached. Let us instead look for a pattern that might give us the result more easily. We note that the first term is 1, the second term is 3, the third term is 5, etc. How would we find the nth term? After some thought, we should discover that if we double the number of the term and subtract 1 we obtain the term. The first term is $2(1) - 1 = 1$, the second term is $2(2) - 1 = 3$, the third term is $2(3) - 1 = 5$, etc. In general, it appears as if the nth term is $2n - 1$. Notice we say it *appears* as if this is the formula to find the nth term. We have only shown that it holds true for

$n = 1$, $n = 2$, and $n = 3$. We would like to be able to say that without a doubt it holds true for all natural numbers. This is where axiom 4 shows its strength. Axiom 4 says that if we can show that the formula holds for $n = 1$ and, assuming it holds for some number $n = k$, show that it holds for the successor of k (i.e., $k + 1$), then the formula must hold for all natural numbers n. If the formula holds for $n = k + 1$, it would appear as $2(k + 1) - 1$. To prove this we first note that we already have seen that the formula holds for $n = 1$, $2(1) - 1 = 1$. Assume for some $n = k$ we have $2k - 1$ as the kth term. To obtain the successor of the kth term we add 2. The $(k + 1)$ term therefore is $(2k - 1) + 2$. This is the same as $(2k + 2) - 1$, which is equivalent to $2(k + 1) - 1$, which is the desired result. We therefore conclude that the formula works for all natural numbers. Axiom 4 is used extensively in mathematical proofs and is given the special name *mathematical induction.*

Example 3   The axioms also describe the set $\{\frac{1}{3}, \frac{1}{6}, \frac{1}{12}, \frac{1}{24}, \ldots\}$. This is left for you to verify. Notice that the elements of this set are not what we normally think of as natural numbers. Which number plays the role of a in axiom 2? Can you find the pattern that will enable you to find the successor of $\frac{1}{24}$?

We indicated earlier that this was a very forceful set of axioms. Using these axioms and proper definitions of addition and multiplication, we can prove such properties as associativity and commutativity of the natural numbers under these operations. Through other clever definitions we can, using these axioms of natural numbers as a base, arrive at all the properties of the real numbers. It is not our purpose to develop these properties here; however, we should appreciate the skillfulness of Peano in developing such a short list of axioms from which so many results could be derived.

PROBLEM SET 6.5

1. The set in example 2 is an arithmetic sequence. Give an example of another arithmetic sequence.

2. The set in example 3 is a geometric sequence. Give an example of another geometric sequence.

3. In your example for exercise 1, guess a formula for the nth term. Show that the formula will always hold by using axiom 4.

4. Consider the set $\{1,4,7,10, \ldots\}$. Guess a formula for the nth term and show that you are correct by using mathematical induction.

Chapter 7

TRIGONOMETRY AND CALCULUS

TRIGONOMETRY

Circular Measure

Inventions and Uses

Trigonometric Ratios

CALCULUS

Pebbles in the Sand

Instantaneous Velocity

Finding Maximum Area

7.1. Trigonometry

I. CIRCULAR MEASURE

Perhaps Og, our cave-dwelling ancestor, had no use whatsoever for any phase of arithmetic or mathematics. During his reign, we may assume, he had no need even for counting. The largest amounts that he encountered in which he had an interest were the members of his clan, and he could tally these by checking off fingers or toes. Og was primarily interested in hunting, food gathering, and protection against the elements. He had no need for describing the "sizes" of things, other than to determine whether they were too large to tackle, but, in contrast, he did need to characterize "sorts" of things in his world.

When man learned to sow grain and keep beasts which bore young at certain periods of the year, he had to take stock of the seasons. He noticed that the moon rises and sets a little later each night between one full moon and the next. Thus, he began to group days into moons or months. Primitive people also recognized that the constellations change with the seasons — rising and setting a little earlier every night — and were able to reckon the number of moons which intervene between one dry or wet season and another. As early as 4000 B.C. the Egyptians had already fixed the length of the year as 365 days by the interval of time between two successive occasions when Sirius, the dog star, was visible immediately before sunrise.

The earliest geometrical problems arose from the need for a calendar to regulate the seasonal pursuits of agriculture. Monuments were erected in line with the rising, setting, or transit of heavenly bodies. At Stonehenge, in England, the position of a massive stone marked the day of summer solstice, when the sun rises farthest north along the eastern boundary of the horizon (the day of the shortest noon shadow, June 21st on our calendar). Thus, to primitive man, not only were sundown and sunrise signals of sleep and awakening, but the recurring phases of the moon coincided with the rhythm of the female fertile life, and seasonal changes became a crude clock for seed scattering.

In the ancient priestly lore, the heavens revolved on an axis passing through the celestial pole. The sun, moon, planets, and stars revolved in circular orbits. Each day the sun seemed to slip back a little slantwise across the celestial sphere in relation to specific stars which rose earlier on successive nights. Thus, the circular track of the sun was mapped out in 360 steps, each corresponding with a day and a night. There seems to be only little doubt that the *degree* had its origin in these 360 natural divisions of the sun's journey around the earth. Long before the Christian era, the angle which the sun's slanting rays makes with the equinox could be calculated within a fraction of a degree. The measurement of direction put numbers to a new use. The Great Pyramid of Cheops was constructed on a geometrical plan such that the perimeter of the four sides' — facing exactly north, south, east, and west — had the same ratio to its height as the ratio of the circumference to the radius of a circle, that is, 2π. The rays of Sirius, whose heliacal rising announced the beginning of the Egyptian year and the flooding of the river Nile which brought prosperity to the land, were at right angles to the south face and shone directly down a ventilating shaft illuminating the head of the Pharaoh in the royal chamber. At the same instant, rays from the pole star, Draco, shone into the royal chamber through the main shaft located on the north face of the pyramid. The astonishing accuracy of these constructive feats was the fruit of centuries of recorded observations. The means of recording the direction in which something lies still bear the physical reality from which the measurement of the angle took its origin.

Heights were calculated by the length of a shadow and the angle of the sun above the horizon, which depends on certain simple truths about the relation between lengths of sides of a triangle. Earliest mathematical discoveries belong to this class of problems. Babylonians, for example, knew how to make an angle of 60° by inscribing a figure of six equal sides in a circle. All over the ancient world, as long as five or six thousand years ago, is evidence of a simple formula, or recipe, for making an angle of 90° which depends on the fact that a triangle with sides of three, four, and five units of length is right-angled. This was later to be elaborated upon and put into a different arrangement and known as the famous theorem of Pythagoras (550 B.C.).

With the progress of building, the right angle of 90°, based on the plumb line and water level, became increasingly important. The measurement of other angles became a fraction of the right angle instead of "so many" degrees. Of all angles less than 90°, the easiest to make were 60°, 45°, and 30°. Each of these contains a multiple of 15°, the arc through which the sun rotates about the axis of the celestial sphere in one hour.

When the temple construction mania exhausted the resources of priests and their greatest mathematical achievement, the measurement of the angle, it was relinquished orally to a craftsman class of slaves. No record of architectural mensuration has been left by this subject class other than the geometrical perfection of their achievements. The primary reason the Greeks are spoken of as the first mathematicians is that the Egyptians left no literature telling how they achieved their great feats of measurement.

This mighty building delirium led to a system of taxation of land in Egypt. The Nile was constantly overflowing and washing away landmarks, giving rise to dispute over property rights and taxes due. This brought into being the craft of surveying. Egyptian surveying supplemented the measurement of the angle with the measurement of area.

II. INVENTIONS AND USES

A great city was founded at the mouth of the Nile in 332 B.C., when Egypt surrendered to Alexander the Great. Alexandria was made up of a mixed population of Egyptians, Jews, and Greeks, and drew into itself all the learning of the ancient world in the arts of medicine, machinery, navigation, and mathematics. The first phase in the Alexandrian contribution is witnessed by the invention of *trigonometry,* which means the measurement of triangles. Trigonometry gave number and measurement back to geometry, which had been divorced by the great philosophers and thinkers. Mathematics was once again put into practical use and applied to the world's work.

The Old Testament (II Chronicles 4:2) states of Solomon, "Also he made a molten sea of ten cubits from brim to brim, round in compass, and five cubits the height thereof; and a line of thirty cubits did compass it round about." The circumference was, then, three times the diameter, $30 \div 10 = 3$. The Hebrews, as early as 975 B.C., were content to use 3 as the value of π. About the time of the celebrated Tennessee evolution dispute, a bill was introduced into the legislature of one of the agricultural states intending to restore π to its biblical value. Fortunately, it did not pass. Otherwise, machines with fast rotating wheels would probably vibrate more than a teenage dance party. Today, in calculations that demand only an approximation, we are often content to use 3.14 or $22/7$ for the value of π.

Archimedes (287-212 B.C.), the gentleman who ran through the streets of Syracuse clad only in a towel shouting "Eureka!" after he had made a great scientific discovery while floating in the public bath, showed the relationship of the circumference and diameter of circles and how to compute π as accurately as needed. Archimedes succeeded in getting a wonderfully close approximation by sand-sketching regular polygons (equal sides) inside and outside a circle. He could then calculate the perimeter (boundary) of each polygon. By continuing to double the number of sides of each of the two polygons and computing the perimeter of each, Archimedes concluded that the perimeter of the circle was always just a little bit less than the perimeter of the outside (circumscribed) polygon and a little bit more than the inside (inscribed) polygon, but was somewhere between $3\frac{1}{10}$ and $3\frac{10}{71}$, if the diameter of the circle was one unit in length (see figure 7.1). That is,

$$3\tfrac{1}{10} < \pi < 3\tfrac{10}{71}$$

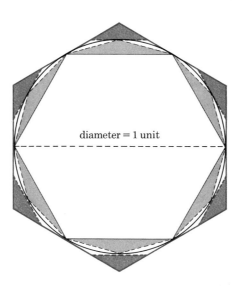

diameter = 1 unit

Figure 7.1 The shaded portions indicate the amount lost from the circumscribed polygon and the amount gained from the inscribed polygon after doubling the number of sides only once.

Archimedes used his knowledge to demonstrate the ratio of weight and distance from a fulcrum. He designed catapults and applied the density ratio to measure purity of precious metals. His measurement of π went hand-in-hand with the introduction of machinery based on the use of wheels. He helped the launching of a ship by suggesting the use of cogs, invented a rotating screw irrigation pump, and made the first known model in which the rotation of the celestial sphere and the changing positions of the stars were represented by the motion of a wheel. It is probable that he was the first to use tables of the functions of angles. There was a very close connection between the rapid development of astronomy and the practical achievements of navigation and land surveying during this era.

The distances of heavenly bodies were calculated by measuring the two base angles with an astrolabe from two different locations to a star, and also the distance between the two locations. The latter became unnecessary to measure after Eratosthenes measured the diameter and circumference of the earth and lines of latitude and longitude were assigned. This classical work of Eratosthenes was based upon four logical assumptions: (1) rays of light coming from a source at a great distance appear to be parallel, (2) a line crossing two parallel lines makes equivalent corresponding angles, (3) when the sun is directly overhead, a line joining the sun to the observer passes through the center of the earth, and (4) at noon the sun lies above some point on the observer's meridian of longitude.

Eratosthenes, librarian of Alexandria, knew that the sun was reflected in a deep well near Syene only on one day of the year. Also, on this day the shadow of an object disappeared when the sun was at its zenith at noon, vertical to the horizon. On this same day at Alexandria, 500 miles due north of Syene, the shadow of a pillar at noon showed the sun to be $7\frac{1}{2}°$ south of the vertical (see figure 7.2). Eratosthenes deduced that since the sun's rays were parallel, then the two radii — from earth's center to Alexandria and Syene, respectively — made an angle of $7\frac{1}{2}°$ at the center of the earth. Now, since $7\frac{1}{2}°$ is approximately $\frac{1}{50}$ of the distance around a whole circle, then the entire circle, the circumference of the earth, must be 50 times the 500 miles between the two cities, or 25,000 miles. The radius could then be calculated by the use of π and the relationship:

$$C = 2\pi r$$

$$25000 = (2)\,\frac{22}{7}\,r\left(\pi \text{ is approximately}\,\frac{22}{7}\right)$$

$$\text{or } r = \frac{25000 \cdot 7}{2 \cdot 22}$$

then $r =$ approximately 4000 miles

This measurement of the circumference depends upon a very simple application of elementary geometry, presupposing that we are able to measure the distance apart of two places on the earth.

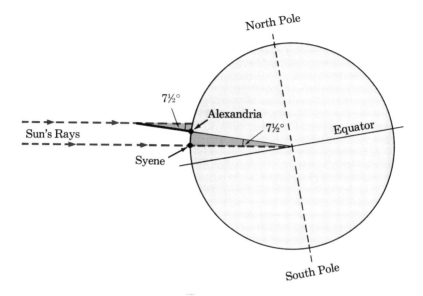

Figure 7.2

III. TRIGONOMETRIC RATIOS

The basis of the branch of mathematics known as trigonomety involves relationships or ratios of the sides of a right triangle with respect to its angles.

Referring to figure 7.3 we define the following ratios.

$$\text{sine angle } A = \frac{\text{opposite side}}{\text{hypotenuse}} = \frac{a}{c}$$

$$\text{cosine angle } A = \frac{\text{adjacent side}}{\text{hypotenuse}} = \frac{b}{c}$$

$$\text{tangent angle } A = \frac{\text{opposite side}}{\text{adjacent side}} = \frac{a}{b}$$

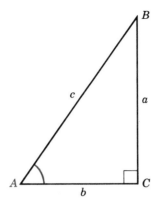

Figure 7.3

We can see that, as the measure of angle A increases or decreases, the ratios of the sides also change, and each angle of a different size has a unique ratio. We should also note that, for a given angle, the size of the triangle has no effect on the ratio.

Consider the right triangle in figure 7.4. Angle C is $90°$, and angle A is $30°$. From geometry we know that the sum of the angles of a plane triangle is $180°$. Therefore angle B contains $60°$.

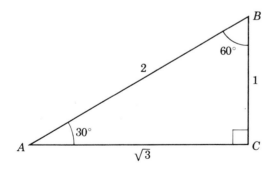

Figure 7.4

Notice that the lengths of the sides satisfy the Pythagorean theorem, which states that the sum of the squares of the two legs is equal to the square of the hypotenuse (the side opposite the $90°$ angle). That is, $(\sqrt{3})^2 + (1)^2 = (2)^2$.

Using the definitions of the trigonometric functions, we obtain:

$$\text{sine } 30° \quad = \quad \frac{1}{2} = \ .500$$

$$\text{cosine } 30° \ = \frac{\sqrt{3}}{2} = \ .866 \text{ (approximately)}$$

$$\text{tangent } 30° = \frac{1}{\sqrt{3}} = \ .577 \text{ (approximately)}$$

$$\text{sine } 60° \quad = \frac{\sqrt{3}}{2} = \ .866 \text{ (approximately)}$$

$$\text{cosine } 60° \ = \quad \frac{1}{2} = \ .500$$

$$\text{tangent } 60° = \frac{\sqrt{3}}{1} = 1.732 \text{ (approximately)}$$

In a similar manner, the triangle in figure 7.5 yields the following ratios.

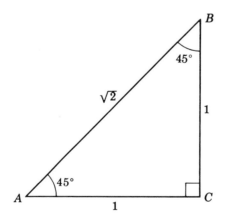

Figure 7.5

$$\text{sine } 45° \quad = \frac{1}{\sqrt{2}} = .707 \text{ (approximately)}$$

$$\text{cosine } 45° \quad = \frac{1}{\sqrt{2}} = .707 \text{ (approximately)}$$

$$\text{tangent } 45° = \quad \frac{1}{1} = 1.000$$

If we further investigate the right triangle with our side relation-ships, we find that, as the measure of one of the acute (less than 90°) angles gets closer and closer to 0°, the length of the side opposite that angle approaches 0 (figure 7.6), and the sine of the angle approaches 0°. We are prompted, therefore, to conclude that

$$\text{sine } 0° = \frac{0}{AB} = .000$$

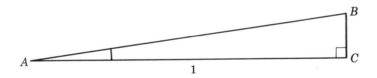

Figure 7.6

Referring again to figure 7.6, we note that as angle A approaches 0°, the length of the hypotenuse AB approaches the length of the adjacent side. Hence, we are led to the conclusion

$$\text{cosine } 0° \quad = \frac{1}{1} = 1.000$$

$$\text{tangent } 0° = \frac{0}{1} = \quad .000$$

As angle A approaches 0°, we see that angle B approaches 90°. Thus, the following relationships seem to be true of angle C.

$$\text{sine } 90° \quad = \frac{1}{1} = 1.000$$

$$\text{cosine } 90° \quad = \frac{0}{1} = .000$$

$$\text{tangent } 90° = \frac{1}{0} \quad (\text{undefined})$$

We may now summarize the data that we have accumulated thus far, in figure 7.7. The values of the trigonometric ratios of angles given in figure 7.7 are approximate (accurate to three decimal places). For greater accuracy other tables may be used.

θ	sine θ	cosine θ	tangent θ
0°	.000	1.000	.000
30°	.500	.866	.577
45°	.707	.707	1.000
60°	.866	.500	1.732
90°	1.000	.000	undefined

Figure 7.7

By finding the ratios of the sides of other right triangles with different angles, we could extend the table to include entries for as many angles between 0° and 90° as we wish. For our purposes, the table in figure 7.7 will be sufficient.

We are now ready to apply this information to the solution of some problems. Consider the following situation.

Example 1   An observer stands 70 feet from the base of a cliff. The angle that his line of sight to the top of the cliff makes with the horizontal *(angle of elevation)* is 60°. Find the height of the cliff to the nearest foot.

Solution   We represent the physical problem with the diagram in figure 7.8.

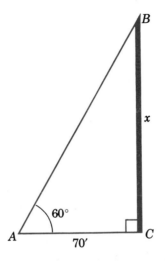

Figure 7.8

If we represent the height of the cliff with the letter x, we see that the two sides of the triangle that we are involved with in regard to the given angle are the opposite and adjacent. We are therefore prompted to use the tangent ratio

$$\text{tangent } 60° = \frac{x}{70}$$

Multiplying each side of the equation by 70 yields

$$x = 70 \text{ (tangent } 60°)$$

Finding the tangent of 60° in the table (figure 7.7), we obtain

$$x = 70 \text{ (1.732)}$$
$$= 121.240 = 121 \text{ feet (to the nearest foot)}$$

We might also take note that we could have approached the problem by using angle B. Since the sum of the measures of the angles of a triangle is 180°, we may conclude that angle $B = 30°$. Using this angle, we are involved with the following relation:

$$\text{tangent } 30° = \frac{70}{x}$$

Solving for x, we obtain

$$x = \frac{70}{\text{tangent } 30°}$$

Again consulting figure 7.7, we have

$$x = \frac{70}{.577}$$

$$= 121 \text{ feet (to the nearest foot)}$$

PROBLEM SET 7.1

1. At a point 50 feet from the base of a flagpole, the angle of elevation to the top of the pole is 30°. Find the height of the flagpole to the nearest foot.

2. The string from a flying kite makes an angle of 45° with the ground. If there are 120 feet of string between the kite and the ground, how high is the kite to the nearest foot?

3. The diagonal of a rectangle is 450 feet in length and makes an angle of 30° with the longer side. Find the dimensions of the rectangle to the nearest foot.

4. A man is standing on the bank of a river. On the bank directly across the river from him is a large boulder. He walks upstream along a straight line parallel to the bank a distance of 80 feet. He now finds that the angle between the line that he walked along and his line of sight to the boulder is 60°. How wide is the river to the nearest foot?

5. The guy wire from a telephone pole is fastened to the ground 65 feet from the base of the pole. The wire makes a 30° angle with the ground. How long is the guy wire to the nearest foot?

7.2. Calculus

I. PEBBLES IN THE SAND

The tools of algebra and geometry are useful to man in solving many of his problems concerning nature. These are basic problems, however, and do not involve other real situations which must be interpreted today. The reason that algebra and geometry alone are not enough is that these tools are satisfactory for static situations, but not for problems involving change. We live in a dynamic world. Everything is undergoing change, from the pulsating vastness of the universe to the structure of an atomic nucleus. Animals and plants are born, grow, and die. Water and air are in constant motion, shifting and eroding the surface of the earth. Stresses from deep within the earth are also continually changing the form and position of the continents.

How, then, can we possibly study the real world with tools which do not allow for movement? Obviously, a different tool is needed — one which can be applied to dynamic situations. Such a tool does exist. It is called the *calculus*. The original meaning of this word is "pebbles." The fundamentals of the calculus were established in the 17th century independently by Pierre Fermat, Gottfried Wilhelm Leibniz, and Isaac Newton of France, Germany, and England, respectively. These men contributed greatly to the mechanics of the calculus, but the logical and rigorous foundations of the subject were to take almost two more centuries to develop.

II. INSTANTANEOUS VELOCITY

To help illustrate the usefulness of calculus, we look at the following situation. A motorist driving from Buffalo, New York, to Cleveland, Ohio (a distance of 180 miles) left Buffalo at 1:00 p.m. and arrived in Cleveland at 5:00 p.m. To find his average speed, we simply divide the total distance by the time required to travel that distance. In this case,

$$\frac{180 \text{ miles}}{4 \text{ hours}} = 45 \text{ miles per hour}$$

The average speed was 45 miles per hour. But suppose we want to know what his speed was at exactly 2:00 p.m. We cannot be certain that it was 45 m.p.h. It is highly unlikely that he traveled at a constant speed throughout the trip. Remember, 45 m.p.h. is his *average* speed. We are now asking for an *instantaneous* speed. More information would, of course, have to be given to answer this question, but this is the type of question that leads us to the realm of the calculus.

Consider a similar problem. A stone is dropped from the top of a 600-foot cliff. The distance d that a falling body travels is found by the formula

$$d = 16t^2$$

where t stands for the time in seconds. We will ask two questions. The first is to find the average velocity of the stone for the first 5 seconds. (We use the term "velocity" rather than "speed" here, since we know the direction of travel of the stone. Velocity involves not only speed, but also direction. This perhaps would have more meaning in a situation where we throw a stone upward and wish to know the velocity after a given number of seconds. The velocity would not only tell us the speed, but would also indicate whether the stone was moving upward or downward at that instant.) To answer this question we need two things: the distance the stone has traveled and the time it has traveled. The latter we have given to us. We find the distance by use of the formula

$$d = 16t^2 = 16(5)^2 = 400 \text{ feet}$$

We now divide the distance by the time

$$\frac{400 \text{ feet}}{5 \text{ seconds}} = 80 \text{ feet per second}$$

This is the average velocity. A moment's thought, however, will convince us that the velocity of a falling body is not constant, but increases with the time that it is falling. If we let $t = 0$ (the instant we release the stone), at that moment the velocity is zero; but as the stone travels downward, it steadily gains velocity.

This leads us to the second question. What is its velocity at 3 seconds? This is asking for a velocity at a particular instant. We are not involved with an average velocity here, but rather with an instantaneous velocity. Let us begin by finding the average velocity between $t = 0$ and $t = 3$. At $t = 3$

$$d = 16(3)^2 = 144 \text{ feet}$$

and $$\frac{144 \text{ feet}}{3 \text{ seconds}} = 48 \text{ feet per second}$$

This is only the average velocity. We know that at 3 seconds the velocity must be greater than 48 feet per second. Now let's find the average velocity between $t = 1$ and $t = 3$. The distance traveled will be the difference between the distance at 3 seconds and the distance at 1 second. Also, the time traveled is $3 - 1 = 2$ seconds. Thus,

$$\frac{16(3)^2 - 16(1)^2}{3 - 1} = \frac{128}{2} = 64 \text{ feet per second}$$

Notice this average velocity is larger than the average velocity for the entire first 3 seconds, and is therefore closer to the exact velocity at 3 seconds. If we find the average velocity between $t = 3$ and another time t very close to $t = 3$, then we should be getting a closer approximation of the exact velocity at $t = 3$. Consider the following.

$t = 2$ to $t = 3$ $\quad \dfrac{16(3)^2 - 16(2)^2}{3 - 2} = \dfrac{80}{1} = 80 \text{ feet per second}$

$t = 2.5$ to $t = 3$ $\quad \dfrac{16(3)^2 - 16(2.5)^2}{3 - 2.5} = \dfrac{44}{.5} = 88 \text{ feet per second}$

$t = 2.9$ to $t = 3$ $\quad \dfrac{16(3)^2 - 16(2.9)^2}{3 - 2.9} = \dfrac{9.44}{.1} = 94.4 \text{ feet per second.}$

We could continue the process, getting as close to $t = 3$ as we wish. Consider t_0 to represent the value we wish to get closer and closer to 3. We could find the average velocity by

$$\frac{16(3)^2 - 16(t_0)^2}{(3 - t_0)}$$

The distributive property enables us to write

$$\frac{16(3)^2 - 16(t_0)^2}{3 - t_0} = \frac{16(3^2 - t_0^2)}{(3 - t_0)}$$

which can be expressed as

$$\frac{16(3 + t_0)\,(3 - t_0)}{(3 - t_0)} = 16(3 + t_0) = 48 + 16t_0$$

Now, as t_0 takes on values closer and closer to 3, $16t_0$ takes on values closer and closer to $16(3) = 48$. Thus, $48 + 16t_0$ is getting closer and closer to $48 + 16(3) = 96$. We say that as t_0 approaches 3, the *limit* of $48 + 16t_0$ is 96. Sometimes we write it as

$$\lim_{t_0 \to 3} 48 + 16t_0 = 48 + 16(3) = 96$$

Thus, the instantaneous velocity at 3 seconds is 96 feet per second.

The Greek philosophers were also aware of the problems caused by change. One of the most often quoted problems of this nature was given by the philosopher Zeno (5th century B.C.) — the paradox of Achilles and the tortoise. Achilles, a mythical Greek hero who was very fleet of foot, was to run a race with the tortoise. Now, since Achilles could run ten times as fast, the tortoise was to get a ten-yard head start. According to Zeno, then, this lead created an unfair advantage for the tortoise, for Achilles would never be able to overtake him. At the start of the race Achilles would run this ten yards and reach the place where the tortoise started, but the tortoise would have gone one-tenth as far as Achilles and would therefore be one yard ahead. Achilles would run

this one yard, but, again, the tortoise would have run his tenth of Achilles' distance, and would still be one-tenth yard in front. After running this tenth-yard, Achilles would still find the tortoise one-tenth of one-tenth yard ahead of him. Achilles would run the hundredth-yard. Meanwhile, the tortoise would go one-tenth of one-hundredth of a yard and would now be one-thousandth of a yard in the lead. So, said Zeno, by repeating the argument as many times as you wish, Achilles would always be getting nearer the tortoise but would never catch up.

The early Greek mathematician, knowing that adding larger and larger quantities to a pile made the pile grow more rapidly without coming to a stop, took for granted that the same would be true for adding smaller and still smaller quantities indefinitely. In one case the pile grew more rapidly, and in the other it grew more slowly, but went on forever. There was nothing in their logic to suggest that when enough single straws were loaded onto the camel's back it would break, or that they had reached a limit.

The concept of limit is basic to the calculus, and enables us to transform a dynamic situation into a static one. In other words, it is a "stop action" device. Perhaps this statement should be expanded. Consider a situation that may conjure up a vivid glimpse into your past. Little Tony has a mania for peanuts. One day he buys a pound from the friendly grocer, finds a shady retreat, and has a feast. When he finishes the lot and is ready to dispose of the hulls, he has a clever idea. Tony runs back to the market and tells the man that he has been tricked. The boy claims that he had purchased peanuts, but had no use for the hulls. The grocer, knowing the ways of boys and for reasons of his own, trades Tony a half pound more of peanuts for the hulls. As you might guess, Tony does away with these nuts, again returns the hulls to the grocer, and trades for one quarter pound of peanuts. Suppose, now, that Tony can keep this up indefinitely. Suppose, too, that the grocer plays the game, and that he can make the needed weights as accurately as demanded. How many pounds of peanuts — not hulls — will Tony get from the grocer? The weights are

$$\tfrac{1}{2} + \tfrac{1}{4} + \tfrac{1}{8} + \tfrac{1}{16} + \tfrac{1}{32} + \tfrac{1}{64} + \cdots$$

This is similar to the dilemma of Achilles in his chase after the tortoise. The answer to our question may become more obvious if we consider another situation.

Let's start with a board one unit long and saw it at the exact center. Then, saw one of the halves into two equal parts, one of the quarters into two equal parts, and so on, using a very thin mathematical saw. We shall leave open the question as to whether we ever reach the end, but obviously enough we will never do any sawing beyond the end of the board. Now, if we add all the pieces together we can never have more than that with which we started, the one-unit board, and, just as clearly, Tony's racket will never yield him more than one pound of nut meats, if that much.

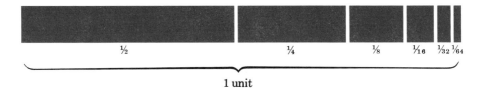

Figure 7.9

One further question. You are to add an infinite number of terms, each of which is finite in size. Suppose you are offered a bet as to whether the sum is finite or infinite and you may choose to bet either way. Which would you choose? There is an old saying that if two men engage in a bet, one is a crook and the other a fool. If you should accept the challenge in this bet based only upon the given information, you would not be the crook, for you would lose no matter which side you chose. There are cases in which the sum reaches a limit and others where the sum is infinite. Say, for example, that you begin with the number 5, which is most certainly finite, and keep adding 5's an infinite number of times. The sum will be infinite, that is, larger than any number that you name.

Let's now look at a geometric interpretation of our previous problems. We should recall that the graph of $d = 16t^2$ is a parabola. Locating several points and sketching the curve, we would obtain figure 7.10.

Notice if we locate a point on the graph for $t = 3$ and also a point for $t = 1$, we can draw a straight line through these points. Such a line is called a *secant* line. Also note that the vertical distance between the two points is 128 and the horizontal distance is 2. The quotient of the vertical distance divided by the horizontal distance is called the *slope* of the line. In this case it is

$$\frac{128}{2} = 64$$

Notice that the slope of this line represents the average velocity between $t = 1$ and $t = 3$.

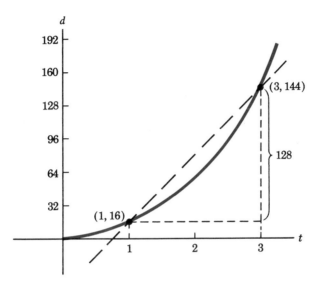

Figure 7.10

As we choose points on the graph corresponding to values of t closer and closer to $t = 3$, our secant line gets closer and closer to the position shown in figure 7.11. Also, the slope of the secant line approaches that of the line in figure 7.11.

This line touches the curve at only one point. Such a line is called a *tangent* line. The slope of this line must be the limit of the slope of the secant line as it approaches this position. In this case the slope is 96.

Let us now find the slope of a tangent line for any point on the curve. For any point on the graph corresponding to a fixed point t take another "movable" point, t_0 (see figure 7.12).

Draw the secant line containing these two points. The vertical distance between these points is $16t^2 - 16t_0^2$ and the horizontal distance is $t - t_0$. The slope, therefore, is

$$\frac{16t^2 - 16t_0^2}{t - t_0}$$

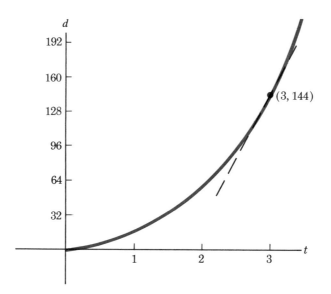

Figure 7.11

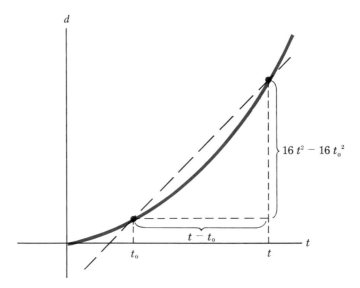

Figure 7.12

To find the slope of the tangent line at the fixed point t we move t_0 closer and closer to t, and each time we find the slope of the secant line. Taking the limit of the slope as t_0 approaches t, we obtain

$$\lim_{t_0 \to t} \frac{16t^2 - 16t_0^2}{t - t_0}$$

$$= \lim_{t_0 \to t} \frac{16(t^2 - t_0^2)}{t - t_0}$$

$$= \lim_{t_0 \to t} \frac{16(t + t_0)(t - t_0)}{t - t_0}$$

$$= \lim_{t_0 \to t} 16(t + t_0)$$

Now, as t_0 gets close to t, $16(t + t_0)$ gets close to $16(t + t)$. Thus,

$$\lim_{t_0 \to t} 16(t + t_0) = 16(2t) = 32t$$

While this geometrically is the slope of the tangent line for any point t, it is also the velocity of the falling stone for any time t. Thus, at 1 second the speed is $32(1) = 32$; at 2 seconds it is $32(2) = 64$; and at 3 seconds it is $32(3) = 96$. This last figure agrees with our original calculation.

III. FINDING MAXIMUM AREA

Consider the following problem. A farmer has 800 feet of wire fencing. He wishes to enclose a rectangular area along the bank of a river. Since he may use the river bank as one side of the rectangle, he does not need to use fencing on that side. What should the dimensions of the rectangle be in order to obtain the maximum area? If we let x represent the width of the rectangle, then $800 - 2x$ represents its length (figure 7.13).

The area of a rectangle is found by taking the product of its width and length. Therefore, if A represents the area of the rectangle, then

$$A = x(800 - 2x)$$

or

$$A = 800x - 2x^2$$

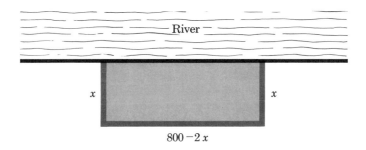

Figure 7.13

This equation also represents a parabola. We see its graph in figure 7.14. The value of x which gives the largest area A must be between 0 and 400. If $x = 0$, then the rectangle would have no width, and if $x = 400$ it would have no length. The correct value of x, of course, corresponds to the highest point on the curve. We might be able to guess at the correct value in this case, but let us be more precise. Consider the tangent line at this point (figure 7.14). It is perfectly horizontal. Since there is no vertical change in moving from one point on the tangent to another, its slope must be zero.

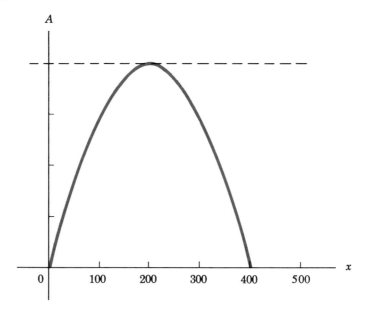

Figure 7.14

Now consider the slope of any secant line on the curve (figure 7.15). The vertical distance in moving from x_0 to x is

$$800x - 2x^2 - (800x_0 - 2x_0^2)$$

and the horizontal distance is

$$x - x_0$$

The slope of the secant line is

$$\frac{800x - 2x^2 - (800x_0 - 2x_0^2)}{x - x_0}$$

$$= \frac{800x - 2x^2 - 800x_0 + 2x^2}{x - x_0}$$

$$= \frac{800x - 800x_0 - (2x^2 - 2x_0^2)}{x - x_0}$$

$$= \frac{800(x - x_0) - 2(x^2 - x_0^2)}{x - x_0}$$

$$= \frac{800(x - x_0) - 2(x + x_0)(x - x_0)}{x - x_0}$$

$$= 800 - 2(x + x_0)$$

Now take the limit of this expression as x approaches x_0.

$$\lim_{x \to x_0} 800 - 2(x + x_0) = 800 - 2(x + x) = 800 - 4x$$

Remember this represents the slope of the tangent line to the curve at any point x. We are particularly interested in the point on the graph where the slope is 0. Therefore, we could set the slope $(800 - 4x)$ equal to 0 and solve for x. This value of x then is the value which makes the slope 0. Thus,

$$800 - 4x = 0$$

or

$$-4x = -800$$

hence

$$x = 200$$

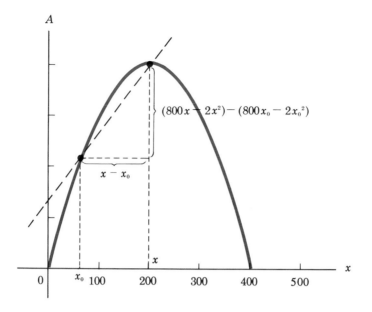

Figure 7.15

When $x = 200$ the slope of the tangent line is 0, and since the only place on the curve where the tangent line is 0 is at the highest point, the $x = 200$ will yield the largest area. We note also that

$$800 - 2x = 800 - 2\,(200)$$
$$= 400$$

Thus, the dimensions of the rectangle should be 200 feet by 400 feet.

PROBLEM SET 7.2

1. A ball is dropped from the top of a 400-foot building. Using the formula $d = 16t^2$, find the average velocity during the first 3 seconds. Find its velocity at 2 seconds.

2. A particle moves along a straight line according to the formula $d = 2t^2 + 3t + 1$, where d and t represent distance in feet and time in seconds, respectively. Find the instantaneous velocity at $t = 5$.

3. A stone is thrown upward from the ground according to the formula $d = 96t - 16t^2$, where d and t represent distance in feet and time in seconds, respectively.

   (a) What is the initial velocity (i.e., when $t = 0$)?

   (b) What is the velocity at $t = 1$?

   (c) What is the velocity at $t = 4$?

   (d) How high does the stone travel? (*Hint:* Find at what time the velocity is 0.)

   (e) How long is the stone in the air before it strikes the ground?

4. A rectangular area is to be enclosed by 1000 feet of fencing. What should the dimensions of the rectangle be in order to give maximum area? Would a circular fence give more area?

5. Fly-by-Night Airlines is offering a special flight to Mexico City. The fare is $495 if only one person makes the trip. A $5 reduction is given to each person for each additional fare. That is, if two people go, the fare is $490 each. If three people make the trip the price for each ticket is $485, etc. The plane's capacity is 60 passengers. How many people are needed to provide the airline maximum revenue for the flight?

6. How far would the tortoise have traveled before being overtaken by Achilles in the problem described in the text? (*Hint:* To solve the problem, think of the tortoise's progress as being the sum of lengths which form an infinite series.)

Answers to Odd-Numbered Problems

CHAPTER 1

Problem Set 1.1

1. (a) no   (b) no   (c) no

    (d) statement   (e) no   (f) statement

    (g) no   (h) open sentence   (i) no

    (j) no   (k) statement   (l) statement

    (m) open sentence   (n) open sentence   (o) open sentence

    (p) open sentence   (q) open sentence   (r) no

3.

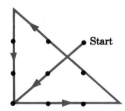

5. Place four coins on each pan of the balance. Discard the heaviest four coins. From the four lightest coins place two coins on each pan. Again, discard the heaviest two and then balance the remaining two by placing one coin on each pan.

7. 77

9. The tie cost $2.00 and the shirt cost $7.50.

11. ½ period

13. "Which door would the other guard tell me leads to freedom?"

15. 11 seconds

Problem Set 1.2

1. (a) $\sim p$ (b) $p \cap q$ (c) $\sim q \cap p$ (d) $p \cap q$ (e) $q \cap \sim q$

   (f) $p \cap q$

3.   (a) 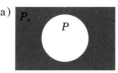   (b) 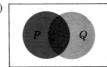   (c)

   (d)   (e)

5. (a) {5}   (b) {1,3,5,7,9}   (c) { } (empty set—no solution)

7. (a) $3 + 2 = 5$, $2 + 5 = 7$ (b) $3 + 2 = 9$, $2 + 5 = 7$

   (c) $3 + 2 = 5$, $2 + 5 = 9$ (f) $x + 2 = 5$, $2(3 + 4) = 6 + 8$

   (g) Saturday is one of the first two days of the week, Sunday is one of the first two days of the week.

Problem Set 1.3

1. (a) $p \cup q$ (b) $\sim p \cup q$ (c) $\sim p \cup (\sim q)$

   (d) $\sim (p \cup q)$ or $\sim p \cap (\sim q)$ (e) $\sim (\sim p \cup (\sim q))$

   (f) $(p \cup q) \cap (\sim q)$

3. (a) 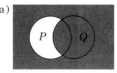 (b) 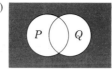 (c)

(d)  (e)  (f)

(g) 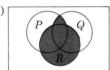 (h) 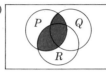 (i)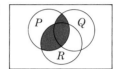

(j)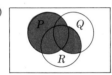

5. 15 or 16

Problem Set 1.4

1. (a) $p \to q$ (b) $q \to p$ (c) $\sim p \to (\sim q)$

(d) $\sim q \to (\sim p)$ (e) $q \to (\sim p)$ (f) $q \to p$

(g) $p \to q$ (h) $q \to p$ (i) $q \to p$

(j) $q \to p$ (k) $q \to p$ (l) $\sim q \to (\sim p)$

3.

Problem Set 1.5

1.

p	q	~p	∩	q	q	→	p	~p	→	(~q)	(~p	∩	q)	→	p
T	T	F	F	T	T	T	T	F	T	F	F	F	T	T	T
T	F	F	F	F	F	T	T	F	T	T	F	F	F	T	T
F	T	T	T	T	T	F	F	T	F	F	T	T	T	F	F
F	F	T	F	F	F	T	F	T	T	T	T	F	F	T	F

3. (a) and (c) agree, (b) and (h) agree with Figure 1.23, (f) and (g) agree, (j) and (k) agree.

Problem Set 1.6

1. (a) ~~not~~ logically true   (b) logically true   (c) logically true

(d) logically true   (e) not logically true

3. (a) fallacy   (b) valid   (c) valid   (d) valid

5. (a) valid   (b) not valid   (c) not valid   (d) valid

7. (a) valid   (b) fallacy   (c) valid   (d) valid

9. (a) valid   (b) valid   (c) not valid

Problem Set 1.7

1. Answers will vary.

3.

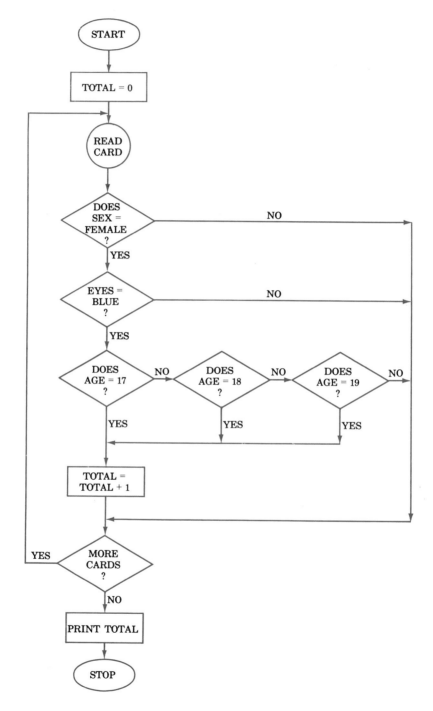

CHAPTER 2

Problem Set 2.1

1. (a) 10,112   (b) 1,316   (c) 1,041   (d) 34,203

3. (a) 66   (b) 47   (c) 741   (d) 1969

5. LXXXVIII = 88;   C = 100;   thus C is larger.

7. The numeral 27 represents 2 tens and 7 ones.
   The numeral 72 represents 7 tens and 2 ones.
   Interchanging the digits of a two-digit number will result in a different two-digit number except when both digits are the same (i.e., 11, 22, 33, etc.).

Problem Set 2.2

1. (a) 124   (b) 83   (c) 606   (d) 69   (e) 231   (f) 58   (g) 494
   (h) 53   (i) 107

3. (a) 1423_5 (b) 24302_5 (c) 1200_5

5. (a) 1022_5 (b) 146_7 (c) 13233_4 (d) 1200_8
   (e) 1102_3 (f) 1110_8 (g) 110000_2 (h) 101_2
   (i) 10000101_2

7. Base 5. His total earnings were $154.

9. one + two = b i j s
   one + one = b d a i
   "thousand" represents the largest number.

Problem Set 2.3

1. A googol is written with a 1 followed by one hundred zeros.
   A googoplex is written with a 1 followed by googol zeros.

3. 9 one-digit numbers.
   90 two-digit numbers.
   As a general rule we say there are $9(10^{n-1})$ n-digit numbers.

5. (a) $3(1 + 2) = 3 \cdot 1 + 3 \cdot 2 = 3 + 6 = 9$

(b) $5(2 + 3) = 5 \cdot 2 + 5 \cdot 3 = 10 + 15 = 25$

(c) $4(2 + 7) = 4 \cdot 2 + 4 \cdot 7 = 8 + 28 = 36$

(d) $6(10 + 3) = 6 \cdot 10 + 6 \cdot 3 = 60 + 18 = 78$

(e) $(2 + 3)5 = 2 \cdot 5 + 3 \cdot 5 = 10 + 15 = 25$

(f) $(a + b)(c + d) = (a + b)c + (a + b)d = ac + bc + ad + bd$

7.
```
      3 2 5
      1 4 7
    ─────────
    2 2 7 5
  1 3 0 0
  3 2 5
  ─────────
  4 7 7 7 5
```

9. No (e.g., $3 \div 2$ is not a natural number).

11. (a) yes (b) yes (c) yes—the identity element for union is the empty set. The identity element for intersection is the universal set. (d) yes (e) yes

Problem Set 2.4

1. (a) 546   (b) 3465   (c) 1545   (d) 1656

3. 3 and 5, 5 and 7, 11 and 13, 17 and 19, 29 and 31, 41 and 43, 59 and 61, 71 and 73

5. (a) 7   (b) 17   (c) 11   (d) 19   (e) 31   (f) 331

Problem Set 2.5

1. (a) -12 (b) -83 (c) -2590 (d) 37   (e) -35

(f) 28   (g) -11 (h) -141 (i) -26 (j) -310

3. (a) 11   (b) -4 (c) -11

(d) -51 (e) -58 (f) 22

(g) 51   (h) -3 (i) 57

(j) 0   (k) 1   (l) -1

5. (a) -17 (b) 31   (c) 33

   (d) 54   (e) 4   (f) 0

   (g) 16   (h) -4

7. $14 - 7 + 3 + 2 - 13 = -1$ (basement)

   $7 + 3 + 2 + 13 = 25$ floors $25(14) = 350$ feet.

9. $69 - (-35) = 69 + 35 = 104$ points needed to have a score of 69 at the end of the second hand. Then $72 - 69 = 3$ more points needed for a score of 72.

Problem Set 2.6

1. (a) odd, $2(9) + 1$ (b) even, $2(-17)$

   (c) odd, $2(-149) + 1$ (d) even, $2(-75)$

   (e) even, $2(806)$ (f) even, $2(-1)$

   (g) odd, $2(0) + 1$ (h) even, $2(105)$

   (i) even, $2(0)$ (j) odd, $2(174) + 1$

3. The sum of two odd integers is even.

   $(2a + 1) + (2b + 1) = 2a + 2b + 2 = 2(a + b + 1)$

5. $2a(2b + 1) = 2(2ab + a)$

Problem Set 2.7

1. (a) $\dfrac{4}{6}, \dfrac{6}{9}, \dfrac{-2}{-3}, \dfrac{-8}{-12}$ (b) $\dfrac{42}{132}, \dfrac{63}{198}, \dfrac{-21}{-66}, \dfrac{-84}{-264}$

   (c) $\dfrac{-16}{18}, \dfrac{16}{-18}, -\dfrac{-16}{-18}, \dfrac{-8}{9}$ (d) $\dfrac{2}{2}, \dfrac{3}{3}, \dfrac{-1}{-1}, \dfrac{-4}{-4}$

   (e) $\dfrac{0}{1}, \dfrac{0}{2}, \dfrac{0}{-3}, \dfrac{0}{-7}$ (f) $-\dfrac{3}{2}, \dfrac{3}{-2}, -\dfrac{-3}{-2}, \dfrac{-6}{4}$

   (g) $\dfrac{3}{5}, -\dfrac{-3}{5}, -\dfrac{3}{-5}, \dfrac{6}{10}$ (h) $-\dfrac{5}{3}, \dfrac{-5}{3}, -\dfrac{-5}{-3}, \dfrac{10}{-6}$

   (i) $\dfrac{-12}{15}, -\dfrac{4}{3}, \dfrac{4}{-3}, -\dfrac{-12}{-15}$ (j) $\dfrac{-a}{-b}, \dfrac{2a}{2b}, -\dfrac{3a}{-3b}, -\dfrac{-5a}{5b}$

3. (a) $\dfrac{31}{35}$　(b) $\dfrac{17}{63}$　(c) $\dfrac{-6}{231}$　(d) $\dfrac{213}{385}$　(e) $\dfrac{5}{21}$

　(f) $\dfrac{87}{70}$　(g) $\dfrac{-144}{1155}$　(h) $\dfrac{3}{35}$　(i) $\dfrac{-98}{25}$　(j) $\dfrac{443}{1122}$

5. (a) $\frac{3}{5} \langle \frac{2}{3}$　(b) $\frac{7}{9} \langle \frac{15}{17}$　(c) $\frac{12}{13} = \frac{84}{91}$　(d) $\frac{212}{413} \rangle \frac{121}{257}$

7. (a) $\dfrac{3600}{480} = \dfrac{\cancel{2}\cdot\cancel{2}\cdot\cancel{2}\cdot\cancel{2}\cdot 3\cdot\cancel{3}\cdot\cancel{5}\cdot 5}{\cancel{2}\cdot\cancel{2}\cdot\cancel{2}\cdot\cancel{2}\cdot 2\cdot\cancel{3}\cdot\cancel{5}} = \dfrac{15}{2}$ minutes.

Problem Set 2.8

1. (a) rational　　(b) rational　　(c) rational　　(d) irrational
　(e) rational　　(f) irrational　　(g) irrational　　(h) rational

3. (a) $\frac{3}{10}$　(b) $\frac{4271}{100}$　(c) $\frac{5}{9}$　(d) $\frac{7}{20}$　(e) $\frac{215}{99}$
　(f) $\frac{43}{333}$　(g) $\frac{1769}{550}$　(h) $\frac{70636}{499995}$

5. $.\overline{9} = \dfrac{.\overline{9}(10-1)}{9} = \dfrac{9.\overline{9} - .\overline{9}}{9} = \dfrac{9}{9} = 1.\overline{0}$

Problem Set 2.9

1. (a) real and complex　　　(b) real and complex
　(c) real and complex　　　(d) imaginary and complex
　(e) imaginary and complex　(f) complex
　(g) real and complex　　　(h) imaginary and complex
　(i) real and complex

3. (a) $\sqrt{5} + 0i$　(b) $0 + 8i$　(c) $-7 + 5\sqrt{2}i$

CHAPTER 3

Problem Set 3.1

1.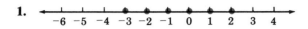

3.

5.

7.

9.

11.   A:

B:

A ∪ B:

Problem Set 3.2

1. {2}

3. {4, 5, 6, 7}

5. {12, 13, 14, 15, 16, 17, 18, 19}

7. ∅

9. {9}

11. {3}

13. {3}

15. {6}

17. {$^{11}\!/_5$}

19. ∅

21. {−13, 13}

23. {−7}

25. {all real numbers}

27. {$^{1}\!/_3$}

Problem Set 3.3

The answers will vary. The following are some possible solutions.

1. $(1,1), (2,2), (-4,-4), (6,6), (0,0)$

3. $(0,0), (-3,-1), (6,2), (-15,-5), (9,3)$

5. $(1,-1), (-3,3), (2,-2), (0,0), (-8,8)$

7. $(0,2), (3,0), (-3,4), (6,-2), (-6,6)$

9. $(3,1), (8,4), (13,7), (-2,-2), (-7,-5)$

11. $(1,-11), (0,-24), (2,2), (3,15), (-1,-35)$

13. $(-4,0), (-4,8), (-4,2), (-4,-3), (-4,-9)$

15. $(4,0), (-2,0), (6,0), (-1,0), (0,0)$

Problem Set 3.4

1.

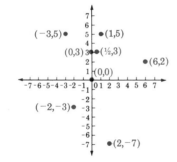

3.

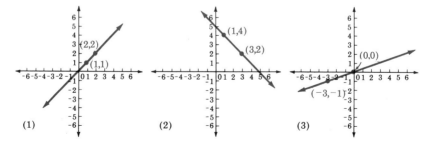

(1)   (2)   (3)

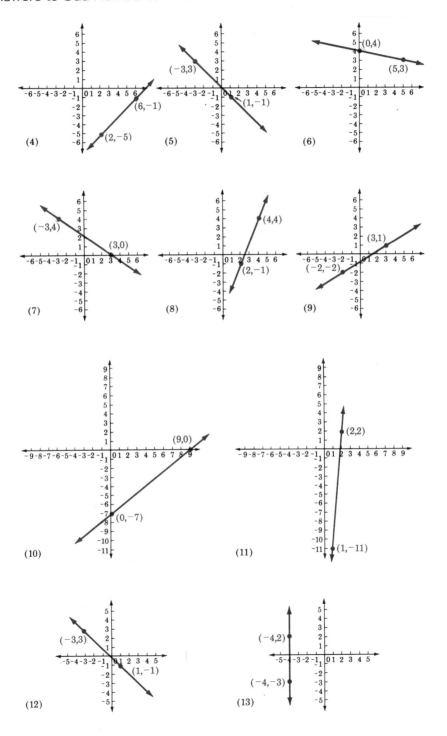

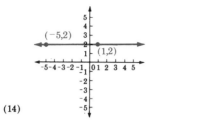

(14)

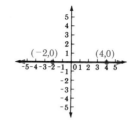

(15)

5.

x	y
−1	6
0	2
1	0
2	0
3	2
4	6

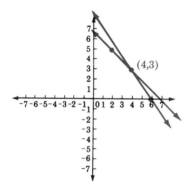

7.

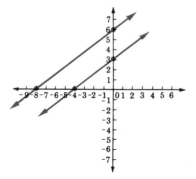

9.

Problem Set 3.5

1.
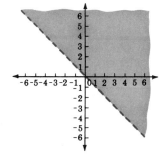

3.
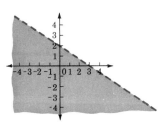

5.
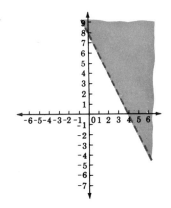

7.
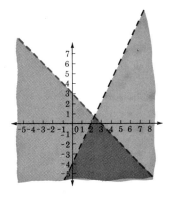

9. See Figure 3.11, Section 3.6.

Problem Set 3.6

1. (a), (c), and (f) are convex.

3. (a) $(0,0)$, $(7,7)$, $(7,-2)$, $(0,-2)$

   (b) $(1,2)$, $(1,15\frac{1}{4})$, $(12\frac{2}{5},2)$

   (c) $(0,3)$, $(4,2)$, $(2,-4)$, $(-2,0)$

5. The profit on corn is
$$125c - 30c - 21c = 74c$$

and the expected profit on soybeans is

$$84s - 25s - 16.8s = 42.2s$$

Thus the total profit may be expressed as

$$P = 74c + 42.2s$$

By substituting the values at each vertice we obtain:

P at $A = 74(0) \ + 42.2(0) \ = \$0.00$

P at $B = 74(25) + 42.2(0) \ = \$1850.00$

P at $C = 74(25) + 42.2(15) = \$2483.00$

P at $D = 74(0) \ + 42.2(40) = \$1688.00$

Therefore the maximum profit of \$2483 may be obtained by planting 25 acres of corn and 15 acres of soybeans.

Problem Set 3.7

1. $x + 5$

3. $3x + 8$

5. $x + 2$

7. $2w + 3$

9. $10d + 25(d + 4)$

11. $x + 18$

13. Let $x =$ the number
$x + 5 = 17$
$x = 12$

15. Let $x =$ the number
$3x + 8 = 65$
$x = 19$

17. Let $x =$ first odd integer
$x + 2 =$ second odd integer
$x + (x + 2) = 400$
$x = 199$
$x + 2 = 201$

19. Let $w =$ width
$2w + 3 =$ length
$2w + 2(2w + 3) = 102$
$w = 16$
$2(w + 3) = 35$

21. Let $d =$ number of dimes
$d + 4 =$ number of quarters
$2d =$ number of half-dollars
$10d + 25(d + 4) + 50(2d) = 505$
$d = 3$
$d + 4 = 7$
$2d = 6$

23. Let $x =$ Tom's age
$x + 18 = 3x$
$x = 9$

25. Answers will vary.

27. Answers will vary.

CHAPTER 4

Problem Set 4.1

1. 2^n where $n = 7$ gives 2^7 or 128.

3. $1, 4, 7, 10, 13, 16, 19, 22, \ldots$ (There appears to be a common difference of 3 between terms.)

5. (a) $1, 3, 5, 7, 9, \ldots, (2n - 1), \ldots$

   (b) $1, \dfrac{1}{2}, \dfrac{1}{3}, \dfrac{1}{4}, \dfrac{1}{5}, \dfrac{1}{6}, \ldots, \left(\dfrac{1}{n}\right), \ldots$

   (c) $-5, -1, 3, 7, 11, 15, \ldots, (4n - 9), \ldots$

   (d) $\dfrac{-1}{4}, 0, \dfrac{1}{6}, \dfrac{2}{7}, \ldots, \left(\dfrac{n - 2}{n + 3}\right), \ldots$

   (e) $1 + 3 + 5 + 7 + 9 + 11 + 13 + 15 = 64$

7. (a) The sequence appears to be found by multiplying the succeeding term by 4, thus we have

   $1, 4, 16, 64, 256, 1024$

   If $N = 8$ we have

   $L = F \cdot D^{N-1}$

   $= 1 \cdot 4^{8-1} = 4^7 = (2^2)^7 = 2^{14} = 16{,}384$ (see Figure 4.7)

   (b) $27, 9, 3, 1, \dfrac{1}{3}$ Common ratio seems to be $\dfrac{1}{3}$

   For $N = 8$, we have

   $L = F \cdot D^{N-1}$

   $= 27 \cdot \left(\dfrac{1}{3}\right)^{8-1} = 27 \cdot \left(\dfrac{1}{3}\right)^7 = 3^3 \cdot \dfrac{1}{3^7} = \dfrac{1}{3^4} = \dfrac{1}{81}$

   (c) $L = F \cdot D^{N-1}$

   $= 2 \cdot 3^5 = 2 \cdot 243 = 486$

9.

17	24	1	8	15
23	5	7	14	16
4	6	13	20	22
10	12	19	21	3
11	18	25	2	9

Sum of each row = 65
Sum of each column = 65
Sum of each diagonal = 65
Sum of all entries = $5 \cdot 65 = 325$

11. Kelly gets $2500

    Jo gets $2750

    Niki gets $3000

    Tony gets $3250

    Patty gets $3500

13. The sum of ears of corn for all 5 seasons is:

    1st year 1 ear or 100 grains

    2nd year $(100)^2$ grains or 100 ears

    3rd year $(100)^2$ ears

    4th year $(100)^3$ ears

    5th year $(100)^4$ ears

    $100^4 = (10^2)^4 = 10^8 = 100 \cdot 10^6$ ears

    $\dfrac{100 \cdot 10^6}{75} = \dfrac{100}{75} \cdot 10^6 = \dfrac{4}{3} \cdot 10^6 = 1,333,333.3\bar{3}$ bushels. At \$1 per bushel, Ralph has \$1,333,333.33.

Problem Set 4.2

1. (a) 362,880   (b) 144

   (c) $(4 + 5)! = 9! = 362,880$ (d) $\dfrac{10!}{9!} = \dfrac{10 \cdot 9!}{9!} = 10$

   (e) $\dfrac{12!}{6!6!} = \dfrac{12 \cdot 11 \cdot 10 \cdot 9 \cdot 8 \cdot 7 \cdot 6!}{6 \cdot 5 \cdot 4 \cdot 3 \cdot 2 \cdot 1 \cdot 6!} = 924$

   (f) $(n + 1)! = (5 + 1)! = 6! = 720$ (g) $n! + 1 = 5! + 1 = 121$

   (h) not defined   (i) 1,320

   (j) $n = 12, r = 3$ evaluates to 220
       $n = 9, r = 0, {}_9C_0 = 1$

3. (a) 35   (b) 1   (c) 1   (d) $\dbinom{9}{3} = {}_9C_3 = 84$

   (e) 3   (f) not defined   (g) 250   (h) 80,730

5. ${}_6C_2 = \dfrac{6 \cdot 5}{1 \cdot 2} = \dfrac{6 \cdot 5}{1 \cdot 2} \cdot \dfrac{4 \cdot 3}{3 \cdot 4} = {}_6C_4 = 15$

7

0 Heads	1 Heads	2 Heads	3 Heads	4 Heads	5 Heads
T T T T T	H T T T T	H H T T T	H H H T T	H H H H T	H H H H H
	T H T T T	H T H T T	H H T H T	H H H T H	
	T T H T T	H T T H T	H H T T H	H H T H H	
	T T T H T	H T T T H	H T H T H	H T H H H	
	T T T T H	T H T T H	H T T H H	T H H H H	
		T T H T H	T H T H H		
		T T T H H	T T H H H		
		T H H T T	H T H H T		
		T T H H T	T H H H T		
		T H T H T	T H H T H		
1	5	10	10	5	1

This is line 5 of Pascal's triangle.

9. $_{26}C_3 = \dfrac{26 \cdot 25 \cdot 24}{3 \cdot 2 \cdot 1} = 2600$

11. $_{40}C_{20}$. There are two ways; they must be alternately G,B,G,B,... or B,G,B,G,...

13. (a) 36

(b) Answering the first four leaves 5 questions of which he must answer any 3, therefore it can be done in 10 ways.

(c) $_5C_5 + {}_5C_4 + {}_5C_3 = 1 + 5 + 10 = 16$

(d) 36

15. (a) one   (b) $2^{12} - 1 = 4095$

17. $n - r + 1 = 67$

19. In one suit there are 14 ranks to be divided in order in groups of 5. $n - r + 1 = 14 - 5 + 1 = 10$. But there are 4 suits, for a total of 40.

21. (a) 1287   (b) $4 \cdot 1287 = 5148$ (c) 4   (d) There are 4^5 ways to choose a specified straight. If the ace can be used as either high or low card, then $n - r + 1 = 14 - 5 + 1 = 10$ possible straights. Therefore there are $10 \cdot 4^5 = 10{,}240$ straights including straight flushes, or $10{,}240 - 40 = 10{,}200$ straights.

23. $_{n+r-1}C_n = {}_{5+3-1}C_5 = 21$ ways

Problem Set 4.3

1. $n = 1$, $2^1 = 2 = {}_1C_1 + {}_1C_0$

   $n = 2$, $2^2 = 4 = {}_2C_2 + {}_2C_1 + {}_2C_0$

   $n = 3$, $2^3 = 8 = {}_3C_3 + {}_3C_2 + {}_3C_1 + {}_3C_0$

   etc. There are $n + 1$ terms in each of the sums.

3. One suggestion may be to divide the names into two equal groups "A" and "B." The first question would be to ask if the girl's name was among group A. If it is, you have eliminated all of group B. If not, the name is in group B. Divide the appropriate group and repeat the process for the second question; repeat for the third question and you can determine the name of any of the girls you may choose.

5.

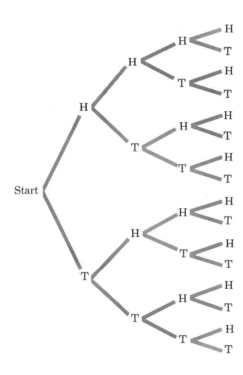

7.

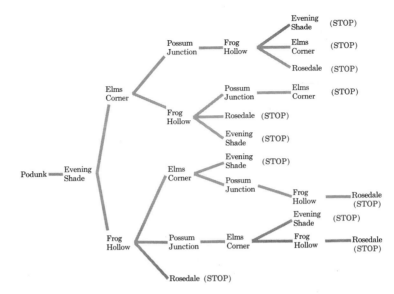

There are eleven different routes; 4 end at Evening Shade, 5 end at Rosedale, and 2 end at Elms Corner. Counting Podunk, 6 is the greatest number of towns. Rosedale has a slight advantage for an overnight stay.

9. 42 schedules

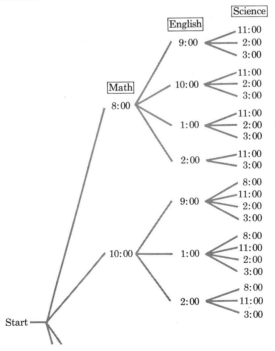

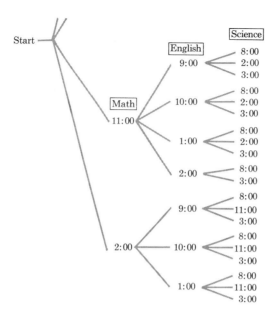

11. $_{54}C_5 \cdot {}_{46}C_4 = (3,162,510)(163,185)$

13. (a) $7! = 5040$

    (b) $7 \cdot 6 \cdot 5 = 210$

15. (a) $_{18}C_4 = 3060$

    (b) $18' \cdot 17 \cdot 16 = 4896$

17. (a) $11!$

    (b) $_{11}C_3 \cdot {}_8C_3 \cdot {}_5C_5 = \dfrac{11!}{3! \, 3! \, 5!} = 9240$

19. (a) $7! = 5040$

    (b) $2! \, 2! \, 1! \, 2! = 8$

    (c) $_7C_2 \cdot {}_5C_2 \cdot {}_3C_2 \cdot {}_1C_1 = (21)(10)(3)(1) = 630$

    (d) After removing the two A's there are 5 letters to be arranged in
        $_5C_2 \cdot {}_3C_2 \cdot {}_1C_1 = 30$ ways. If the two A's are to be side by side they
        must be inserted as a unit. There are $6 \times 30 = 180$ ways.

    (e) 450

21. (a) $7! = 5040$

    (b) $\dfrac{7!}{3! \, 2! \, 1! \, 1!} = 420$

23. 63 (Every player loses once, except for the lone survivor. 63 losses = 63 games.)

25. (a) $_{10}C_4 = 210$ (b) $_6C_4 \cdot {}_4C_0 = 15$

     (c) $_6C_3 \cdot {}_4C_1 = 80$ (d) $_6C_2 \cdot {}_4C_2 = 90$

     (e) $_6C_1 \cdot {}_4C_3 = 24$ (f) $_6C_0 \cdot {}_4C_4 = 1$

     (g) 210

27. $_{16}C_3 = 560$ ways of choosing a combination of 3 numbers. You would expect to win $\frac{1}{560}$ or 18% of the time; therefore it would be a fair game if you paid approximately .2 of one cent for each dollar you had a chance to win.

Problem Set 4.4

1. $P(5) = \frac{1}{6}$

3. (a) $P(\text{even}) = \frac{1}{2}$ (b) $P(\text{odd}) = \frac{1}{2}$

     (c) $P(n > 10) = \frac{1}{12}$ (d) $P(n < 3) = \frac{1}{36}$

     (e) $P(n > 5) = \frac{13}{18}$ (f) $P(\text{at least } 5) = \frac{5}{6}$

5. (a) $P(\text{A spades}) = \frac{1}{52}$ (b) $P(7) = \frac{1}{13}$

     (c) $P(\text{black jack}) = \frac{1}{26}$ (d) $P(\text{red}) = \frac{1}{2}$

     (e) $P(\text{king} \cup \text{queen}) = \frac{2}{13}$ (f) $P(\text{A spades} \cup \text{face}) = \frac{1}{4}$

     (g) $P(\text{red } 7 \cup \text{black } 9) = \frac{1}{13}$

7. $\dfrac{_{13}C_5}{_{52}C_5} = P(\text{heart flush}) = \dfrac{1287}{2,598,960} \approx .0005$

     $P(\text{royal flush}) = \dfrac{4}{2,598,960} \approx .0000015$

     $P(\text{royal flush clubs}) = \dfrac{1}{2,598,960} \approx .000000375$

9. (a) $P(\text{HHH}) = \dfrac{_5C_3}{2^5} = \dfrac{5}{16}$

     (b) $P(\text{HHHH}) = \dfrac{_5C_4}{32} = \dfrac{5}{32}$

     (c) $P(\text{HHHHH}) = \dfrac{_5C_5}{32} = \dfrac{1}{32}$

(d) P (at least 3H) $= P$ (HHH) $+ P$ (HHHH) $+ P$ (HHHHH) $= \frac{1}{2}$

(e) P (at most 3H) $= 1 - P$ (at least 3H) $+ P$ (HHH) $= \frac{13}{16}$

11. P (one blue) $= \frac{1}{7}$; P (blue $\cup$ green) $= \frac{3}{7}$; P (black $\cup$ white) $= \frac{4}{7}$;

P (two black) $\approx (\frac{3}{7})(\frac{5}{13}) = \frac{15}{91}$ assuming that all black socks are mates.

13. Mr. Cantwin's genes are *Ii* and Mrs. Cantwin's genes are *Ii*, then

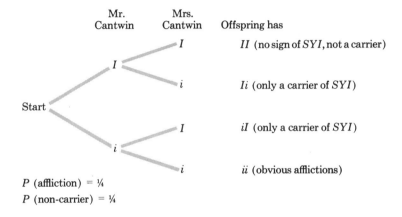

P (affliction) $= \frac{1}{4}$
P (non-carrier) $= \frac{1}{4}$

Problem Set 4.5

1. $1:1$

3. (a) $\frac{7}{12}$ (b) $\frac{7}{18}$ (c) $\frac{1}{3}$

5. Odds for an odd number are $9:10$. The odds against a number 13 to 21 are $29:9$. $P(\text{odd}) = \frac{9}{19}$. $P(13 \leq n \leq 21) = \frac{9}{38}$.

7. $P(n < 7) = \frac{5}{12}; P(n \geq 7) = 1 - (\frac{5}{12}) = \frac{7}{12}$

$E = (\frac{5}{12})(1) + (-\frac{7}{12})(1) = -(\frac{1}{6})$. Thus expected winnings are $17\cent$ loss.

9. $P(H) = \frac{1}{2}; E(1) = \frac{1}{2} \cdot 1 = \frac{1}{2}; E(2) = 1; E(3) \frac{3}{2}; E(50) = 25$

11. $E = \$0.001$ or one-tenth of a cent. A fair price might be to add about one-tenth of a cent for each chance of winning the prize.

Problem Set 4.6

1. (a) $P(\text{1st maple}) = \frac{5}{20} = \frac{1}{4}$; $P(\text{2nd maple} \mid \text{1st maple}) = \frac{4}{19}$; $P(\text{1st} \cup \text{2nd}) = (\frac{1}{4})(\frac{4}{19}) = \frac{1}{19}$

   (b) $P(P \cap P) = P(P) \cdot P(P \mid P) = (\frac{9}{20})(\frac{8}{19}) = \frac{18}{95}$
   $P(C \cap C) = P(C) \cdot P(C \mid C) = (\frac{6}{20})(\frac{5}{19}) = \frac{3}{38}$
   $P(M \cap M) = P(M) \cdot P(M \mid M) = \frac{1}{19}$
   $P(\text{same flavor}) = (\frac{18}{95}) + (\frac{3}{38}) + (\frac{1}{19}) = \frac{61}{190}$

   (c) $P(P \cap C) = P(P) \cdot P(C \mid P) \Rightarrow P(C \mid P) = \dfrac{P(P \cap C)}{P(P)} =$
   $\dfrac{(\frac{9}{20})(\frac{6}{19})}{(\frac{9}{20})} = \frac{6}{19}$

   (d) If the first is peppermint then the probability that the second is peppermint is $\frac{8}{19}$. Therefore probability of *not* peppermint is $1 - (\frac{8}{19}) = \frac{11}{19}$.

3. $P(\text{all boys}) = \frac{1}{32}$; $P(B \mid 4B) = \frac{1}{2}$

5. (a) $P(\text{fail chem} \mid \text{fail physics}) = \frac{1}{2}$

   (b) $P(P_c \mid C_c) = \frac{2}{5}$

   (c) $P(P_c \cup C_c) = \frac{7}{20}$

   (d) $P(P_c \cap C_c \mid P_c) = \frac{1}{2}$

   (e) $P(P_c \cap C_c \mid C_c) = \frac{2}{5}$

7. (a) $P(C \mid P) = \frac{1}{4}$

   (b) $P(P \mid C) = \frac{1}{2}$

   (c) $P(C \cup P) = \frac{5}{12}$

   (d) $P(C_c \mid P_c) = \frac{5}{6}$

CHAPTER 5

Problem Set 5.1

1. Answers will vary, e.g., for the bill on population control Senator Buster may poll subscribers to *Medical Journal*, believing these subscribers (probably doctors, medical technicians, etc.) are more informed. On the other hand, subscribers to *Ladies' Home Journal* are the ones who will more probably be most affected by the bill.

3.

	Mean	Median	Mode
Forwards	6.02′	6.04′	6.17′
Guards	5.93′	5.92′	5.92′
Centers	6.50′	6.42′	none

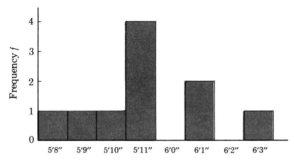

Height of guards in feet and inches

100th percentile not defined. 10 below 99th. 7 below 50th. 9 below 75th.

5. mean

7. 100

9. (a) median

(b) mean

(c) median (possibly the mean)

11. *Jim*

Course	Sem. hrs.	Grade pts.	Total pts.
Calculus	5	2	10
Physics	4	2	8
History	3	4	12
Phys. Ed.	1	4	4
	13		34

Jim's GPR = $34 \div 13 \approx 2.62$

Mary

Calculus	5	4	20
Physics	4	3	12
History	3	2	6
Phys. Ed.	1	1	1
	13		39

Mary's GPR = $39 \div 13 = 3.00$

Therefore Mary has the better grade point ratio.

13.

	Mean	Median	Mode	Range	Mid-range
(a)	6.00	6.0	none	8	6.0
(b)	3.50	4.0	5	7	3.5
(c)	3.75	2.5	1	9	5.5
(d)	11.11	8.0	4&10	48	26.0
(e)	.2	1.0	2	12	0

Problem Set 5.2

1. $\overline{X} = \dfrac{\Sigma x}{n} = 3$

$$\sigma = \sqrt{\dfrac{\Sigma(x - \overline{X})^2}{n}} = 2$$

$$\sigma = \sqrt{\dfrac{x^2}{n} - \overline{X}^2} = 2$$

$$\Sigma(x_n - \overline{X}) = 0$$

3. $\sigma = .41$

5. $\sigma = .3$

7. Answers will vary, e.g.
   Low $= \{69,71,70,72,72,68,70,71,68,64\}$ Might possibly be ten successive scores each for 18 holes of golf.
   High $= \{14,32,5,21,23,29,7,2,19,10\}$ Scores made by a basketball player in successive games.

9. The longer length of time between accidents at First and Wrongway indicates that the accidents are scattered more throughout the day, thus one should be more cautious at any time in proceeding through that intersection. At the Last Street and Rightway intersection the accidents are more clustered, and may indicate more danger at rush hours than during the rest of the day.

11. $\sigma = 5.3$

Problem Set 5.3

1. Class participation project.

3. A's = $100(.036) = 3.6$
   B's = $100(.238) = 23.8$
   C's = $100(.452) = 45.2$
   D's = $100(.238) = 23.8$
   F's = $100(.036) = 3.6$

5. Negative z scores lie to the left of the mean. Positive z scores lie to the right of the mean. A '0' z score is the mean.

7. Better in mathematics.

9. Upper is 84 and lower is 66.

11. 30.8% expected to pass.
    19.2% of scores between 100 and 110, or approximately 2,880 $P(x > 110) \approx .308$

    The normal curve is also the probability curve.

13. 66.4 is upper IQ limit.

Problem Set 5.4

1. (a) high   (b) high   (c) 0   (d) low to moderate   (e) 0

3. Lower = 44.53,   Upper = 45.47

5. 95% interval is $4 \mp .231$
   99% interval is $4 \mp .336$

CHAPTER 6

Problem Set 6.1

1. (a) Axiom 1″ guarantees there are at least two points, call them A and B. Axiom 2″ says there is a line containing the two points. Axiom 4″ states there is a point not on the line. Therefore this point cannot be A or B, but must be a third point, C.

   The set of axioms does allow for more than 3 points.

(b) By part (a) we have concluded there are at least 3 points not on the same line. Points A and B are contained in a line. Since point C does not lie on that line, there is a line containing A and C by axiom 2″. Using the same axiom we may give the third line as that containing B and C.

The set of axioms does allow for more than 3 lines.

3. Theorems such as:

(a) "Each glib contains exactly two globs." In order for axioms 1 and 3 to be satisfied, each glib would have to contain exactly 2 globs.

(b) "Each glob is on exactly three glibs."

Let W, X, Y, Z represent the 4 globs from axiom 1. Take any one of the 4 globs, say W. That glob is on a glib with X. It is also on another glib with Y and on a third glib with Z (axiom 2). Theorem (a) guarantees the three glibs to be distinct. Since there are no other globs, then W cannot be on any other glib, hence it is on exactly 3 glibs.

(c) "There are exactly 6 glibs."

Let W, X, Y, Z represent the 4 globs from axiom 1. Let A represent the glib containing globs W and X. Also B contains X and Y, C contains Y and Z, and D contains Z and W (axiom 2). Also by axiom 2 there must be a glib E containing W and Y, and another glib F containing X and Z. By theorem (a) we know that these glibs are distinct, thus a total of 6 glibs.

Problem Set 6.2

1. (a) $2\,R\,1$, $14\,R\,7$, $18\,R\,9$, $28\,R\,14$

(b) No

3. (a) A, D, E   (b) A, B, C, D, E, F

Problem Set 6.3

1. The element 0 is the only element having an inverse.

3. The set is associative, 0 is the identity element for the set, and each element has an inverse. Therefore the set forms a group.

5. It forms a group.

+	0	1	2	3
0	0	1	2	3
1	1	2	3	0
2	2	3	0	1
3	3	0	1	2

Problem Set 6.4

1.

+	0	1	2	3	4
0	0	1	2	3	4
1	1	2	3	4	0
2	2	3	4	0	1
3	3	4	0	1	2
4	4	0	1	2	3

×	0	1	2	3	4
0	0	0	0	0	0
1	0	1	2	3	4
2	0	2	4	1	3
3	0	3	1	4	2
4	0	4	3	2	1

The set forms a field.

3. No. The element 1 is the only element having an inverse under multiplication.

5. (a) axiom 3   (b) axiom 6   (c) axiom 3

Problem Set 6.5

1. Answers will vary. If a is the first term and k is a constant, the sequence will be of the form:

$$a, a + k, a + 2k, a + 3k, \ldots$$

3. Answers will vary.

CHAPTER 7

Problem Set 7.1

1.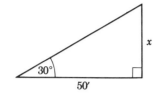

$$\tan 30° = \frac{x}{50}$$
$$x = 50 \tan 30°$$
$$= 50(.577)$$
$$= 28.85 = 29' \text{ (to the nearest foot)}$$

3.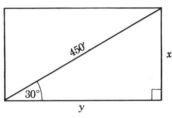

$$\sin 30° = \frac{x}{450} \qquad\qquad \cos 30° = \frac{y}{450}$$
$$x = 450 \sin 30° \qquad\qquad y = 450 \cos 30°$$
$$= 450(.500) \qquad\qquad = 450(.866)$$
$$= 225 \text{ feet} \qquad\qquad = 390 \text{ feet}$$

5.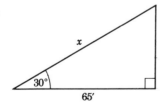

$$\cos 30° = \frac{65}{x}$$
$$x = \frac{65}{\cos 30°}$$
$$= \frac{65}{.866}$$
$$= 75 \text{ feet}$$

Problem Set 7.2

1. $d = 16\,t^2 = 16\,(3)^2 = 144$ feet

$$\frac{144 \text{ feet}}{3 \text{ sec.}} = 48 \text{ ft./sec. (average velocity)}$$

To find the velocity at 2 seconds we take

$$\lim_{t_0 \to 2} \frac{16(2)^2 - 16(t_0)^2}{2 - t_0} = \lim_{t_0 \to 2} 16(2 + t_0) = 64 \text{ ft./sec.}$$

3. (a) $\lim_{t_0 \to 0} \dfrac{96(0) - 16(0)^2 - 96t_0 + 16t_0^2}{0 - t_0}$

$$= \lim_{t_0 \to 0} \frac{-t_0(96 - t_0)}{-t_0}$$

$$= \lim_{t_0 \to 0} 96 - t_0 = 96 \text{ ft./sec.}$$

(b) $\lim_{t_0 \to 1} \dfrac{96(1) - 16(1)^2 - 96t_0 + 16t_0^2}{1 - t_0}$

$$= \lim_{t_0 \to 1} 80 - 16t_0 = 64 \text{ ft./sec.}$$

(c) $\lim_{t_0 \to 4} \dfrac{96(4) - 16(4)^2 - 96t_0 + 16t_0^2}{4 - t_0}$

$$= \lim_{t_0 \to 4} 32 - 16t_0 = -32 \text{ ft./sec.}$$

(d) We wish to find the time t when

$$\lim_{t_0 \to t} \frac{96t - 16t^2 - 96t_0 + 16t_0^2}{t - t_0} = 0.$$

$$\lim_{t_0 \to t} \frac{96(t - t_0) - 16(t^2 - t_0^2)}{t - t_0}$$

$$= \lim_{t_0 \to t} 96 - 16(t + t_0)$$

$$= 96 - 32t = 0$$

$$t = 3 \text{ seconds}$$

Then to find the distance it travels

$$d = 96(3) - 16(3)^2$$

$$= 144 \text{ feet}$$

(e) Solve: $96t - 16t^2 = 0$

$$t(96 - 16t) = 0$$

$$t = 0 \text{ or } t = 6$$

The stone was in the air 6 seconds before it struck the ground.

5. If we let x represent the number of people on the flight, then the total revenue may be represented by $x(500 - 5x)$.

$$\lim_{x_0 \to x} \frac{x(500 - 5x) - x_0(500 - 5x_0)}{x - x_0}$$

$$= \lim_{x_0 \to x} 500 - 5(x + x_0)$$

$$= 500 - 10x$$

We then set

$$500 - 10x = 0$$

$$x = 50$$

Thus 50 people would provide the airline with maximum revenue.

index

Patterns in the Sand

designed by Glencoe Press.

composed by the Typographic Service Company,
Los Angeles, California.

printed and bound by the Stecher-Traung-Schmidt
Corporation, San Francisco, California.

cover design by Jerry Braude, Los Angeles,
California.